FLOWERS
OF THE FIELD

BY THE
REV. C. A. JOHNS, B.A., F.L.S.

REVISED THROUGHOUT AND EDITED BY
CLARENCE ELLIOTT

WITH AN APPENDIX INCLUDING
THE PIPE-WORT TRIBE (ERIOCAULEÆ), THE SEDGE TRIBE (CYPERACEÆ),
AND THE GRASS TRIBE (GRAMINEÆ)

WITH 96 COLOURED ILLUSTRATIONS BY E. N. GWATKIN
AND 245 CUTS IN THE TEXT

FOURTH IMPRESSION

LONDON
GEORGE ROUTLEDGE & SONS, Limited
NEW YORK: E. P. DUTTON AND CO.
1911

'These to his memory since he held them dear.'

———

I dedicate the coloured illustrations in this work to the loving and reverent memory of my father,

JAMES THOMAS GWATKIN,

for many years a member of the Brighton Natural History Society, once its President, and for some years its Honorary Librarian.

E. N. G.

EDITOR'S PREFACE

In preparing the present edition of Johns' *Flowers of the Field*, it has been found necessary to make a good many additions and alterations ; most of them, however, are of an unobtrusive nature.

To have made a thoroughly scientific work of it was deemed undesirable, for it would have meant so much pulling to pieces and putting together again, that the charming classic, the simple book in which for so many years keen unscientific amateurs have been wont to burrow, and find quite successfully the names of the plants which they collected, would no longer have remained.

' Johns,' though founded on a scientific basis, is not a scientific book, and it has been the aim of the editor to exclude from the present edition all those bewildering technical terms which terrify the uninitiated, and to retain that unscientific simplicity which for so long has made ' Johns ' the book of all others beloved of amateurs.

Some plants not included in the older editions have been added, and the descriptions of many individual species have been somewhat elaborated, but the rearrangement of Orders and Genuses has been comparatively slight. The greatest change will be found in the illustrations. The majority of the old familiar cuts which give so well what may best be called the ' expression ' of the plants they represent are reproduced in the present edition, but in addition to these some 268 other species are illustrated in the coloured plates, which are reproduced from a collection of water-colour drawings by Miss Gwatkin. These speak for themselves. Though advanced botanists are apt to think lightly of illustrations, the cry of amateurs is always, ' Give us plates,' and undoubtedly plates are a great help to the beginner—*if they are good.*

The *Introduction to British Botany* is given practically as it stands in the older editions, and by a careful study of this the beginner may easily gather sufficient knowledge to enable him to make the best use of the text of the book. The chapter of the Introduction describing the Linnæan system of classification has been omitted as unnecessary, and even likely to confuse the beginner, who would be apt to laboriously study it, only to find that it is *not* the system used in the text of the book.

The Index, which has been prepared by another hand, is quite exhaustive, and will doubtless appeal to the uninitiated, whilst the Glossary of Terms will explain any words unfamiliar to beginners.

Clarence Elliott

INTRODUCTION TO BRITISH BOTANY

AND EXPLANATION OF TERMS, ETC.

THOUGH the highest claim of this volume is to introduce the lover of Nature to an acquaintance with the common British plants, the author has given to his first chapter the somewhat presuming title of an "*Introduction to British Botany*," lest those into whose hands the work may fall should pass over the earlier part of it as a treatise or summary of contents so little connected with what follows, that the perusal of it may be omitted or deferred with safety. So far is this from being the case, that the reader who is unacquainted with the elements of botany will find the body of the work of little use, unless he carefully peruses the earlier pages, and makes himself thoroughly acquainted with the general plan.

The limits of a work of this kind will not allow any account of the internal structure of plants, or of the functions of their various organs. Nor, indeed, is such description necessary in a work which professes merely to teach the unscientific how to find out the names of the flowers they may happen to fall in with in the course of their country rambles. Such a knowledge of plants as this, it may be said, and said with truth, is not Botany; nevertheless, it is a step towards Botany: for there can be no doubt that scientific treatises on this subject would often be studied with pleasure, if the reader were familiar with simply the outward appearance of the examples quoted : just as we take greater interest in accounts of astronomical discoveries, if we have seen and handled a telescope, than if we had merely had one described to us, no matter with what accuracy and minuteness. The reader, then, or, inasmuch as even the elementary knowledge of a science can only be attained by study, the *student* who wishes to make this volume practically useful in enabling him to find out the names of our common wild flowers, is recommended to read with care and attention the following pages, into which the author has introduced nothing but what is essential to the proper understanding of the body of the work, and so to the attainment of his object.

Before a novice can commence the study of any science he must make himself acquainted with the terms employed by writers on that science ; he must not be frightened if things new to him should have strange names. Unmeaning and hard to be remembered they must appear to him at first, but this will be only as long as they remain mere sounds. When he has gained a knowledge of the *things* for which they stand, they will lose their formidable appearance, and, hard as they may still be to pronounce, they will very soon become familiar to the mind, if not to the tongue. In a scientific treatise on Botany, taken in its widest sense, these terms must of necessity be very numerous. Not so, however, with a popular description of the plants growing wild in a single country of limited extent ; the author, therefore, has endeavoured to keep technical terms as much as possible out of sight, in the hope that the lover of Nature may be beguiled into forming an acquaintance with the outward appearance of the plants of his neighbourhood, and eventually be induced to study their characters, or to extend his researches beyond the limits of his own country. He has, consequently, avoided the use of Latin words wherever English ones would do as well, and has often preferred to express by several words what might have been defined by one, because that one was probably strange to the reader. With respect to the organs of plants, he has not noticed the existence of any but those with which it is necessary that the student should be familiar before he refers to the body of the work for a description of any plant which he may have found ; these, with their principal peculiarities, may be described at once. They are, ROOT, STEM, LEAF, STIPULES, BRACTS, FLOWER, CALYX, COROLLA, STAMENS, PISTILS, FRUIT, SEED, RECEPTACLE, and NECTARY.

THE ROOT.—The most frequent form of the *root* is a tuft of fibres, each of which ends in a porous substance serving to absorb moisture from the soil. In many instances, however, the nourishment thus obtained, instead of being transmitted at once to that part of the plant which rises above the ground, is lodged in another organ, which, though partaking in some measure the properties of root and stem, is distinct from both. This, too, with the fibres attached to it, is called a *root*, the fibres themselves being named *rootlets*. The principal forms of the root are :—

The *Creeping Root*, familiar examples of which are afforded by Couch-grass and Great Bindweed.

The *Spindle-shaped Root ;* examples, Carrot and Parsnep.

A spindle-shaped root which ends abruptly is termed *premorse* (bitten off), as in Premorse Scabious, p. 146.

The *Tuberous Root* consists of one or more roundish solid masses, having the power of producing rootlets and buds from several parts of its surface, as the Potato.

The *Bulbous Root* is a solid roundish mass, producing rootlets at the lower extremity, and a bud at the other ; it consists either of fleshy scales, as in the White Lily ; concentric circles, as in the Onion ; or is of one uniform substance throughout, as in the Crocus. This last is sometimes called a *corm*.

THE STEM.—The stem is said to be *simple* when it bears leaves, or leaves and flowers only without branches, as in Grass of Parnassus, Plate 33.

A *compound stem* is repeatedly and irregularly branched, as in Flax-seed, p. 49.

The term *erect*, when applied to the stem, has the same meaning as *perpendicular*.

An *ascending stem* is one which is horizontal when first it leaves the root, and then becomes erect. When several stems grow from one root, the central one is often *erect*, the rest *ascending*, as in the common Mallow.

A *prostrate stem* trails along the ground without ever becoming erect.

A *creeping stem* differs from the last by sending out roots from its joints. Some plants have erect stems with creeping *scions*, or shoots from the base, as the Creeping Buttercup, p. 6.

THE AXIL.—This name is given to the angle formed by a leaf where it leaves the stem. A bud or flower which springs from this angle is termed *axillary*.

THE LEAF.—*Leaves* which spring directly from the root are called *radical ;* those which grow on the stem are either *alternate*, as in Balsam, p. 60 ; *opposite*, as in the Pink, p. 39 ; or *whorled :* the leaves of Bedstraw, Plate 37, grow in *whorls*.

Leaves which have no stalks are termed *sessile* (sitting), as in Eryngo, Plate 35.

A leaf which consists of but one piece is said to be *simple*, as in Marsh Marigold, Plate 3 ; a *ternate leaf* consists of three *leaflets* on a common stalk, as in Medick, p. 67 ; a *quinate*, of five, as in Marsh Cinquefoil, Plate 27. Other forms of the *compound leaf* are the pinnate (from *penna*, a feather), where a number of leaflets are ranged along the opposite sides of a common stalk, as in Saint-foin, p. 77.

A simple leaf is sometimes *wavy* at the edge, as in the Oak, Plate 82 ; 3-, 5-, or 7-*lobed*, as in the Mallows, Plate 13 ; and these *lobes* are often deeply *cut*, as in Geranium, Plates 15 and 16. A leaf of five or more narrow lobes united near the main stalk is termed *palmate* (from *palma*, the palm of the hand), as in Hellebore, p. 8. The *pedate* leaf differs from the palmate, in having the two side lobes divided a second time at the edge nearest the stalk. A leaf which is lobed after the manner of a pinnate leaf is termed *pinnatifid* (from *penna*, a feather, and *findo*, to cleave).

If a stalk is attached to a leaf at or near its centre, such a leaf is termed *peltate* (from *pelta*, a buckler), as in Cotyledon, Plate 32.

a 2

A leaf through which a stalk passes is termed *perfoliate* (from *per*, through, and *folium*, a leaf), as in Hare's-ear, p. 122.

Two leaves united by their bases, and allowing the stem to pass through them, are termed *connate* (from *con*, together, and *nascor*, to grow), as in Chlora, Plate 59.

The margin of the leaf is either *entire*, as in Soapwort, Plate 10 ; *crenate*, as in Marsh Pennywort, Plate 34 ; *serrate* (saw-edged), as in Rose, Plate 29 ; *toothed*, as in Enchanter's Nightshade, Plate 30 ; or *fringed*, as in Rock-rose, Plate 8.

With respect to form, the varieties of leaves are very numerous, and the terms employed to define them not less so. Those which occur in this volume are :—

Hair-like, or *capillary*, as in Fennel, p. 124.

Linear, as in the Grasses and Pink, p. 39.

Strap-shaped, as in Corrigiola, p. 103.

Oblong, as in Rock-rose, Plate 8.

Elliptical, oval, with both ends alike, as in the leaflets of Rose, Plate 29.

Egg-shaped, oval, with the base broader than the extremity, as in Pear, p. 90.

> *Inversely egg-shaped*, oval, with the base narrower than the extremity, as in Brook weed, p. 239.
>
> *Rounded*, as in Pyrola, p. 186.
>
> *Heart-shaped*, as in Violet, Plate 9.
>
> *Inversely heart-shaped*, as in the leaflets of Medick, p. 67.
>
> *Kidney-shaped*, as in Ground Ivy, Plate 71.
>
> *Arrow-shaped*, as in Tower Mustard, p. 25.
>
> *Halberi-shaped*, arrow-shaped, but with the barbs turned outwards.
>
> *Angular*, as in Danish Scurvy-Grass.

DANISH SCURVY GRASS

Sword-shaped, as in Iris, Plate 68.

STIPULES.—The base of the leaf-stalk is not unfrequently furnished with two sheathing wings ; these are called stipules. The leaf of the Rose has oblong stipules at its base.

BRACTS.—Beneath the flower are frequently situated small leaves called *bracts*. Sometimes they are mere scales, as in the Broom-rape, Plate 67 ; but more frequently they are only to be distinguished from true leaves by their smaller size, as in Evening Primrose, p. 94.

In the Umbelliferous Tribe, p. 111, they often grow, several in a whorl, at the base of the general and partial umbels ; and in Compound Flowers, p. 146, they are yet more numerous at the base

of the heads of flowers. When they grow in this form they are termed an *involucre* (from *involvo*, to wrap up, because they enclose the flowers before expansion).

THE FLOWER.—This, as it is the most ornamental, so it is the most important part of the plant, being rarely produced until the juices fit for its nourishment have been selected by the roots and matured by the leaves, and containing all the apparatus necessary for perfecting seeds. In flowering plants, besides the parts which are indispensable to the ripening of seeds, there are others which evidently serve as a protection, and others, again, the use of which is not known. The flower, however, generally being essential to the continuance of the species, has been selected as the part on which to found every arrangement of plants which can lay claim to accuracy or utility. A thorough knowledge of its structure is therefore necessary, before the student can proceed to discover the names of the commonest plants which are flung with so bountiful a hand over our hills and fields.

THE CALYX.—This name is given to that part of the flower which in the bud stage is outside all the rest, and which when the flower is expanded encircles the more delicate parts. It is usually green, and consists of several leaves, termed *sepals ;* but these sepals are often united at the base and form a cup, (hence the name *calyx,* a cup).

It is unnecessary here to describe the various forms of the calyx, which are very numerous. It may be remarked, however, that when the calyx is divided into two distinct lobes, one of which over-hangs the other, it is termed *gaping ;* in the Mallow Tribe it is *double ;* and in Compound Flowers, the Valerian and Teazel Tribes, it is at first a mere ring, but afterwards becomes a chaffy or feathery appendage to the seed, termed a *pappus.*

THE COROLLA.—Within the calyx is the *corolla* (little crown), a ring of delicate leaves called *petals,* usually coloured—that is, not

green—and often fragrant. The petals are either distinct, as in the Rose, in which the expanded part is termed the *limb,* the lower the *claw ;* or united below, when the expanded part is termed the *border,* the lower the *tube.* The corolla more frequently has as many petals or divisions as there are sepals ; and if these are all of the same size and shape, the corolla is said to be *regular.*

The most common forms of the regular corolla of one petal are ;—

Salver-shaped, as in Primrose, Plate 74.

Funnel-shaped, as in Cowslip, Plate 74.

Wheel-shaped, when the tube is no longer in proportion than the axle of a wheel, as in Speedwell, Plate 69.

Bell-shaped, as in Campanula, p. 384.

Trumpet-shaped, as in Convolvulus, Plate 57.

When the irregular corolla of one petal is divided into two lobes, one of which overhangs the other, it is termed *labiate*, or *lipped*, as in the Natural Family *Labiatæ ;* if the lips are open, it is said to be *gaping*, as in Yellow Dead Nettle ; if closed, *personate*, (from *persona*, a mask), as in Toadflax. In the Compound Flowers, p. 146, there are frequently two kinds of florets in one flower : those of the *disk*, or centre, being tubular, without an evident border ; those of the *ray*, or margin, strap-shaped, as in the Daisy.

Among *regular* flowers of many petals, the only form which it will be necessary to mention here is the *cruciform*, consisting of four petals placed cross-wise, as in the Cruciferous Tribe, p. 16.

The most remarkable among the *irregular* is the papilionaceous, (from *papilio*, a butterfly), consisting of five petals, of which the upper one, called the *standard*, is usually the largest ; the two side ones are termed *wings*, and the two lower ones, which are often combined, form the *keel*, p. 62.

Both calyx and corolla are not always found in the same flower, and when one only is present, it is sometimes difficult to decide by what name it should be called. In this case the term *perianth* (from the Greek *peri*, around, and *anthos*, a flower) is a convenient one. Some flowers have neither calyx nor corolla, as Water Star-wort. When the *perianth* is said to be double, it is to be understood that calyx and corolla are both present.

THE STAMENS.—Within the perianth, and frequently attached to it, is a row of delicate organs called *stamens*, of which the lower part is termed the *filament*, the upper the *anther*. When the filament is slender throughout, it is said to be *thread-like ;* but if it be thick at the base, and taper to a point, it is said to be *awl-shaped*. The anther varies in shape, but is most frequently oblong, and composed of two lobes and as many cells, which are filled with a fine dust, called *pollen*. If there be no filament, the anther is said to be *sessile*. In a majority of flowers the number of stamens equals that of the petals ; a few plants have but one stamen : very often the number of stamens is some multiple of the petals—that is, there are twice or thrice, etc., as many, and not a few flowers have from twenty to several hundred. Sometimes the filaments are united at the base into one or more sets, as in Hypericum, p. 52 ; sometimes they form a hollow tube, the anthers being distinct, or *free*, as in Mallow, p. 49 ; and sometimes the filaments are free, and the anthers are united into a ring, as in the Compound Flowers, p. 146.

THE PISTIL.—This is the central part of the flower, and in its commonest form is a delicate column composed of three parts—the *ovary*, the *style*, and the *stigma*.

The *ovary*, (from *ovum*, an egg), sometimes called the *germen*, contains the rudiments of the future seed.

The *style*, (from *stylos*, a column), is to the pistil what the shaft is to a pillar, connecting the ovary with—

The *stigma*, which is sometimes a mere viscid point, but more frequently an enlargement of the summit of the style, and is variously shaped, being globular, flat, lobed, etc. If there be no style, the stigma is said to be sessile.

In the majority of flowers there is but one pistil ; but very often there is a single ovary, which bears several styles and stigmas. In this case the ovary usually consists of several cells, each of which, with its style and stigma, is termed a *carpel ;* and the same name is given to each of the ovaries in such flowers as Marsh Marigold, p. 7, where they are distinct ; and in Blackberry, p. 86, where they are united.

Both calyx and corolla, it has been said above, may be absent. Not so with respect to stamens and pistils ; for, unless they are present, no seed can be perfected. It is not, however, essential that they should both be found in the same flower. Sometimes on the same plant flowers are to be found, some of which bear stamens only, others pistils only ; and not unfrequently these organs grow, not only in separate flowers, but on different plants. In either case, those flowers alone which contain pistils produce seeds, and are therefore termed *fertile ;* while those containing stamens only, are called *barren*. The external structure of barren and fertile flowers is often very dissimilar, as in Willow, p. 264, and Oak, p. 266. When the ovary is inserted above the base of the perianth, it is said to be *superior*, as in Crowfoot, p. 6 ; when below, *inferior*, as in Rose, p. 88. In like manner the perianth is said to be superior or inferior, according as it is inserted above or below the ovary.

THE FRUIT.—As the flower withers, the ovary enlarges and becomes the *fruit*, that is, the seed, with its case or covering, also called a *pericarp*, (from *peri*, around, and *carpos*, fruit). Among the various forms of fruit, the principal are—

The *capsule* (from *capsula*, a little box), a dry case, either opening by *valves*, as in Pink, p. 39 ; by *teeth*, as in Lychnis, p. 42 ; by *pores*, as in Poppy, p. 13 ; or by splitting all round, as in Pimpernel, p. 237.

The *silique* and *silicle*, described at p. 16.

The *pod*, or *legume*, a long seed-vessel, differing from the silique in having no partition, and bearing the seeds in a single row, as in the Pea and Bean Tribe, p. 63.

The *berry*, a juicy or mealy fruit, bearing the seeds immersed in pulp, as in Elder, Currant, etc.

The *nut*, a dry fruit, composed of a hard shell, containing a seed, as in Hazel, p. 267 ; and Gromwell, p. 200.

The *drupe*, a nut enclosed in pulp, as the Plum and Cherry.

The *cone*, a collection of *imbricated* or overlapping scales, each of which covers two seeds.

THE SEED.—A seed is said to be *dicotyledonous* when it is composed of two lobes, or *cotyledons*, which enclose the *plumule*, or embryo of the future plant. As the seed germinates, the cotyledons either rise above the ground, as in Mustard, or remain buried, as in the garden Pea. Plants bearing seeds of this structure compose the first Natural Class, DICO-TYLEDONOUS PLANTS, or EXOGENS, p. 1. When the seed is not separable into two parts, it is termed *monocotyledonous ;* and plants bearing such seeds compose the Second Natural Class, MONOCOTY-LEDONOUS PLANTS, or ENDOGENS, p. 269.

RECEPTACLE.—This name is given to that part of the flower on which all the others rest. It is most conspicuous in the Compound Flowers, p. 146, where it is sometimes *conical*, as in Daisy, p. 173 ; *chaffy*, as in Cat's-ear, p. 156 ; *bristly*, as in Thistle, p. 161 ; or *dotted*, as in Dandelion, p. 160.

NECTARY.—Any distinct organ in a flower which contains honey ; for instance, the scale at the base of the petals in Crowfoot, p. 5 ; the spurs of the Columbine, p. 8, etc.

INFLORESCENCE.—This term is used to denote the arrangement of flowers on the stem.

A flower-stalk springing directly from the root, and bearing no leaves, is termed a *scape*, as in Primrose, Plate 74.

When it is inserted in the angle between the main stem and a leaf, it is termed *axillary*, as in Balsam, p. 60.

When it is at the extremity of the main stem, having no leaves beyond it, it is said to be *terminal*, as in Grass of Parnassus, p. 111.

A flower-stalk which bears but one flower, is said to be *simple*, as in Grass of Parnassus.

A stalk bearing a number of sessile flowers, arranged one above another, is termed a *spike*, as in Plantain, p. 241.

When, instead of being sessile, the flowers are supported on simple stalks, the inflorescence is a *cluster*, as in Melilot, p. 68.

A *panicle* differs from a cluster in being branched, as in Spurrey, p. 45.

A *corymb* differs from a cluster in bearing the lower flowers on long stalks, while the upper are sessile, or nearly so, as in Wall-flower, p. 28.

In a *cyme* the stalks are irregularly branched, but the flowers are nearly level, as in Elder, p. 135.

The *umbel* is a mode of inflorescence in which the flower-stalks spring from a common centre, and bear each a single flower, as in Ivy, p. 131. When the stalks bear, instead of a single flower, a second umbel, the inflorescence is a *compound umbel*, the primary division being termed a *general umbel*, the secondary a *partial*. This mode of inflorescence is common in the Umbelliferous Tribe, p. 110.

A *head* resembles a simple umbel, except that the flowers are all sessile, as in Scabious, p. 146.

A *catkin* resembles a spike, except that the flowers are enclosed each within a scale-like bract, as in Hazel, Plate 81.

Other terms which are employed in the body of the work will be explained as they occur, or in the description which precedes the summary of each Natural Order. A glossary will also be found at the end of the volume, containing definitions of most of the common terms in use.

It is not necessary to give an account of the Linnæan system of classification, nor of the various others which have been proposed. Suffice it to say, the one generally adopted in Britain is a modification of those of Jussieu and De Candolle. Here the whole Vegetable Kingdom is divided into three great CLASSES.

CLASS I. DICOTYLEDONS.

In this Class are placed such plants as produce seeds divisible into two lobes, or *cotyledons*. It is subdivided into four *Sub-classes*, THALAMIFLORÆ, CALYCIFLORÆ, COROLLIFLORÆ, and MONOCH-LAMYDEÆ.

Sub-class I. THALAMIFLORÆ.

Flowers furnished with calyx and corolla ; *petals* distinct, inserted into the receptacle, or *thalamus ; stamens* springing from the base of the *ovary*.

Sub-class II. CALYCIFLORÆ.

Flowers furnished with calyx and corolla ; *sepals* distinct, or united ; *petals* distinct ; *stamens* inserted in the *calyx*, or close to its base.

Sub-class III. COROLLIFLORÆ.

Flowers furnished with calyx and corolla ; *petals* united, bearing the stamens.

Sub-class IV. MONOCHLAMYDE.E.*

CLASS II. MONOCOTYLEDONS.

Perianth single, or none.

Seeds with a single *cotyledon*. It is subdivided into two *Sub-classes*, PETALOIDE.E and GLUMACE.E.

Sub-class I. PETALOIDE.E.

Flowers with petals.

Sub-class II. GLUMACE.E.

Flowers formed of chaffy scales, or *glumes*. This Sub-class contains the Grasses and Sedges.

CLASS III. ACOTYLEDONS.

Flowerless plants. Here are placed the Ferns, Mosses, Liverworts, Lichens, Sea-weeds, and Fungi, not included in the present work.

Each of the *Natural Orders*, or *Tribes*, alluded to above, consists of a number of plants which are more or less like one another in various respects, especially in the organs of fructification. The plants comprised in each Tribe are again distributed into *genera*, or *families*, each genus including all plants which resemble one another yet more closely in the essential characters of fructification. A *species*, or *kind*, is an assemblage of individual plants agreeing with each other in *all* essential points ; and individuals which differ one from another in minor points, such as an irregular formation of leaves or mode of growth, unusual colour of flowers, extraordinary number of petals, etc., are termed *varieties*. These words are frequently used loosely in common conversation, but the habit cannot be too carefully avoided in botanical descriptions, as calculated to produce great confusion. Throughout these pages they will be employed exclusively with the meanings above assigned, which will be rendered clearer by the following examples : The wild sweet-scented Violet is called by botanists *Viola odorata ;* the former name, *Viola*, indicating that it belongs to the *genus* so called, and being, therefore, termed its *generic* name. Besides the scented Violet, we have in England the Dog-Violet, the Marsh-Violet, the Pansy, and several others, all belonging to the same *genus*, and, therefore, described under the name *Viola*. But the Dog-Violet differs from the Sweet-scented in having acute sepals, and leafy stems, whereas the latter has blunt sepals, and the leaves spring

---

* From the Greek *monos,* one, and *chlamys,* a mantle or covering; the plants of this Sub-class never having both calyx and corolla.

directly from the roots. The Dog-Violet is therefore a distinct *species, Viola canina.* The Marsh-Violet and Pansy differ also in important characters ; they are, therefore, also considered distinct species, the fact being indicated by the addition of the *specific* or *trivial* names, *palustris* and *tricolor,* to the *generic* name *Viola.* The flowers of the scented *Violet* are sometimes white and sometimes blue ; garden specimens are often tinged with pink, and still more frequently, double. These characters being either unimportant or inconstant—for blue flowers generally have a great tendency to sport to white, and double flowers are not perpetuated by seed— the blue, white, pink, and double sweet Violets are not considered distinct species, but mere *varieties.* Now there are many plants which bear a close resemblance to a Violet in the structure of their flowers and seeds, but yet differ so far that they cannot be reduced under the same *genus ;* they are therefore placed with it in the same *Tribe,* called VIOLACEÆ, all the genera in which, differ in essential points from the genera which compose other Tribes, but agree with a vast number in having *two-lobed seeds* and *leaves with netted veins,* two of the characters of DICOTYLEDONOUS PLANTS. In this Class it is arranged with plants furnished with both calyx and corolla, and having their petals distinct and inserted with the stamens into the receptacle.

The plant of which we have been speaking belongs, then, to the

CLASS I.   DICOTYLEDONS.

SUB-CLASS I.   THALAMIFLORÆ.

Order or *Tribe* IX.   VIOLACEÆ.

Genus I, Viola.

Species 2, *odorata.*

Variety, blue, white, or *double.*

LIST OF COLOURED PLATES

a 2*

NATURAL ARRANGEMENT OF PLANTS

CLASS I

DICOTYLEDONOUS OR EXOGENOUS PLANTS

THE characteristics by which plants belonging to this class may be distinguished from members of the less extensive class, Monocotyledons, are mainly as follows :—

The seeds are composed of two lobes or *cotyledons*, which enclose the *plumule*, or embryo of the future plant. As germination commences, the plumule lengthens downwards into a root, called in its early stage a *radicle*. At the same time the upper extremity lengthens into a *stem*, which is composed of *bark, woody fibre, spiral vessels, cellular tissue*, and a central column of *pith*. The stem increases in diameter by deposits beneath the bark, but *outside* the existing fibre. Hence the plants belonging to this class are called EXOGENOUS (increasing by additions on the outside). In all trees and shrubs of this class the wood is arranged in concentric layers, the hardest part being nearest the pith. The *leaves* are netted-veined, as opposed to the parallel-veined leaves of Monocotyledons. (Compare the leaves of a common primrose with those of a lily of the valley.)

The parts of the *flowers* are usually arranged in fours, fives, or some multiple of those numbers.

With a little observation the student will quickly come to be able to recognize the essential characteristics of Dicotyledons and Monocotyledons, whose general aspects are really very distinct.

SUB-CLASS I

THALAMIFLORÆ

Flowers furnished with calyx and corolla ; *petals* distinct, inserted into the receptacle or *thalamus ; stamens inferior*, i.e. springing from below the base of the ovary.

B

NATURAL ORDER I

RANUNCULACEÆ.—THE RANUNCULUS TRIBE

Sepals distinct, generally 5; *petals* distinct, generally 5, sometimes irregular in form, minute, or wanting; *ovaries* generally numerous; *fruit* consisting of several one- or many-seeded carpels, but in Actæa a berry. An extensive tribe of plants, inhabiting for the most part the temperate regions of the globe. All the British species are herbaceous, with the exception of clematis, which is a woody climber. The leaves are generally much divided, the flowers showy, including as they do many garden favourites. Sepals and petals often graduating into one another, sometimes extended into spurs. Most of them possess acrid and poisonous properties if taken into the stomach, and not a few produce wounds if applied to the skin. Some species were formerly used in medicine, and the extract of monk's-hood is still employed to relieve pain in affections of the nerves. The Hellebore was held in high repute among the ancients as a specific for madness ; the beautiful garden Christmas Rose belongs to this family. The Celery-leaved Crowfoot, *Ranunculus sceleratus,* is one of the most widely diffused plants, being as common in America, and on the banks of the Ganges, as in our own marshes.

Carpels one-seeded

1. CLEMATIS (Traveller's Joy).—*Sepals* 4–6, resembling petals ; *petals* wanting ; *carpels* surmounted by a long feathery tail. (Name from the Greek, *clema,* a vine-shoot.)

2. THALICTRUM (Meadow Rue).—*Sepals* 4–5, resembling petals ; *petals* wanting ; *carpels* without tails. (Name from the Greek, *thallo,* to flourish.)

3. ANEMONE (Wind-flower).—*Sepals* 5–15, resembling petals ; *petals* wanting ; *involucre* of 3 leaves distinct from the flower. (Name from the Greek, *anemos,* the wind, from the exposed place of growth.)

4. ADONIS (Pheasant's Eye).—*Sepals* 5 ; *petals* 5–10, usually red, without a nectary at the base ; *carpels* without tails. (Name from *Adonis,* a youth who was killed by a wild boar, and whose blood is fabled to have stained flowers.)

5. RANUNCULUS (Crowfoot, Buttercup, Lesser Celandine, etc.).—*Sepals* 5 (rarely 3) ; *petals* 5 (rarely numerous), with a nectary at the base. (Name from the Latin, *rana,* a frog, an animal which frequents the kind of places where these plants grow.)

6. MYOSURUS (Mouse-tail).—*Sepals* 5, spurred ; *petals* 5,

minute ; *carpels* numerous, forming a lengthened spike. (Name, Greek for a mouse's tail.)

Carpels many-seedea

7. TROLLIUS (Globe-flower).—*Sepals* about 15, resembling petals ; *petals* 5 or more, small, narrow, flat. (Name said to be derived from an old German word, signifying a *globe*.)

8. CALTHA (Marsh Marigold).—*Sepals* 5, resembling petals ; no true *petals*. (Name from the Greek, *calathus*, a cup.)

9. HELLEBORUS (Hellebore).—*Sepals* 5, petal-like, persistent ; *petals* small, tubular ; *carpels* 3-10. (Name from the Greek, *helein*, to injure, and *bora*, food.)

10. AQUILEGIA (Columbine.)—*Sepals* 5, petal-like, soon falling off ; *petals* 5, with curved, tubular spur. (Name from the Latin, *aquila*, an eagle, to the claws of which its nectaries bear a fancied resemblance.)

11. DELPHINIUM (Larkspur).—*Sepals* 5, petal-like, soon falling off ; the upper one helmet-shaped, with a long spur at the base ; *petals* 2, concealed within the spur of the sepal ; *carpels* 1-5. (Name from *delphin*, a dolphin, to which animal the upper sepal bears a fancied resemblance.)

12. ACONITUM (Monk's-hood).—*Sepals* 5, petal-like, the upper one helmet-shaped, but not spurred ; *petals* 2, forming a spur which is concealed beneath the helmet-shaped sepal ; *carpels* 3-5. (Name of uncertain origin.)

13. ACTÆA (Bane-berry).—*Sepals* 4, petal-like, soon falling off ; *petals* 4 ; *fruit* a many-seeded berry. (Name from the Greek, *acte*, the elder, from the similarity of the leaves of the two plants.)

14. PÆONIA (Peony).—*Sepals* 5, not falling off ; *petals* 5-10 ; *carpels* 2-5. (Name from *Pæon*, a Greek physician, who is said to have cured wounds with it.)

1. CLEMATIS

1. *C. vitalba* (Traveller's Joy).—The only British species. A hedge shrub, common where limestone or chalk enters largely into the composition of the soil ; climbing other shrubs by the help of its twisting leaf-stalks, its stout woody stem and young branches often carrying it to a height of several yards. Well distinguished in summer by its loose panicles of greenish white, fragrant flowers, and in winter by its tufts of feathery seed-vessels, popularly known by the name of " Old Man's Beard." It received its name from " decking and adorning waies and hedges where people travel."—Fl. May, June. Perennial.

2. THALICTRUM (*Meadow Rue*)

1. *T. Alpinum* (Alpine Meadow Rue). *Stem* unbranched; *flowers* in a simple terminal cluster, drooping when fully expanded. A graceful little alpine plant, 4–6 inches high, common on the mountains of Scotland ; occasionally in the north of England and North Wales.—Fl. June, July. Perennial.

2. *T. minus* (Lesser Meadow Rue).—*Stem* zigzag, branched ; *leaves* thrice pinnate ; *leaflets* three-cleft, glaucous ; *flowers* in loose panicle, drooping, pale greenish yellow ; *sepals* tinged with pink ; *stamens* conspicuously yellow. A very variable species, usually found in limestone and chalky pastures, where it grows from 1–2 feet high ; on richer soils it grows more luxuriantly and the foliage loses its glaucous appearance. Great Britain and Ireland ; uncommon.—Fl. June, July. Perennial.

THALICTRUM ALPINUM
(*Alpine Meadow Rue*)

3. *T. flavum* (Yellow Meadow Rue).—*Stem* erect, branched, 3–4 feet high ; *flowers* crowded, not drooping, yellow ; *leaves* twice pinnate. Not uncommon about the banks of ditches and streams in England, Ireland, and the south of Scotland.— Fl. June, July. Perennial.

3. ANEMONE (*Wood Anemone*)

1. *A. nemorosa* (Wood Anemone, Wind-flower).—*Rootstock* creeping beneath the surface of the soil ; *flower* drooping ; *sepals* 6 ; *carpels* without tails. Plant from 3–6 inches high. This is one of our most beautiful spring flowers, adorning our woodlands at the season when primroses and violets are in perfection. The sepals are generally white, but not unfrequently tinged with pink externally ; more rarely they are of a delicate sky-blue, both within and without.—Fl. March to May. Perennial.

2. *A. pulsatilla* (Pasque-flower).—*Flower* slightly drooping ; *sepals* 6 ; *carpels* with feathery tails. The whole plant is clothed with silky hairs. The large, solitary flowers are of a dull violet hue, and are thickly covered with silky hairs on the outside. High chalky pastures. Rare.—Fl. about Easter (*Pâques*), hence the name. Perennial.

Two other species are described by British botanists—*A. apennina*, with blue flowers of 12 or more sepals, and *A. ranunculoides*, which has yellow flowers. They are not natives, but have apparently become thoroughly established in many places.

PLATE II.

Lesser Celandine
　　　Water Crowfoot
Creeping Buttercup

Bulbous Buttercup
Wood Anemone
　　Celery-leaved Buttercup

4. ADONIS (*Pheasant's Eye*)

1. *A. autumnalis.* — The only
British species. A pretty herbaceous plant, 8–12 inches high;
leaves finely cut; *flowers* resembling buttercups in shape; *sepals*
5; *petals* 5–8, bright scarlet, dark
at the base. It occurs as a weed
in cornfields, but is not very common, nor is it a real native of
Britain.—Fl. September to October.
Annual.

5. RANUNCULUS (*Buttercup, etc.*)

Flowers white

1. *R. aquatilis* (Water Crowfoot). — *Stem* submerged; *lower
leaves* deeply cleft into hairlike
segments; *upper ones* floating,
three-lobed, variously cut; *flowers*
large, white, conspicuous, borne
singly on axillary flower stalks.
A very variable plant. When
growing in swiftly running water
the plant is wholly composed of
hairlike leaves; but when growing
in stagnant water it produces flat-
tened leaves as well.—Fl. May to July. Perennial.

ADONIS (*Pheasant's Eye*)

2. *R. hederaceus* (Ivy-leaved Crowfoot).—*Leaves* all rounded
and lobed; *petals* scarcely longer than the calyx; *stamens* 5–10.
Smaller than the last, growing either in water or close to the
water's edge.—Fl. all the summer. Perennial.

Flowers yellow; leaves undivided

3. *R. lingua* (Great Spear-wort).—*Leaves* narrow, tapering to
a point, sessile; *stem* erect, 2–3 feet high; *flowers* bright yellow,
more than an inch in diameter. The largest British species,
a handsome plant, but not common; found in watery places.
—Fl. summer. Perennial.

4. *R. flammula* (Lesser Spear-wort).—*Leaves* narrow, tapering
to a point, slightly stalked; *stem* creeping at the base. Sides of
watery places; much smaller than the last; *flowers* about ½ inch
in diameter; leaves sometimes clothed with silky hairs.

5. *R. ficaria* (Lesser Celandine).—*Leaves* heart- or kidney-

shaped, angular ; *sepals* 3 ; *petals* about 9. One of our brightest
and earliest spring flowers, studding every bank with its glossy-
yellow, starlike flowers.—Fl. March to May. Perennial.

Flowers yellow ; leaves divided ; carpels smooth

6. *R. auricomus* (Wood Crowfoot, or Goldilocks).—*Radicle
leaves* kidney-shaped, lobed, on longish stalks ; *stem leaves*
deeply divided, without stalks. Whole plant about a foot high.
Flowers mostly irregular, owing to some of the petals being imperfectly developed. Common in woods.—Fl. April, May.
Perennial.

7. *R. sceleratus* (Celery-leaved Crowfoot).—*Leaves* smooth, cut
into oblong segments ; *stem* hollow, juicy, erect, branched ;
carpels collected into an oblong head. A highly acrid species,
from 6 inches to 2 feet high, growing in watery places in most
parts of the world. *Leaves* glossy ; *petals* small, pale yellow.
—Fl. June to August. Annual.

8. *R. bulbosus* (Bulbous Buttercup).—*Calyx* reflexed ; *flower-
stalks* channelled ; *root* bulbous ; whole plant about a foot high.
A common British meadow plant.—Fl. May, June. Perennial.

9. *R. repens* (Creeping Buttercup).—*Calyx* spreading ; *flower-
stalks* channelled ; *root* creeping. A common and most troublesome weed, increasing by creeping shoots, or *scions*, which take
root wherever a leaf is produced.—June to August. Perennial.

10. *R. acris* (Meadow Crowfoot).—*Calyx* spreading ; *flower-
stalks* cylindrical, not furrowed ; plant from 2–3 feet high ; *root*
composed of long fibres. Meadows—very common throughout
Britain. Well distinguished from the preceding by the above
characters, as well as by its slender stem and by the narrower
segments of its upper leaves.—Fl. June, July. Perennial.

A double variety is common in gardens, under the name of
Bachelor's Buttons.

Flowers yellow ; leaves divided ; carpels not smooth

11. *R. hirsutus* (Pale Hairy Buttercup).—*Calyx* reflexed ;
root fibrous ; *carpels* margined, and rough with small tubercles ;
plant 6 inches to 1 foot high ; *flowers* pale yellow. Meadows
and waste ground.—Fl. June to October. Annual.

12. *R. arvensis* (Corn Crowfoot).—*Calyx* spreading ; *carpels*
large and prickly ; *leaves* deeply divided ; *flowers* pale yellow ;
plant about 18 inches high, nearly glabrous. One of the most
poisonous of the genus, yet its seeds are said to be a favourite
food of partridges. A common weed in cornfields, especially in
the south of England.—Fl. June to August. Annual.

13. *R. parviflorus* (Small-flowered Crowfoot).—*Stem* prostrate, hairy; *seeds* covered with small hooked prickles. Well distinguished by its hairiness, prostrate mode of growth, and inconspicuous flowers which grow opposite the leaves. Fields and waste places —not common.—Fl. May to August. Annual.

Most of the plants of this genus are acrid, and are said to be injurious to cattle if mixed largely with their food. *R. flammula* and *sceleratus* are used in the Hebrides to raise blisters; these are, however, of objectionable use, being likely to produce sores difficult to heal. *R. aquatilis* is by some botanists separated into several species. Another species, *R. alpestris*, which grows on the Clova mountains, has divided leaves and white flowers.

6. MYOSURUS (*Mouse-tail*)

1. *M. minimus* (Common Mouse-tail).—A small annual plant, 3–6 inches high; *petals* yellow; *leaves* narrow, fleshy; easily distinguished from every other British plant by the arrangement of its ripe carpels into the appearance of a mouse's tail. Found in gravelly or chalky cornfields, chiefly in the south of England.—Fl. May. Annual.

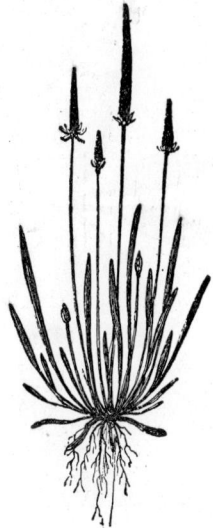

MYOSURUS (*Mouse-tail*)

7. TROLLIUS (*Globe Flower*)

1. *T. Europæus* (Globe Flower).—A large and handsome plant, common in gardens, and growing wild in upland woods and pastures in Scotland, Wales, and the north of England; rare in Ireland. The flowers are composed of about fifteen pale yellow sepals, which converge into the form of a globe, enclosing the petals and stamens.—Fl. June, July. Perennial.

8. CALTHA (*Marsh Marigold*)

1. *C. palustris* (Marsh Marigold, King Cup).—A large showy plant, resembling a gigantic buttercup; *leaves* kidney-shaped, large and glossy; *flowers* golden-yellow, often nearly four inches across. Abundant in marshes or by the sides of streams. A double variety is common in gardens.—Fl. Spring. Perennial.

9. HELLEBORUS (*Hellebore*)

HELLEBORUS VIRIDIS
(*Green Hellebore*)

1. *H. viridis* (Green Helle-bore, Bear's - foot). — *Leaves* digitate; *sepals* spreading; *petals* tubular, shorter than the calyx, containing honey which is said to be poisonous. A coarse, herbaceous plant, re-markable for the light green hue of its flowers. Height 12–18 inches.—Fl. March, April. Perennial.

2. *H. fœtidus* (Stinking Helle-bore, Setter-wort).—*Leaves* pe-date; *sepals* converging. Best distinguished from the preced-ing by its evergreen leaves, which are not divided to a com-mon centre, and by the purple hue of its sepals. Fl.—March, April. Perennial.

These two species may possi-bly be natives of one or two of the southern counties of Eng-land; but they are generally considered naturalized garden escapes. Both are found on cal-careous soils, and both are remarkable for their large green sepals and for the large tubular petals, in whose honey small flies may sometimes be found caught. Closely allied with this genus is the common garden flower, *Eranthis hyemalis* (Winter Aconite), a pretty little plant, with yellow flowers and glossy leaves, appear-ing very early in spring.

10. AQUILEGIA (*Columbine*)

1. *A. vulgaris* (Common Columbine).—The only British species, common in gardens, to which it is in spring very ornamental, with its delicate folded leaves, and no less so in summer, with its gracefully borne flowers, of curious shape and many delicate shades of colour. When growing wild its flowers are blue, white, or dull purple. It may be distinguished from all other British flowers by having each of its five petals terminated in an in-curved hornlike spur. It derives its English name, Columbine, from the fancied resemblance of its flowers to a nest of doves, *columba* being the Latin for a dove. Open woods.—Fl. June, July. Perennial.

PLATE III.

Columbine.

Marsh Marigold   Globe Flower

11. DELPHINIUM (*Larkspur*)

1. *D. ajacis* (Common Larkspur).—*Flowers* blue, pink, or white, in *racemes*, easily distinguished from other flowers by their spurred *calyx*. A not uncommon weed in cornfields, but not a native. Height 1–1½ feet. Many very beautiful species are cultivated in gardens.—Fl. June to August.

DELPHINIUM (*Larkspur*)   ACONITUM (*Monk's-hood*)

ACONITUM (*Monk's-hood*)

1. *A. napellus* (Common Monk's-hood, Wolf's-bane).—A common garden plant, 1–2 feet high, with handsome dark blue flowers. The whole plant, especially the root, is very poisonous, and derives its name, Woolf's-bane, from being used to poison the meat used as bait in wolf-traps. A doubtful native in parts of England and Wales.—Fl. June, July. Perennial.

13. ACTÆA (*Bane-berry*)

1. *A. spicata* (Bane-berry, Herb Christopher).—The only British species. *Stem* triangular, 1–2 feet high; *flowers* white; *fruit* almost black.

ACTÆA (*Bane-berry*)

Poisonous. A rare plant, found only in a few limestone localities in the north of England. Fl. May. Perennial.

14. PÆONIA (*Peony*)

1. *P. corallina* (Entire-leaved Peony). — A handsome, herbaceous plant, 1–2 feet high. *Flowers* deep red; *seed-vessels* downy. Not a native of Britain, but naturalized on the slopes of the Steep Holmes, an island in the Severn. Many beautiful species and varieties are cultivated in gardens.—Fl. May, June. Perennial.

PÆONIA (*Peony*)

NATURAL ORDER II

BERBERIDEÆ.—THE BARBERRY FAMILY

Sepals 3, 4, or 6, in a double row, often coloured, soon falling off, surrounded by petal-like scales ; *petals* either equal in number to the sepals, or opposite to them, or twice as many, often with a gland at the base ; *stamens* equal in number to the petals, and opposite to them ; *anthers* opening by a valve from the base upwards; *ovary* solitary, 1-celled, 1- to 3-seeded, generally turning to a berry. Shrubs, growing principally in mountainous parts of the temperate zones, especially in the north of India. Several species have thorny stems and astringent bark, and furnish a yellow dye ; the berries are acid—those of our species, *Berberis Asiatica*, are dried in the sun like raisins. Several handsome species are cultivated in gardens under the name of *Mahonia*.

1. BERBERIS (Barberry).—*Sepals* 6 ; *petals* 6, with 2 glands at the base of each ; *fruit*, a berry with 1–3 seeds. (Name said to be of Arabic origin.)

2. EPIMEDIUM (Barrenwort).—*Sepals* 4; *petals* 4, with a scale at the base of each ; *pod* many-seeded. (Name of uncertain origin.)

1. BERBERIS (*Barberry*)

1. *B. vulgaris* (Common Barberry).—A pretty shrub, not uncommon in woods and hedges, remarkable for the light colour of its bark, which is yellow within, and for its 3-forked spines. The flowers are yellow, and grow in drooping clusters ; the *filaments* are elastic and irritable, so that when touched ever so lightly by the legs of an insect they spring forward and close on the pistil, scattering the pollen from the anthers as they do so ; after some time they recover their original position. The berries are oblong, red when ripe and gratefully acid, and may be made into an agreeable preserve. Probably not a true native.—Fl. June. Perennial.

BERBERIS
(*Barberry*)

2. EPIMEDIUM (*Barrenwort*)

1. *E. Alpinum* (Alpine Barrenwort).—The only species found in Britain, occurring here and there in mountainous woods in some parts of Scotland and the north of England, but not really indigenous. Never growing more than a foot high ; each *stem* bears a single leaf, which is composed of 3 delicate heart-shaped leaflets.—Fl. May. Perennial.

EPIMEDIUM
ALPINUM (*Alpine
Barrenwort*)

Natural Order III

NYMPHÆACÆ.—Water Lily Tribe

Sepals 3–6, gradually passing into petals, and these into *stamens*, all being inserted on a fleshy disk, which surrounds the ovary; *stigma* sessile, rayed; *fruit* many-celled, many-seeded.

Herbaceous, aquatic plants, with peltate, floating leaves, and large, often fragrant flowers. The roots of some species are roasted and eaten; the seeds contain a considerable quantity of starch, and in seasons of scarcity are used as food. The East Indian *Nelumbium speciosum* is said to have been the sacred bean of Pythagoras. Its curious seed-vessels, filled with vegetating seeds, are thought to have originated the

NYMPHÆA ALBA (*White Water Lily*)

form of the cornucopia of the ancients. One plant of this order, *Victoria regia*, the largest and most beautiful of aquatic plants, produces blossoms 15 inches, and leaves more than 6 feet in diameter. The seeds are eatable, and are called in South America, Water Maize.

1. NYMPHÆA (Water Lily).—*Sepals* green on the outside; *petals* white, inserted on a fleshy disk. (Name from its growing in places which nymphs were supposed to haunt.)

2. NUPHAR (Yellow Water Lily).—*Sepals* yellow; *petals* small, yellow, inserted on the receptacle. (Name of Greek origin.)

1. NYMPHÆA (*Water Lily*)

1. *N. alba* (White Water Lily).—*Leaves* 6–8 inches in diameter, cordate, floating on the surface of the water; *flowers* about 5 inches in diameter and without scent. The only British species, and perhaps the most magnificent of our native flowers, inhabiting clear pools and slow rivers. The flowers rise above the water under the influence of light, and expand only during sunshine, in the middle of the day. Towards evening they close and sink beneath the surface.—Fl. July. Perennial.

2. NUPHAR (*Yellow Water Lily*)

1. *N. lutea* (Common Yellow Water Lily).—*Stigma* with 14–20 rays, which do not extend to the margin. Rivers and ditches, frequent. Much smaller than the last in all its parts. *Flower* yellow,

and nearly globose, raised some three inches out of the water, smelling like brandy, whence, in Norfolk and other parts of England, it is called Brandy-bottle. The Turks prepare a cooling drink from the flowers, which they call *Pufer*, a corruption of the ancient name Nouphar.—Fl. July. Perennial.

2. *N. pumila* (Least Yellow Water Lily).—*Stigma* of 8–10 rays, which extend beyond the margin. Much smaller than the preceding, from which it differs principally in the toothed edge of the stigma. It grows in several of the smaller Highland lakes.—Fl. July, August. Perennial.

NUPHAR LUTEA
(*Common Yellow Water Lily*)

NATURAL ORDER IV

PAPAVERACEÆ.—THE POPPY TRIBE

Sepals 2, soon falling off ; *petals* 4 ; *stigma* rayed, or lobed ; *capsule* 1-celled, many-seeded ; *seeds* inserted on incomplete partitions, which radiate from the sides of the capsule, but do not meet at the centre. Herbaceous plants, and, under the names of Opium, Laudanum, and Morphia, ranks among the most valuable of medicines. That produced from *Papaver somniferum* is alone used. The seeds of all contain a considerable quantity of oil, which is mild and wholesome.

1. PAPAVER (Poppy).—*Stigma* sessile, rayed ; *capsule* opening by pores beneath the stigma. " Named, because it is administered with *pap* (*papa* in Celtic) to induce sleep."—Sir W. J. Hooker.

2. MECONOPSIS (Welsh Poppy).—*Style* short ; *stigma* of few rays ; *capsule* opening by pores beneath the top. (Name in Greek signifying, *bearing resemblance to a poppy*.)

3. GLAUCIUM (Horned Poppy).—*Stigma* 2-lobed; *capsule* pod-like, 2-celled, 2-valved. (Name from the *glaucous* hue of the foliage.)

4. CHELIDONIUM (Celandine). — *Stigma* 2-lobed; *capsule*, pod-like, 1-celled, 2-valved ; *seeds* crested. (Named from *chelidon*, a swallow, because, Pliny tells us, that bird discovered that its juice was efficacious in restoring sight to its young when blinded.)

5. RŒMERIA (Rœmeria).—*Stigma* sessile, rayed ; *capsule* 3-4 valves ; *flowers* violet.

PLATE IV.

Common Red Poppy

Opium Poppy   Pale Poppy

1. PAPAVER (*Poppy*)

Capsules bristly

1. *P. Argemone* (Long Rough-headed Poppy, Pale Poppy).— *Capsule* club-shaped; *bristles* erect; *leaves* twice pinnatifid. A small species, with light scarlet petals, black at the base, occurring sparingly in cornfields. (The name Argemone, from *argos*, slothful, was formerly given to Poppies, from their narcotic effects.)—Fl. June, July. Annual.

2. *P. hybridum* (Round Rough-headed Poppy).—*Capsule* nearly globular; *bristles* spreading; *leaves* twice pinnatifid. Sandy or chalky cornfields—uncommon. *Flowers* deep scarlet. —Fl. June, July. Annual.

Capsules smooth

3. *P. dubium* (Long Smooth-headed Poppy).—*Capsule* oblong, often twice as long as broad; *bristles* on the flower-stalks close pressed; *leaves* twice pinnatifid; *flowers* scarlet.—Fl. June, July. Annual.

4. *P. rhœas* (Common Red Poppy).—*Capsules* nearly globular; *bristles* spreading; *leaves* pinnatifid, cut; *flowers* large, rich scarlet, often black at the base. The common poppy of corn-fields. From this species the well-known garden Shirley Poppies were raised, ranging through many beautiful and delicate shades of crimson, pink, and white.—Fl. June, July. Annual.

5. *P. somniferum* (Opium Poppy).—*Capsule* globular, smooth; *whole plant* glaucous, and smooth, with the exception of a few hairs on the flower-stalk, about 2 feet high. *Flowers* usually white with a purple stain at the base of the petals; but the colours of the garden varieties are endless. Common in gardens, and sometimes found apparently wild in waste ground, but its native country is unknown. Opium is procured by puncturing the unripe capsules of this plant, and collecting the juice which exudes and hardens. The seeds are destitute of narcotic proper-ties, and afford a wholesome oil, which is said to be used in adulterating olive oil.—Fl. July, August. Annual.

2. MECONOPSIS (*Welsh Poppy*)

1. *M. Cambrica* (Yellow Welsh Poppy).—The only British species, easily distinguished from any of the foregoing by its golden-yellow flowers, and juice of the same colour; and from the Horned Poppy by its slender growth, and green, not glaucous foliage. Rocky places in Wales, Devonshire, and Westmoreland, etc.—Fl. June, July. Perennial. A pretty variety with orange-coloured double flowers has recently been introduced into gardens.

3. GLAUCIUM (*Horned Poppy*)

1. *G. luteum* (Yellow Horned Poppy).—*Pod* roughish; *leaves* embracing the stem, wavy, very rough and glaucous. A handsome plant, conspicuous on the sandy seashore, with its hoary foliage and large yellow flowers. The *pods* are cylindrical, 6–10 inches long, and might at first sight be mistaken for flower-stems bare of leaves; *juice* yellow.—Fl. June to August. Biennial.

4. CHELIDONIUM (*Celandine*)

1. *C. majus* (Common or Greater Celandine).—The only British species; not uncommon in waste places and among ruins, bearing its yellow flowers, which are much smaller than those of any others of the Poppy tribe, in stalked *umbels;* the *leaves* are irregularly pinnate, slightly hairy, and abound, as well as the rest of the plant, in an orange-coloured juice, which is a violent acrid poison. It is a popular remedy for warts, and has been employed successfully in removing films from the cornea of the eye—a property which, Pliny tells us, was discovered by swallows; and hence it derived its name from *chelidon*, a swallow. According to the same author it comes into flower at the time when those birds arrive, and fades at their departure.—Perennial. The Lesser Celandine is a species of Ranunculus, and bears little resemblance, either in appearance or properties, to the present plant.

5. RŒMERIA (*Violet Horned Poppy*)

1. *R. hybrida* (Common Rœmeria, Violet Horned Poppy).—Distinguished by its purple-red *flowers*, and its *capsules*, which are 3-valved and 2–3 inches long, with a few hairs. Not indigenous, but naturalized in cornfields in Norfolk and Cambridgeshire.—Annual.

NATURAL ORDER V

FUMARIACEÆ.—THE FUMITORY TRIBE

Sepals 2, deciduous, minute; *petals* 4, irregular, the outer two more or less united, and swollen or spurred at the base, the inner two smaller and crested; *stamens* 6, in two sets; *ovary* 1-celled; *style* threadlike; *stigma* lobed; *seed-vessels* 1 or 2-seeded; *seeds* shining, crested. Herbaceous plants, with brittle stems, and watery juice, growing mostly in temperate climates. Closely allied to the Poppies, from which they may well be distinguished by their irregular corollas, and watery (not milky) juice.

1. CORYDALIS (Fumitory).—*Petals* 4, of which one is spurred

PLATE V.

Greater Celandine

Welsh Poppy   Yellow Horned Poppy

at the base; *seed-vessel* a many-seeded pod. (Name from the Greek name of *Fumitory*.)

2. FUMARIA (Fumitory).—Petals 4, of which one is swollen at the base; *seed-vessel* 1-seeded. (Name from *fumus*, smoke; the smoke of this plant being said by the ancient exorcists to have the power of expelling evil spirits.)

1. CORYDALIS (*Fumitory*)

1. *C. claviculata* (Climbing Corydalis). —*Stem* climbing; *leaves* pinnate, ending in branched tendrils. Bushy places, in many parts of Great Britain. A long and slender plant, with delicate green stems and foliage, rising to the height of several feet by the help of the bushes among which it grows. Flowers in small clusters, yellowish white.—Fl. June to August. Annual.

Two other species are naturalized in Britain—*C. solida*, distinguished by its unbranched stem and purple flowers, and *C. lutea* (Yellow Corydalis), not uncommon on old walls; it is, like the last, destitute of tendrils, and bears bright yellow flowers.

CORYDALIS CLAVICULATA
(*Climbing Corydalis*)

2. FUMARIA (*Fumitory*)

1. *F. capreolata* (Ramping Fumitory).—*Sepals* as broad as the corolla and half as long; *fruit* globose, notched; plant generally climbing by the help of its twisted leaf-stalks; *foliage* of a delicate green; *flowers* pale pink, or cream-coloured, tipped with purple. Hedges and cornfields, common.—Fl. May to August. Annual.

2. *F. officinalis* (Common Fumitory).—*Sepals* narrower than the corolla; *fruit* nearly globose, terminating abruptly. Distinguished from the last by its smaller sepals and petals, which are rose-coloured, tipped with purple; it generally grows erect. In fields and waste places, common.—Fl. nearly all the year round. Annual.

Several smaller varieties of Fumitory are not unfrequently met with, which some botanists consider distinct species, and name as such. In these the fruit is more or less pointed, and there are other minute differences which cannot be detected without accurate examination. They are described by Hooker and Arnott, under the names of *F. parviflora, vaillantii,* and *micrantha.*

NATURAL ORDER VI

CRUCIFERÆ.—THE CRUCIFEROUS TRIBE

A very large and important Order, well described by the name *cruci-ferous*, or cruciform, there being invariably 4 *petals*, which are placed cross-wise; *stamens* 6, of which two opposite ones are shorter than the rest; *seed-vessel* either a long pod, a *silique*, composed of two valves and a central par-tition, or a shorter pod called *silicle*, or pouch, which is for the most part, but not always, similarly con-structed. At the base of the stamens are generally two green glands, which secrete honey. Most of the plants of this Order possess, in their wild state, stimulant properties, and an acrid flavour, though none of them are poisonous; in medicine they afford a valuable remedy for scurvy. Under cultivation

CRUCIFORM
FLOWER

many of them assume a succulent habit of growth, and hold the first rank among esculent vegetables. The various kinds of cabbage, kale, broccoli, turnip, radish, and cress are the most remarkable examples. They contain a great deal of nitrogen gas, to the presence of which is to be attributed their unpleasant odour when rotting. Some contain a large portion of sulphur. Oil is contained in the seeds of many, in such quantities as to be a valuable article of commerce. There are some twelve hundred species, distributed chiefly over the northern hemisphere, par-ticularly in the cold and temperate regions. Upward of two hundred grow in the frigid zone, where they form a large proportion of the vegetation. In the tropics they are uncommon, and in certain districts the Order is quite unrepresented. This Order contains all the plants which were placed by Linnæus in the class Tetradynamia, that is, all such as are distinguished by having 6 stamens, 4 long and 2 short. Modern botanists found the main distinctions of the genera on the position of the radicle or embryo root, with relation to the cotyledons, or seed-lobes; but as this arrangement presents difficulties to the young student in botany, it is not considered advisable to adopt it here.

Seed-vessel, a pouch (silicle) *or short pod. Pouch 2-valved, with a central vertical partition.*

1. THLASPI (Penny Cress).—*Pouch* rounded, flat, notched; *valves* boat-shaped, winged at the back; *seeds* numerous. (Name from the Greek, *thlao*, to flatten.)

2. CAPSELLA (Shepherd's Purse).—*Pouch* inversely heart-shaped, flat; *valves* boat-shaped, keeled, but not winged; *seeds* numerous. (Name, a little *capsa*, or seed case.)

PLATE VI.

Yellow Corydalis   Corydalis Solida
Ramping Fumitory   Common Fumitory

3. HUTCHINSIA.—*Pouch* elliptical, entire ; *valves* boat-shaped, keeled, not winged ; *cells* 2-seeded. (Named in honour of *Miss Hutchins*, of Bantry, an eminent botanist.)

4. TEESDALIA.—*Pouch* rounded, notched ; *valves* boat-shaped, keeled ; *cells* 2-seeded ; *stamens* having a little scale at the base of each, within. (Named in honour of *Mr. Teesdale*, a Yorkshire botanist.)

5. IBERIS (Candytuft).—Two outer *petals* larger than the inner two ; *pod* oval, notched ; *valves* boat-shaped, with winged keel ; two 1-seeded *cells*. (Name from *Iberia*, Spain, where this genus is largely represented.)

6. LEPIDIUM (Pepper-wort).—*Pouch* roundish ; *valves* keeled ; *cells* 1-seeded ; *petals* equal. (Name from the Greek, *lepis*, a scale, from the shape of the pouches.)

7. COCHLEARIA (Scurvy Grass).—*Pouch* globose, or nearly so ; *seeds* in 2 rows. (Name from *cochlear*, a spoon, from the shape of the leaves.)

8. SUBULARIA (Awl-wort).—*Pouch* oval ; *valves* flattened, boat-shaped ; *seeds* numerous ; *leaves* awl-shaped. (Name from *subula*, an awl, from the shape of the leaves.)

9. ALYSSUM (Alyssum).—*Pod* oval, flattened ; *seeds* few.

10. DRABA (Whitlow Grass).—*Pod* oval or oblong ; *valves* slightly convex ; *seeds* many, in two rows. (Name from the Greek, *drabe*, acrid.)

Pod without a central partition

11. CAKILE (Sea Rocket).—*Pouch* angular, with a horizontal joint ; *lower division* containing a pendant seed, the *upper* one an erect seed, and soon falling off. (Name of Arabic origin.)

12. CRAMBE (Sea Kale).—*Pouch* 2-jointed ; *upper cell* containing one pendant seed, *lower joint* seedless. (Name from the Greek, *crambe*, cabbage.)

13. SENEBIERA (Wart Cress).—*Pouch* 2-lobed, rough, not bursting ; *cells* 1-seeded. (Name in honour of *M. Senebier*, an eminent Genevese naturalist.)

Seed vessel, a silique or long pod. Pod opening by two valves.

14. CARDAMINE (Bitter Cress).—*Pod* narrow ; *valves* flat, nerveless, separating with an elastic spring ; *seeds* in a single row. (Name from the Greek, *cardia*, the heart, and *damao*, to fortify, from its supposed strengthening properties.)

15. ARABIS (Rock Cress).—*Pod* linear ; *valves* flat, with one nerve or several veins. (Name from being originally an Arabian genus.)

C

16. BARBAREA (Winter Cress).—*Pod* linear, 4-angled ; *valves* with prominent nerve ; *seeds* in a single row ; *calyx* erect. (Name from *St. Barbara,* to whom it was anciently dedicated.)

17. NASTURTIUM (Cress).—*Pod* nearly cylindrical, short ; *valves* convex, nerveless ; *seeds* irregularly placed in two rows ; *calyx* spreading. (Name from *nasus tortus,* a distorted nose, on account of the pungent properties of the plant.)

18. SISYMBRIUM (Hedge Mustard).—*Pod* rounded or angular ; *valves* convex, with 3 (or rarely 1) nerves ; *stigma* entire ; *seeds* in a single row ; seed-stalks slender. (Name, the Greek name of the plant.)

19. ALLIARIA (Garlic Mustard).—*Pod* long, linear, rounded ; *valves* slightly 3-nerved ; *seeds* striated ; seed-stalks flat. (Name from the Latin, *allium,* garlic.)

20. ERYSIMUM (Treacle Mustard).—*Pod* 4-sided ; *valves* keeled ; *stigma* obtuse, entire or notched ; *seeds* in a single row, smooth, not margined. (Name from the Greek, *eruo,* to cure, on account of the supposed virtues of the plant.)

21. CHEIRANTHUS (Wall-flower).—*Pod* flattened ; *valves* with a prominent nerve ; *stigma* of two spreading lobes. (Name of Arabic origin.)

22. MATTHIOLA (Stock).—*Pod* nearly cylindrical, or flattened ; *stigma* of two erect parallel lobes ; *seeds* generally with a membranous border. (Named in honour of *Dr. Matthiolus,* an Italian botanist.)

23. BRASSICA (Cabbage).—*Pod* nearly cylindrical, beaked ; *seeds* globose. (Name from the Celtic, *bresic* a cabbage.)

Pod without valves

24. RAPHANUS (Radish).—*Pods* swollen, imperfectly jointed, tapering ; *seeds* globular ; *calyx* spreading. (Name in Greek, denoting early appearance or quick growth.)

1. THLASPI (*Penny Cress*)

1. *T. arvense* (Mithridate Mustard, or Penny Cress).—*Pouch* round, flat, with very broad wings and a deep notch ; *leaves* oblong, arrow-shaped at the base, toothed, smooth. Height about a foot. In cultivated or waste ground, but not common. Penny Cress derives its name from the resemblance which its seed-vessels in size and shape bear to silver pennies ; its longer name is

THLASPI ARVENSE
(*Penny Cress*)

received from having been " formerly used in the Mithridate confec-
tion, an elaborate hodge-podge now laid aside."—Sir E. J. Smith.
The *flowers* are white, and very small in comparison with the
pouches.—Fl. all the summer. Annual.

2. *T. perfoliatum* (Perfoliate Penny Cress).—*Pouch* inversely
heart-shaped, not so large as in the last, and with smaller wings ;
style shorter than the notch of the pouch ; *seeds* 3–4 in a cell,
smooth ; *stem-leaves* oblong, heart-shaped at the base, clasping
the stem ; height up to 6 inches. Limestone pastures in Oxfordshire and Gloucestershire, but rare. Flower
white.—Fl. April, May. Annual.

3. *T. alpestre* (Alpine Penny Cress).—*Pouch*
inversely heart-shaped ; *style* longer than the
broad notch of the pouch ; *seeds* numerous ;
stem-leaves narrow and clasping the stem ; *stem*
simple, about 6 inches high ; *flowers* white,
rather larger than in the two foregoing. Mountainous limestone pastures in the north of England, rare.—Fl. June, July. Perennial.

2. CAPSELLA (*Shepherd's Purse*)

CAPSELLA BURSA
PASTORIS (*Common
Shepherd's Purse*)

1. *C. bursa Pastoris* (Common Shepherd's
Purse).—The only species. A common weed,
to be found in almost every part of the world,
varying considerably in luxuriance, according
to soil and situation. In stony ground it
grows only a few inches high, but in rich soil
as much as 2 feet. The whole plant is more
or less rough with hairs ; the *root-leaves* are
pinnatifid, those on the *stem* oblong, toothed,
and arrow-shaped at the base.—Fl. nearly the
whole year round. Annual.

3. HUTCHINSIA

1. *H. petræa* (Rock Hutchinsia).—The only
British species. A pretty little plant, 2–3
inches high, growing on limestone rocks in
several parts of England and Wales. The
leaves are pinnate ; *flowers* minute, *petals*
white, scarcely longer than the calyx ; the
seeds 2 in each cell.—Fl. March, April. Annual.

HUTCHINSIA PETRÆA
(*Rock Hutchinsia*)

4. Teesdalia

1. *T. nudicaulis* (Naked-stalked Teesdalia).—The only British species. A minute and not inelegant plant, bearing several stems, which terminate in small racemes of white *flowers*, the central *stem* being always bare of leaves. The *leaves* are pinnate, about half an inch long, and lie closely pressed to the ground. Though widely spread over England, it is not a common plant. Dry banks.—Fl. May. Annual.

Teesdalia
Nudicaulis
(*Naked-stalked
Teesdalia*)

5. Iberis (*Candytuft*)

1. *I. amara* (Bitter Candytuft).—Plant 6 or 8 inches high, bearing its white or pink *flowers* in a flat head or corymb. *Petals* unequal, the two outer larger than the two inner. An occasional cornfield weed on calcareous soils. —Fl. July. Annual. (Candytuft is a common garden plant, and is particularly effective in the rock garden.)

6. Lepidium (*Pepper-wort*)

1. *L. latifolium* (Broad-leaved Pepper-wort, Dittander).—The largest British species, remarkable for its dull glaucous hue; plant 2–4 feet high; *leaves* egg-shaped, pointed, simple, smooth; *pouch* oval, entire; *flowers* numerous, small, white, in leafy clusters. In salt marshes and on the sea-coast; rare. —Fl. July. Perennial.

Lepidium Latifolium
(*Broad-leaved Pepper-wort*)

2. *L. ruderale* (Narrow-leaved Pepper-wort).—Smaller than the preceding, 6–12 inches high; *leaves* smooth, *lower ones* pinnatifid, toothed, *upper ones* linear, entire; *petals* wanting; *stamens* 2. Waste places near the sea.—Fl. June. Annual.

3. *L. campestre* (Field Pepper-wort).—*Stem* erect, branched above, about a foot high; *leaves* downy, *upper ones* arrow-shaped at the base; *pod* rough with minute scales; *style* scarcely longer than the notch in the pod; *flowers* very small; *anthers* yellow. Common.—Fl. July, August. Annual or biennial.

Lepidium Campestre (*Field Pepper-wort*)

4. *L. Smithii* (Hairy Pepper-wort). — *Leaves* downy, *upper ones* arrow-shaped at the base;

pouch not scaly ; *style* much longer than the notch ; *anthers* violet. (These last two are common hedge plants, of erect growth and downy habit, made more conspicuous by their hoary foliage and numerous pouches than by their minute flowers. *L. campestre* is an annual, and sends up a single stem. *L. Smithii* is perennial, and sends up several stems, which are woody near the base. The latter is the less common of the two.)—Fl. June to August. Perennial.

7. COCHLEARIA (*Scurvy Grass*)

1. *C. officinalis* (Common Scurvy Grass).— *Pouch* nearly globose ; *root-leaves* heart-shaped or kidney-shaped, stalked ; *stem-leaves* oblong, sessile, slightly lobed, toothed at the base, all fleshy and glabrous ; *stem* often much branched ; *flowers* in rather large corymbs, white. On the muddy sea-shore, common.—Fl. May. Annual.

2. *C. Anglica* (English Scurvy Grass).— *Pouch* elliptical, inflated ; *root-leaves* oblong, entire, stalked, not heart-shaped ; *stem-leaves* oblong, toothed at the base, sessile. Leaves more entire and pouches and flowers larger than in the last. Seashores, common. Fl. May to August. Annual.

COCHLEARIA OFFICINALIS
(*Common Scurvy Grass*)

3. *C. Danica* (Danish Scurvy Grass). —Smaller than either of the preceding ; *leaves* all stalked, lobed, and nearly triangular. Cliffs and hedges near the sea, very common.—Fl. March to June. Annual.

Two other forms are—*C. Alpina*, not so large as *C. officinalis*, *pods* narrowing at the ends ; and *C. Grœnlandica.* Mountains, Northern Scotland.

COCHLEARIA DANICA
(*Danish Scurvy Grass*)

4. *C. armoracia* (Horse-radish).—*Root-leaves* stalked, toothed, often a foot long. *Stem* as much as 3 feet high, *stem-leaves* almost stalkless ; *flowers* yellow, small. Remarkable for its long, stringy *roots*, which have a pungent taste and are used in cooking. Really a garden plant, but has become established in some places. Waste ground.—Fl. June to August. Perennial.

The plants of this genus derive their English name from the relief they afford to persons suffering from scurvy, a disease to which sailors are particularly liable, in consequence of their being debarred from the use of fresh vegetables. Many other plants of the same tribe possess antiscorbutic properties to an equal degree, but these are particularly available from always growing near the sea. The use of lime-juice in the navy and merchant service has rendered the attacks of this disease less frequent than they used to be.

8. SUBULARIA (*Awl-wort*)

1. *S. aquatica* (Water Awl-wort).—The only species. The *roots* are composed of long white fibres; the *leaves* all grow from the roots, and are awl-shaped; the *flowers* are small and few; *petals* white. The plant often grows entirely under water; common on the banks of Alpine lakes.—Fl. July. Annual.

SUBULARIA AQUATICA (*Water Awl-wort*)

9. ALYSSUM (*Alyssum*)

1. *A. calycinum* (Small Alyssum).—A small annual, 3–6 inches high. *Flowers* pale yellow; *sepals* persistent, or remaining on the pods. Waste places, rare.—Fl. April to June.

2. *A. maritimum* (Sweet Alyssum).—A pretty garden plant, with trailing ascending *stems* and white, sweet-scented *flowers;* *sepals* falling off. In many places it has become established as a garden escape.—Fl. all summer. Annual or perennial.

10. DRABA (*Whitlow Grass*)

1. *D. aizoides* (Yellow Alpine Whitlow Grass).—*Flower-stalk* leafless, smooth; *petals* notched, twice as long as the calyx; *style* much longer than the stamens; *leaves* narrow, pointed, rigid, glossy, keeled, and fringed. On rocks and walls at Pannard Castle, near Swansea, where it forms dense tufts, conspicuous with bright yellow flowers.—Fl. March, April. Perennial.

2. *D. rupestris* (Rock Whitlow Grass).—A very rare species growing in the crevices of the rocks and among moss, on the summits of some of the Highland mountains. It seldom exceeds 2 inches in height; the *flower-stems* are usually leafless, several growing from the same root; the *leaves* grow in tufts and are slightly hairy.—Fl. July. Perennial.

3. *D. incana* (Twisted Whitlow Grass).—*Stems* 4–12 inches high, bearing small white *flowers;* *stem-leaves* narrow, toothed, hoary; *petals* entire; *pouch* twisted. Remarkable for the down on its leaves, which is forked in a starlike manner. Mountains and sand dunes on the coast, scarce.—Fl. June, July. Biennial.

4. *D. muralis* (Speedwell-leaved Whitlow Grass).—
Stem leafy, branched; *leaves* rough, egg-shaped, blunt,
toothed, embracing the stem; *pedicles* spreading horizontally; *stem* 6–12 inches high; *flowers* white. Limestone mountains, rare.—Fl. May. Annual.

5. *D. verna* (Vernal Whitlow Grass).—*Flower-stalk*
leafless; *petals* deeply cleft; *leaves* all radicle, forming
a rosette, somewhat toothed, hairy. Common on walls
and dry banks.—Fl. February to May. Annual.

DRABA
VERNA
(*Vernal
Whitlow
Grass*)

This species is classed by some botanists as a distinct
genus—*Erophila;* the following forms occur : *E. vul-*
garis, pods twice as long as broad, common form;
E. brachycarpa, pods rounded, not
common; *E. inflata, pods* inflated,
found on Ben Lewers, in Scotland.

11. CAKILE (*Sea Rocket*)

1. *C. maritima* (Purple Sea Rocket).
—The only British species. Common on
the sandy seashore, where it grows in
a bushy manner, with zigzag branched
stems; bearing fleshy, variously cut,
glaucous *leaves;* and *corymbs* of lilac
flowers. The *seed-vessels* are of very
curious construction, each containing
2 seeds, of which the lower is erect,
the upper pendant.—Fl. June to September. Annual.

CAKILE MARITIMA
(*Purple Sea Rocket*)

12. CRAMBE (*Sea Kale*)

1. *C. maritima* (Sea Kale).—Plant about
2 feet high; glabrous, glaucous; *leaves*
thick, waved and toothed; *root* hard,
almost woody. This is the plant which
is so well known in gardens as an esculent
vegetable. The part which is eaten is
the leaf-stalk, blanched by being kept
from the action of the light. It is found
on various parts of the sea-coast, and
differs in no respect from garden specimens, as they appear when the forcing is
over.—Fl. June. Perennial.

CRAMBE MARITIMA
(*Sea Kale*)

13. SENEBIERA (*Wart Cress*)

1. *S. coronopus* (Wart Cress or Swine Cress). —*Pouch* undivided, rough, with little sharp points ; *style* prominent. A common roadside weed, with trailing leafy stems, and clusters of very small whitish flowers.—Fl. all the summer. Annual.

2. *S. didyma* (Lesser Wart Cress).—*Pouch* notched, of two wrinkled lobes ; *style* very short. A common roadside weed in the south and west of England. It differs from the last in having a more slender stem, and more finely cut leaves. It emits a very powerful smell, like that of Pepper-cress, especially when trodden on, or in hot weather, and is particularly nauseous to the taste.—Fl. all the summer. Annual.

SENEBIERA
CORONOPUS
(*Wart Cress*)

14. CARDAMINE (*Bitter Cress*)

1. *C. amara* (Large-flowered Bitter Cress).—*Leaves* pinnate, without stipules ; *root-leaflets* roundish, those of the stem toothed and angular ; *stem* ascending, about a foot high ; *style* oblique. By the banks of rivers and canals, not common. The *flowers* are large and handsome, white, with purple anthers.—Fl. April, May. Perennial.

2. *C. pratensis* (Cuckoo-flower or Lady's Smock). —*Leaves* pinnate, without stipules ; *root-leaves* roundish, slightly angular, those of the *stem* entire ; *style* straight. A common and very pretty meadow plant, with large lilac flowers. A double variety is sometimes found wild, which is remarkably pro- liferous, the leaflets producing new plants when they come in contact with the ground, and the flowers as they wither sending up a stalked flower- bud from their centres.—Fl. May. Perennial.

3. *C. impatiens* (Narrow-leaved Bitter Cress).— *Stem* erect, leafy, about 18 inches high ; *leaves* pinnate ; *auricles* fringed. Moist rocks in some parts of Scotland and the north of England, rare. —Fl. May, June. Annual.

4. *C. hirsuta* (Hairy Bitter Cress).—*Leaves* pin- nate, without stipules ; *leaflets* stalked, toothed ; *pods* erect. A common weed everywhere, varying in size according to soil and situation, from 6–18 inches in height. In dry localities it ripens its seed in March or April, and withers away ; but in

CARDAMINE
HIRSUTA
(*Hairy Bitter Cress*)

PLATE VII.

Common Watercress
Garlic Mustard

Cuckoo Flower
Charlock (Wild Mustard)

CRUCIFEROUS TRIBE

damper places continues in flower all the summer. The leaves and young flower-stems afford an agreeable salad. The *flowers* are white, very small, and often imperfect, and are soon overtopped by the lengthening pods, the valves of which, when ripe, curl up with an elastic spring if touched, and fly off, scattering the seeds to a considerable distance.—Fl. all the summer. Annual.

5. *C. bulbifera* (Bulbiferous Bitter Cress, Coral-root).—*Stem* erect, about 18 inches high, unbranched. Well distinguished from any other British plant in the order, by its purple flowers, its whitish toothed roots, and dark purple, scaly bulbs, which grow in the axils of the upper leaves, and falling off when mature produce new plants. Seeds are seldom produced, the plant depending for propagation upon the axillary bulbils.

CARDAMINE BULBIFERA
(*Bulbiferous Bitter Cress, Coral-Root*)

ARABIS PERFOLIATA
(*Glabrous Rock Cress; Tower Mustard*)

15. ARABIS (*Rock Cress*)

1. *A. perfoliata* (Glabrous Rock Cress, Tower Mustard).—*Stem* erect, about 2 feet high; *stem-leaves* glabrous; clasping the stem; *root-leaves* slightly hairy; *flowers* pale yellow, small. It grows on banks and open places, widely distributed in England, but never very common.

2. *A. turrita* (Tower Cress).—*Stem* about 1 foot high; plant rough with forked hairs; *stem-leaves* clasping the stem; *flowers* whitish yellow; *pods* curved downwards as they ripen. Naturalized on old walls at Oxford and Cambridge, but not a true native of Britain.—Fl. May to July. Biennial.

3. *A. hirsuta* (Hairy Rock Cress).—A stiff, erect plant, about a foot high. *Leaves* rough with hairs, those of the stem numerous, clasping the stem; *flowers* small, white. Frequent in many parts of Great Britain on walls and banks.—Fl. June, July. Biennial.

4. *A. alpina* (Alpine Rock Cress).—*Flowers* larger than in the last; *stem-leaves* toothed, downy. A rare species only found in the Isle of Skye.—Perennial.

5. *A. ciliata* (Fringed Rock Cress).—*Stem* about 6 inches high, smooth; *leaves* smooth on both sides, fringed with hairs at the edges; *flowers* white. Confined to a few localities in South Wales and the west of Ireland.—Perennial.

6. *A. thaliana* (Thale Rock Cress).—*Stem* 6–12 inches high; *stem-leaves* few; *root-leaves* spreading, oblong, toothed; plant covered with short hairs; *flowers* small, white; *seed-pods* twice as long as the stalks which bear them. Walls and banks, common. —Fl. all the summer. Annual.

7. *A. stricta* (Bristol Rock Cress).—Plant about 6 inches high; *stem-leaves* few; *root-leaves* forming a tuft, hairy, pinnate; *flowers* yellowish white. Limestone rocks near Bristol.—Fl. spring. Perennial.

8. *A. petræa* (Northern Rock Cress).—*Stems* about 6 inches, branched below; *root-leaves* usually smooth, pinnate; *flowers* white with a purplish tinge. Mountains in Scotland and Wales.—Fl. summer. Perennial.

ARABIS THALIANA
(*Thale Rock Cress*)

16. BARBAREA (*Winter Cress*)

1. *B. vulgaris* (Common Winter Cress).— Lower leaves lyrate, the terminal lobe roundish; *upper* obovate, toothed. Common in moist waste ground, where it may be readily detected by its smooth, shining, dark green *leaves*, and its erect angular *stem*, bearing numerous bright yellow *flowers*. A variety with double flowers is frequent in gardens under the name of Yellow Rocket. —Fl. May to August. Perennial.

2. *B. præcox* (American Cress).—Distinguished by its slender habit and narrow leaves, but it is only an escape from gardens, and is used for salad.—Biennial.

Botanists have distinguished several forms of *B. vulgaris;* some of them are of rare occurrence, and the differences by which they are distinguished are so slight that it is unnecessary to give them here.

BARBAREA VULGARIS
(*Common Winter Cress*)

17. NASTURTIUM (*Cress*)

1. *N. officinale* (Common Water-cress).—*Leaves* pinnate; *leaflets* roundish or oblong, toothed; *flowers* white. Abundant in rivulets and ponds, and extensively cultivated as a salad. The only plant for which it can be mistaken by water-cress gatherers is the *Procumbent apium*, which may be distinguished by its hollow leaf-stalks and serrated leaflets, which water-cress has not.—Fl. June to August. Perennial.

2. *N. sylvestre* (Creeping Yellow Cress).—*Leaves* pinnate; *root* creeping; *stems* ascending; *flowers* small, yellow; *petals* longer than *sepals*. Watery places, not common.—Fl. June to September. Perennial.

3. *N. palustre* (Marsh Yellow Cress).—Not so large as the last, and *petals* smaller. Found in similar places, but more frequent. —Fl. June to November.

4. *N. amphibium.* Larger than any of the foregoing. *Flowers* yellow; *petals* longer than the *sepals*. Banks of streams and wet places, not common.—Fl. June to August. Perennial.

18. SISYMBRIUM (*Hedge Mustard*)

1. *S. officinale* (Common Hedge Mustard).— *Pods* downy, close pressed to the stem; *leaves* hairy, deeply lobed, with the points turned backward, the terminal lobe large; *stem* rough, with erect *branches*, 1–2 feet high; *flowers* small, yellow. Common in waste places and by roadsides, where it seems to have a peculiar aptitude for collecting and retaining dust. —Fl. June, July. Annual.

SISYMBRIUM OFFICINALE (*Common Hedge Mustard*)

2. *S. Irio* (London Rocket).—*Leaves* pinnately lobed, with the points turned backward, toothed, smooth; *stem* also smooth, erect, branched, about 2 feet high; *flowers* small, yellow. A local plant, growing in waste ground, chiefly about London, where, in the spring following the Great Fire of 1666, it sprang up very plentifully among the ruins, whence its English name.

3. *S. Sophia* (Flixweed).—*Leaves* twice pinnatifid, downy; *petals* shorter than the calyx. More slender than either of the preceding, with an erect branched *stem* about 1 foot high; and small greenish yellow *petals*, which are almost hidden by the calyx; and numerous erect *pods*, which when ripe have the appearance of being bearded, from the numerous projecting seeds. Waste places and roadsides, not uncommon.—Fl. summer. Annual. It was called by the old herbalists *Sophia chirurgorum*, "the Wisdom of Surgeons," from its supposed virtue in curing wounds.

19. ALLIARIA (*Garlic Mustard*)

1. *A. officinalis* (Garlic Mustard, Jack-by-the-Hedge, or Sauce-alone).—*Leaves* broadly heart-shaped, stalked, heavily veined. An early flowering hedge-plant, 1–3 feet high, with delicate green leaves and snow-white flowers. The whole plant emits when bruised a nauseous scent of garlic, from which it derives its Latin and English names.—Fl. April to June. Annual or biennial.

20. ERYSIMUM (*Treacle Mustard*)

1. *E. cheiranthoides* (Treacle Mustard, Worm Seed).—*Leaves* narrow, slightly toothed, roughish with three-forked bristles, dull green ; *pods* erect on spreading stalks ; *stem* branched, 1–3 feet high ; *flowers* small, yellow, with whitish *sepals*. Fields, gardens, and waste places, not common.—Fl. June to August. Annual.
2. *E. orientale* (Hare's-ear Treacle Mustard). — With smooth entire *leaves* clasping the *stem*, which is about 1 foot high ; *flowers* cream-coloured. Grows on some parts of the coast of Essex, Suffolk, and Sussex, but is an escape.—Early summer. Annual.

21. CHEIRANTHUS (*Wall-flower*)

1. *C. Cheiri* (Wall-flower).—The only British species, flourishing best on the walls of old buildings, and producing its sweet-scented yellow flowers nearly all the summer, although scantily supplied with water. Not a true native, but has become thoroughly established in many situations of the kind described above. Many beautiful varieties are cultivated in gardens, some with blood-red flowers, some double. Perennial.

22. MATTHIOLA (*Stock*)

1. *M. incana* (Hoary Shrubby Stock, Gilliflower).—*Stem* shrubby, 1–2 feet high ; *leaves* hoary with down, entire ; *flowers* large, light purple. The origin of the garden Stock. On the southern seashore of the Isle of Wight.—Fl. May, June. Perennial.

CHEIRANTHUS CHEIRI
(*Wall-flower*)

2. *M. sinuata* (Great Sea Stock).—*Stem* herbaceous, spreading; *leaves* oblong, downy, the lower ones imperfectly lobed ; *pods* rough with prickles ; *flowers* dull purple, very fragrant by night.—Fl. August. Biennial. Sandy sea-coasts of Wales and Cornwall.

23. BRASSICA (*Cabbage*)

1. *B. tenuifolia* (Wall Rocket).—*Stem* erect, slender, smooth, leafy ; *leaves* narrow, smooth, deeply divided into narrow segments ; *pods* lined, slightly beaked, erect. A slender, branched plant, from 1–2 feet high, with a tough stem, woody below, scattered foliage, and large light yellow *flowers ;* it grows on old walls, quarries, and waste places, principally in the neighbourhood of large towns.—Fl. all the summer. Perennial.

2. *B. muralis* (Sand Rocket).—An annual, with a bristly stem, is very like the last, but smaller, and grows in barren places near the sea, but is not considered indigenous.

3. *B. Monensis* (Isle of Man Cabbage).—*Leaves* glaucous, pinnatifid ; *stem* nearly leafless, and 6–12 inches high ; *pods* 4-angled ; *flowers* bright lemon-coloured, veined with purple. Sandy seashores on the western coast of Britain, rare.—Fl. summer. Perennial.

4. *B. oleracea* (Sea Cabbage). — *Root* stem-like, fleshy ; *stem* branched, 1–2 feet high ; *leaves* perfectly smooth, glaucous, waved, lobed ; *stem-leaves* oblong, obtuse ; *flowers* lemon-coloured and large. The original of all the varieties of garden cabbage growing on several parts of the sea-coast.—Fl. May to August. Biennial.

5. *B. campestris* (Common Wild Navew).—*Root-leaves* pinnate, with rounded terminal lobe, toothed, roughish ; *stem-leaves* smooth, heart-shaped, tapering to a point ; all somewhat glaucous ; *stem* about 2 feet high, usually unbranched. Borders of fields, common. Often confounded with *Charlock*, from which, however, it may readily be distinguished by the smoothness and glaucous hue of its upper leaves.—Fl. June, July. Annual.

B. rapa, Rape or Colza ; *B. rutabaga*, the Swedish turnip, commonly known as Swede ; and *B. napus*, the Turnip, are all varieties in cultivation.

6. *B. alba* (White Mustard).—*Pods* bristly, rugged, spreading, shorter than the flat two-edged beak ; *leaves* pinnatifid ; *flowers* rather large, yellow. The young leaves of this plant are used as salad. Waste ground.— Fl. June, July. Annual.

BRASSICA CAMPESTRIS
(*Common Wild Navew*)

7. *B. sinapis* (Charlock, Wild Mustard).—*Pods* with many angles, rugged, longer than the awl-shaped beak, spreading ; *leaves* rough, toothed ; plant 1-2 feet high ; *flowers* bright yellow. A common and most pernicious weed in cornfields, sometimes springing up profusely from ground which has recently been disturbed, though unknown there before.—Fl. all the summer. Annual.

8. *B. nigra* (Black Mustard).—*Pods* quadrangular, smooth, slightly beaked, close pressed to the stalk ; *lower leaves* pinnate, with rounded terminal lobe ; *upper leaves* narrow, pointed, undivided, smooth. Taller than either of the preceding, but bearing smaller flowers. The seeds yield the well-known table condiment. —Fl. June, July. Annual.

9. *B. adpressa*.—Resembling the last, but the *foliage* is hoary, the *pods* short, beaked. Found in the Channel Islands.—Biennial.

24. RAPHANUS (*Radish*)

RAPHANUS KAPHANISTRUM
(*Wild Radish*)

1. *R. Raphanistrum* (Wild Radish).— A bristly or almost prickly plant ; *leaves* horizontal, pinnate, with rounded terminal lobe ; *flowers* rather large, straw-coloured, veined with purple ; well distinguished when in seed by its jointed 1-celled pods.—Fl. all the summer. Annual. Cornfields.

A variety named *R. maritimus*, which grows on sea-cliffs, has its leaves composed of large and small leaflets arranged alternately. In both varieties the flowers are sometimes almost white.

An interesting cruciferous plant, rare in England and not indigenous, is *Isatis tinctoria :* erect, smooth, glaucous, 1-3 feet high. It was with this plant—Woad—that the Ancient Britons stained their bodies blue, and it is still in use as a dye.

NATURAL ORDER VII

RESEDACEÆ.—THE MIGNONETTE TRIBE

Sepals 4-6, narrow ; *petals* unequal, ragged, or fringed at the back ; *stamens* 10-24, inserted as well as the petals on an irregular disc, which is placed on one side of the flower ; *stigmas* 3, sessile ; *ovary* 3-lobed, 1-celled, many-seeded, open at the summit ; *seeds* in 3 rows. Herbaceous or somewhat shrubby plants, with alternate leaves and minute stipules, having their flowers in racemes or

PLATE VIII.

Wild Mignonette   Common Rock Rose

spikes. Most of the plants of this Order inhabit Europe and the neighbouring parts of Africa and Asia. *Reseda odorata,* mignonette, is a native of Egypt, and on account of the delicious perfume of its flowers is a universal garden favourite.

1. RESEDA (Mignonette).—*Calyx* many-parted ; *petals* entire, or variously cut, unequal ; *stamens* numerous ; *capsule* 1-celled, opening at the top. (Name from the Latin, *resedo,* to calm, from the supposed sedative qualities of some species.)

1. RESEDA (*Mignonette*)

1. *R. luteola* (Dyer's Rocket, Yellow-weed, or Weld).—*Leaves* narrow, undivided ; *calyx* 4-parted. An erect herbaceous plant, 1–2 feet high, with long blunt shining leaves, and terminal spikes of yellowish flowers, with conspicuous stamens, and short flattened capsules. It was used to dye wool yellow, or, with indigo, green ; the whole plant when in flower being boiled for that purpose. Waste places, especially on chalk or limestone soils.—Fl. summer. Annual or biennial.

2. *R. lutea* (Wild Mignonette).—*Leaves* 3-cleft, lower ones pinnatifid ; *calyx* 6-parted ; *petals* 6, very unequal. More bushy than the last, and not so tall, and may be distinguished by the above characters, as well as by the shorter and broader flower spikes. On chalky hills and waste places.—Fl. July, August. Biennial.

3. *R. alba* (White Mignonette or Shrubby Rocket).—*Leaves* pinnate, glaucous ; *sepals* usually 5 ; *petals* the same ; *flowers* whitish. A garden plant, sometimes found as an escape in waste places.—Fl. summer. Biennial.

NATURAL ORDER VIII

CISTACEÆ.—THE ROCK-ROSE TRIBE

Sepals either 3 equal, or 5 with 2 smaller than the rest twisted in the bud ; *petals* 5, twisted when in bud in a direction contrary to the sepals, soon falling off ; *stamens* numerous ; *ovary* single ; *style* and *stigma* simple ; *capsule* 3–5, or, rarely, 10-valved ; *seeds* numerous. Mostly shrubby, but sometimes herbaceous plants, often with sticky branches ; *leaves* entire ; *flowers* white, red, or yellow, lasting a very short time. The plants of this Order are almost confined to the south of Europe and north of America ; the only species which possesses any remarkable properties is *Cistus Creticus*, which affords the balsam called *Gum Ladanum.*

1. HELIANTHEMUM (Rock-Rose).—*Sepals* 5, the two outer either smaller or wanting ; *petals* 5 ; *stamens* numerous ; *capsule* 3-valved. (Name from the Greek, *helios,* the sun, and *anthos,* a flower, because the flowers expand when the sun shines.)

1. Helianthemum (*Rock-Rose*)

1. *H. vulgare* (Common Rock-Rose).—*Stem* shrubby, prostrate; *leaves* with fringed stipules, oblong, green above, hoary beneath; *calyx* of 5 sepals, the two outer very small, fringed. A beautiful little branching shrub, with loose racemes of large bright yellow flowers, frequent in hilly pastures on a chalky or gravelly soil, where its flowers only expand during sunshine; the stamens if lightly touched spread out and lie down on the petals.—Fl. July, August. Perennial.

2. *H. canum* (Hoary Rock-Rose).—Grows on Alpine rocks in Wales and the north of England; the whole plant is smaller than the above. The *leaves* are without stipules and very hoary beneath; *flowers* small, yellow. Rare.

3. *H. guttatum* (Spotted Rock-Rose).—A herbaceous species, the *flowers* of which are yellow, with a blood-red spot at the base of each petal. Rare—Channel Islands, Cork in Ireland, and in Anglesea.—Annual.

4. *H. polifolium* (White Rock-Rose).—A small shrubby species with white *flowers*, and *leaves* downy on both sides. Grows on Brent Downs in Somersetshire, and on a few parts of the Devonshire coast.

Natural Order IX

VIOLACEÆ.—The Violet Tribe

Sepals 5; *petals* 5, sometimes unequal; *stamens* 5; *anthers* lengthened into a flat membrane; *style* with a swollen stigma; *ovary* 1-celled; *seeds* numerous, in 3 rows. A beautiful and important Order of herbaceous plants or shrubs, strongly marked by the above characters, inhabiting most regions of the world, except those parts of Asia which are within the tropics. Those which grow in temperate regions are mostly herbaceous; but in South America, where they are abundant, most of the species are shrubs. The roots of some species are highly valuable in medicine, furnishing Ipecacuanha, well known for its sudorific and emetic properties. The British species also possess medicinal properties, though they are rarely used.

1. Viola (Violet).—*Sepals* 5, extended at the base; *petals* 5, unequal, the lower one forming a spur; *anthers* united into a tube, two lower ones furnished with spurs, which are enclosed within the spur of the corolla; *capsule* with 3 valves. (*Viola* was the Latin name of some fragrant flower.)

The handsome flowers of the different British species appear to be for ornament rather than use, for they seldom produce any seeds. In the autumn, however, very small flowers are produced,

PLATE IX.

Heartsease
Heartsease (variety)

White Sweet Violet
Dog Violet
Sweet Violet

almost without petals, and borne on short stalks. These insignificant flowers are prolific seed bearers. The Heartsease is an exception to this phenomenon.

1. VIOLA (*Violet*)

1. *V. hirta* (Hairy Violet).—*Leaves* heart-shaped, rough, as well as their stalks, with hairs ; *bracts* below the middle of the flower-stalks ; *sepals* obtuse ; lateral *petals* with a hairy central line. *Flowers* various shades of blue, rarely white, scentless. Best distinguished from the sweet violet (to which it is nearly allied) by its very hairy leaves and capsules, by the position of the bracts, and by the absence of creeping scions.—Fl. April, May. Perennial.

2. *V. odorata* (Sweet Violet).—*Leaves* heart-shaped, slightly downy, especially beneath ; *bracts* above the middle of the flower stalk ; *sepals* obtuse ; lateral *petals* with a hairy central line ; *scions* creeping. One of the most highly prized of all our wild flowers, unrivalled in fragrance, and doubly welcome from its appearing so early in spring. The flowers are deep purple, lilac, pale rose-coloured, or white, and all these tints may sometimes be discovered on the same bank. The roots possess the medicinal properties of Ipecacuanha, and the flowers are used as a laxative for children. An infusion of the petals is employed as a chemical test, being changed to red by acids, and by alkalies to green. The flowers are said to communicate their flavour to vinegar in which they have been steeped, and it is also said that they are used in the preparation of the Grand Seignor's sherbets.—Fl. March, April. Perennial.

3. *V. palustris* (Marsh Violet).—*Leaves* heart- or kidney-shaped, quite smooth ; *sepals* obtuse, *spur* very short ; *root* creeping ; *scions* none. Bogs and marshy ground ; common, more particularly in the north. Flowers delicate lilac, with darker veins ; leaves light green, often purplish beneath.—Fl. April to June. Perennial.

4. *V. canina* (Dog Violet).—*Stem* channelled, leafy, ascending ; *leaves* heart-shaped, acute ; *stipules* long, toothed, fringed ; *bracts* awl-shaped, entire ; *sepals* acute. Hedges, heaths, and rocky ground ; the most common species. Flowers light blue, purple, or white ; more abundant and lasting longer than any of the preceding, but less beautiful and scentless. This species appears to have received its specific name as a reproach for its want of perfume. There are several varieties classed by some as distinct species ; of these the more important are, *V. pumila*, which is small, not more than 3 inches high ; *V. stagnina*—taller than the type, with very pale blue flowers.

5. *V. tricolor* (Pansy or Heartsease).—*Stem* angular, branched ; *leaves* oblong, crenate ; *stipules* deeply cut, terminal lobe broad, crenate. Cultivated fields. Very different in habit from any of

D

the preceding, and varying considerably in the size and colour of its flowers, which are, however, most frequently light yellow, either pure or tinged with purple. The cultivated varieties are countless. —Fl. all the summer. Generally annual.

6. *V. lutea* (Yellow Mountain Violet or Mountain Pansy).—*Stem* angular, branched principally at the base; *leaves* oblong, crenate; *stipules* deeply cut, terminal lobe narrow, entire. Mountain pastures, north of England, and Scotland. Nearly allied to the preceding, and as variable in the size and colour of its flowers. —Fl. June, July. Perennial.

NATURAL ORDER X
DROSERACEÆ.—SUNDEWS

Sepals 5, equal; *petals* 5; *stamens* distinct 5; *ovary* single; *styles* 3–4, often 2-cleft or branched; *capsule* 1-celled with 3 or 4 valves, which bear the seeds at the middle or at the base.

DROSEREÆ (Sundew).—*Styles* elongated; *leaves* clothed with glandular hairs. Delicate, herbaceous marsh plants, often covered with glands; *leaves* alternate, rolled in at the edges before expansion; *flower-stalks* curled when in bud. The leaves of the Droseras are covered with irritable hairs, from the ends of which exudes a sticky acid substance which takes the form of minute drops, and which in the sunshine has the appearance of dew. These glandular hairs are longer towards the edges of the leaves than at the centres. Any small insect which settles on a leaf at once becomes caught by the sticky drops, and in a short time the longer outer hairs bend inward and on to the captive. The juices of the insect are actually absorbed by, and go to nourish the plant. The incurved hairs resume their former position. The leaves of *Dionæa* (Venus' Fly-trap) are furnished with a two-lobed appendage, each half of which is armed with three sharp spines in the middle and a fringe of bristles at the edge. When touched by an insect these two lobes instantaneously close on the ill-fated intruder and crush it to death. After a short time they open again, in readiness for another victim. In this case also the bodies of the trapped insects go to nourish the plant.

1. DROSERA (Sundew).—*Sepals* 5; *petals* 5; *stamens* 5; *styles* 3–5, deeply cleft; *capsule* 1-celled, 3–5-valved. (Name from the Greek, *drosys*, dew, the leaves being covered with red hairs, which exude drops of viscid fluid, especially when the sun is shining, and appear as if tipped with dew.)

1. DROSERA (*Sundew*)

1. *D. rotundifolia* (Round-leaved Sundew).—*Leaves* all from the root, spreading horizontally, round; *leaf-stalks* hairy; *seeds*

PLATE X.

Round-leaved Sundew
Common Soapwort

Long-leaved Sundew
Sea Campion

chaffy. An exceedingly curious little plant, 2–6 inches high, growing in bogs. The root is small and fibrous, and takes a very slight hold on the ground; the leaves are densely covered with red hairs, each of which is tipped with a drop of viscid fluid; from the centre of the tuft of leaves rises a wiry leafless stalk, bearing several small whitish flowers, which only expand in sunny weather; the flowers are all on the same side of the stalk, which in its early stage is curled up, and gradually uncoils itself as the flowers severally expand.—Fl. July, August. Perennial.

2. *D. longifolia* (Long-leaved Sundew).—*Leaves* all from the root, erect, elongated, broad at the extremity, and tapering towards the base; *leaf-stalks* smooth; seeds with a rough, not chaffy coat. Smaller than the last, and, like it, growing in boggy places, but not so frequent.—Fl. July, August. Perennial.

3. *D. Anglica* (Great Sundew).—*Leaves* all from the roots, erect, long and narrow, on very long smooth stalks; *seeds* with a loose chaffy coat. Much like the last, and growing in similar situations, but is stouter and taller and has longer leaves. Rare.—Fl. July, August. Perennial.

Natural Order XI

POLYGALACEÆ.—The Milkwort Tribe

Sepals 5, the two inner larger, generally petal-like; *petals* 3–5, unequal, more or less combined with the filaments; *stamens* 8, in two equal sets; *anthers* 1-celled, opening by pores at the summit; *pistil* 1; *capsule* 1–3-celled; *seeds* pendulous. An extensive tribe of herbaceous or shrubby plants, with clustered, often showy flowers. Many are bitter, and their roots are milky. Medicinally they are said to be useful in affections of the lungs, and to excite perspiration. The most celebrated is a North American herb, *Polygala senega* (Snake-root), to which extraordinary virtues are ascribed. Several species are said to cure snake bites. *Krameria* (Rhatany-root) is astringent, and furnishes a red infusion, used to adulterate port wine. Some of the above properties, but in a less degree, reside in the only British genus, *Polygala*.

1. POLYGALA (Milkwort).—*Sepals* 5, the two inner coloured, wing-shaped; *petals* combined with the filaments, the lower one keeled; *capsule* flattened, 2-celled, 2-valved; *seeds* downy, crested at the base. (Name from the Greek, signifying *much milk*, the juice of the root being milky; or perhaps from the belief that it increased the milk-yield of cows which ate it.)

1. POLYGALA (*Milkwort*)

1. *P. vulgaris* (Common Milkwort).—Lower *petal* crested in a starlike manner; *calyx-wings* about equal in length to the corolla;

POLYGALA VULGARIS
(*Common Milkwort*)

bracts 3, at the base of each flower ; *stems* ascending, herbaceous ; *leaves* narrow. Common on heaths and dry pastures, where it is highly ornamental during the later summer months, with its starlike, blue, pink, or white flowers.—Fl. June to August. Perennial.

Besides the common form, *P. vulgaris*, several more or less distinct varieties have been distinguished, and classed as species. Of these the more important are as follows : *P. oxyptera*, with narrow *leaves ; flowers* small, far apart ; *inner sepals* narrow ; local. *P. depressa—inner sepals* broader than in the type ; common. *P. calcarea—lower leaves* tufted ; *calyx-wings* blunt, with the veins scarcely netted ; has ceased to flower almost before the common milkwort has commenced. *P. amara—*plant small ; *wings* narrow ; *flowers* pink ; confined to Cronkley Fell, Yorkshire. *P. Austriaca—flowers* larger, blue ; confined to Kent.

NATURAL ORDER XII

FRANKENIACEÆ.—SEA HEATHS

Sepals 4-6, united into a furrowed tube, not falling off ; *petals* equal in number to the sepals, furnished with long claws, and usually having scales at the junction of the claw and limb ; *stamens* equal in number to the petals ; *ovary* 1 ; *style* threadlike, 2, 3, or 4-cleft ; *capsule* 1-celled, 2, 3, or 4-valved ; *seeds* very minute, attached to the edges of the valves. Herbaceous or somewhat shrubby plants, with branched stems, opposite leaves without stipules, but a membranous sheathing base, and numerous small sessile flowers in the axils of the upper leaves. An Order of only one genus, the species of which are pretty widely distributed over the temperate and warm sea-coasts of the world.

1. FRANKENIA (Sea Heath).—*Style* cleft into 3 lobes, with the stigma on the inner side ; *capsule* 3 to 4-valved. (Name from *John Franken,* a Swedish botanist.)

FRANKENIA (*Sea Heath*)

1. Frankenia (*Sea Heath*)

1. *F. lævis* (Smooth Sea Heath).—*Leaves* narrow, rolled back at the edges, smooth, fringed at the base ; *flowers* terminal, or from the forks of the stem. A small procumbent plant, with wiry stems, crowded leaves, and pale rose-coloured flowers, growing in muddy salt marshes on the south-eastern coasts of England.—Fl. July. Perennial.

Another species, *F. pulverulenta* (Powdery Sea Heath), formerly grew on the sea-coast of Sussex, but is now extinct.

Natural Order XIII

ELATINACEÆ.—Water-wort Tribe

Sepals 3–5, distinct, or growing together at the base ; *petals* equal in number to the sepals ; *stamens* equalling or twice as many as the petals ; *ovary* 3–5-celled, and with as many styles and globular stigmas ; *capsule* with 3–5 cells and valves ; *seeds* wrinkled, springing from the centre of the capsule. Minute, annual, aquatic herbs, with rooting stems and opposite leaves. Found in most parts of the world.

1. ELATINE (Water-wort). — *Sepals* 3–4, growing together at the base ; *petals* 3–4 ; *stamens* 3–4 or 6–8 ; seeds cylindrical, furrowed, and transversely striated. (Name of doubtful origin.)

1. Elatine (*Water-wort*)

1. *E. hexandra* (Six-stamened Water-wort).—*Flowers* stalked ; *petals* 3 ; *stamens* 6 ; *capsule* 3-celled ; *seeds* straight. A minute plant, forming matted, turfy beds on the margin of lakes, or growing entirely submersed. When left by the subsiding water it assumes a bright red hue, but the pink flowers are at all times inconspicuous. Rare.—Fl. July to September. Annual.

ELATINE HEXANDRA
(*Six-stamened Water-wort*)

2. *E. Hydropiper* (Eight-stamened Water-wort).—*Flowers* sessile ; *petals* 4 ; *stamens* 8 ; *capsule* 4-celled ; *seeds* curved. Yet rarer than the preceding, and growing in similar situations.—Fl. July to September. Annual.

Natural Order XIV

CARYOPHYLLACEÆ.—The Pink Tribe

Sepals 5 or 4, distinct, or connected into a tube ; *petals* equal in number to the sepals ; *stamens* usually twice as many as, sometimes equalling, the petals, and like them inserted on the stalk or ring of the ovary ; *ovary* 1, raised on a short stalk, or inserted in a ring ; *styles* 2–5, each with a *stigma* running along its inner side ; *capsule* 1 or imperfectly 2-5-celled, opening by as many or twice as many teeth, or valves, as there are styles ; *seeds* inserted on a central column. An extensive and well-marked order of herbaceous plants, habitating the temperate and frigid regions of the globe, particularly the northern hemisphere. The stems are swollen at the joints ; the leaves always opposite and undivided, and frequently of a glaucous hue. Among garden flowers, the Pink, Carnation, Sweet William, and Scarlet Lychnis, all belonging to this order, are well known ; and our hedges are much indebted for their showy appearance in spring to the great White Stitchwort, and in summer to the Red and White Robin. Botanists have distributed the plants of this Order into two groups or sub-orders.

Sub-order I. Sileneæ.—*Pink Tribe*

Sepals connected into a tube.

1. Dianthus (Pink).—*Calyx* with 2 or more opposite scales at the base outside ; *styles* 2 ; *capsule* 1-celled, opening at the top with 4 valves ; *seeds* flattened. (Name in Greek signifying *the flower of Jupiter*, from its beauty and fragrance.)

2. Saponaria (Soapwort).—*Calyx* without scales at the base ; *styles* 2 ; *capsule* 1-celled, opening at the top with 4 valves ; *seeds* rounded. (Name from *sapo*, soap, the plant abounding in soapy juice.)

3. Silene (Catchfly).—*Petals* generally crowned at the top of the claw ; *styles* 3 ; *capsule* imperfectly 3-celled, opening at the top with 6 valves. (Name of doubtful origin. The English name was given in consequence of flies being often caught in the viscid fluid which, in some species, surrounds parts of the stem, a provision against insects crawling up to the flowers for the honey, without effecting the cross fertilization which is essential for the formation of seeds. The pollen is carried by a winged insect.)

4. Lychnis (Campion).—*Styles* 5, occasionally 4 ; *capsule* 1-celled, imperfectly divided into 5 cells, opening at the top with 5 or 10 teeth. (Name from the Greek, *lychnos*, a lamp ; " the thick cottony substance on the leaves of some species, or some similar plant, having been employed as wicks to lamps."—Hooker.)

Sub-order II.   ALSINEÆ.—*Chickweed Tribe*

Sepals distinct or very nearly so.

5. SAGINA (Pearl-wort).—*Sepals* 4–5 ; *petals* 4–5, minute or sometimes wanting ; *stamens* 4–10 ; *styles* 4–5 ; *capsule* 4–5-valved ; *seeds* numerous.   (The name in Latin signifies *fattening meat*, but is totally inapplicable to the minute plants of this genus.)

6. MŒNCHIA.—*Sepals* 4, erect; *petals* 4; *stamens* 4 or 8; *styles* 4 ; *capsule* opening at the top with 8 teeth.   (Name in honour of *Conrad Mœnch*, Professor of Botany at Hesse-Cassel.)

7. HOLOSTEUM (Jagged Chickweed).—*Sepals* 5 ; *petals* 5, toothed at the margin ; *stamens* 3–5 ; *styles* 3 ; *capsule* opening at the top with 6 teeth.   (The name signifies in Greek *all bone*, but why it was given is uncertain.)

8. STELLARIA (Stitchwort).—*Sepals* 5 ; *petals* 5, deeply 2-cleft ; *stamens* 10 or sometimes 5 ; *styles* 3 or 5 ; *capsule* opening with 6 valves, or teeth.   (Name from *stella*, a star, which the expanded flowers resemble in shape.)

9. SPERGULARIA (Sand Spurrey).—*Sepals* 5, flat ; *petals* 5, ovate, entire, as large as the sepals ; *stamens* 10, sometimes less ; *styles* usually 3.   (Name from the resemblance to the next genus.)

10. SPERGULA (Spurrey).—*Sepals* 5 ; *petals* 5, ovate, entire, as large as the sepals, *styles* 5, alternate with the sepals.   (Name from the Latin, *spargo*, to scatter, the genus being widely diffused.)

11. POLYCARPON (All Seed).—*Sepals* 5, keeled at the back; *petals* 5, small, notched ; *stamens* 3–5 ; *stigmas* 3, on very short styles ; *fruit* 1-celled, 3-valved.   (Name from the Greek, *polys*, many, and *carpos*, fruit.)

12. ARENARIA (Sandwort).—*Sepals* 5 ; *petals* 5, entire ; *stamens* 10 ; *styles* 3, occasionally 4 ; *capsule* opening with 3 or 6 valves.   (Name from the Latin, *arena*, sand, many species growing in sandy ground.)

13. CERASTIUM (Mouse-ear Chickweed).—*Sepals* 5, occasionally 4 ; *petals* 5, 2-cleft, occasionally very small, or absent ; *stamens* 10 or 5 ; *styles* 5, seldom less ; *capsule* tubular, opening at the end with usually 10 small teeth.   (Name from the Greek, *keras*, a horn, from the shape of the capsule in some species.)

1. DIANTHUS (*Pink*)

1. *D. armeria* (Deptford Pink).—*Stem* from 1–2 feet high ; *leaves* downy ; *flowers* in close tufts, rose-coloured, dotted with white, and scentless ; *calyx-scales* very narrow, downy, as long as the tube.   Waste places, rare.—Fl. July, August.   Annual.

DIANTHUS
ARMERIA
(*Deptford
Pink*)

2. *D. prolifer* (Proliferous Pink).—*Stem* smooth; *leaves* roughish at the edge; *flowers* in heads; *calyx-scales* membranous, pellucid. An erect wiry plant, 6–12 inches high, with narrow leaves; readily distinguished by its heads of rose-coloured flowers, only one of which opens at a time, and by the brown dry scales in which the heads of flowers are enclosed. Gravelly pastures, rare, but not a native.—Fl. June to September. Annual.

3. *D. cæsius* (Cheddar Pink).—*Flowers* mostly solitary; *calyx-scales* 4, blunt, one-fourth as long as the calyx; *petals* jagged; *leaves* linear, glaucous, with rough edges; flowers rose-coloured, fragrant. Limestone cliffs at Cheddar, Somersetshire.—Fl. July. Perennial.

SAPONARIA OFFICINALIS (*Common Soapwort*)

4. *D. deltoides* (Maiden Pink).—*Flowers* solitary, or 2 on a stalk; *calyx-scales* 2–4, tapering to a point, half as long as the calyx; *petals* notched; *stem* and *leaves* roughish. A much branched plant, with ascending stems 6–12 inches high, and rose-coloured flowers with white spots, and a dark ring in the centre, scentless. Gravelly banks and pastures, but not common.—Fl. July, August. Perennial. A white variety sometimes found.

2. SAPONARIA (*Soapwort*)

1. *S. officinalis* (Common Soapwort).—A robust plant, 2–4 feet high, with broad, pointed, smooth leaves, and corymbs or heads of large handsome pink flowers which are often double, sometimes white. It is generally found in the neighbourhood of cultivated ground, and is not considered a native.—Fl. August, September. Perennial.

3. SILENE (*Catchfly*)

1. *S. acaulis* (Moss Campion).—*Stem* much branched, tufted; *leaves* narrow, fringed at the base; *petals* crowned, slightly notched. Confined to the loftiest British mountains, where it forms a densely matted turf, copiously decorated with bright purple flowers.—Fl. June, July. Perennial.

PLATE XI.

Ragged Robin   Bladder Campion

2. *S. inflata* (Bladder Campion).—*Stem* ascending or erect; *leaves* oblong, tapering; *flowers* in loose panicles, white; *calyx* inflated, bladder-like, with a network of veins; *petals* deeply cloven, rarely crowned. A common weed in cornfields and pastures, growing 1–2 feet high, and well marked by its numerous white flowers and veined calyces, often tinged with purple. The foliage and stem are glaucous, and generally smooth; but a variety which is downy all over is occasionally found.—Fl. June to August. Perennial. Also called *S. Cucubalus.*

3. *S. maritima* (Sea Campion).—*Stems* numerous from the same root, spreading; *leaves* oblong, tapering; *flowers* few on each stem, or solitary; *petals* slightly cloven, crowned. Resembling the last, but of humbler stature, though bearing larger flowers. Common near the seashore, occasionally by the sides of mountain streams.—Fl. all the summer. Perennial.

SILENE MARITIMA (*Sea Campion*)

4. *S. Otites* (Spanish Catchfly).—*Stems* erect, with opposite, tufted branches; *stamens* and *pistils* on separate plants; *petals* narrow, not cloven, nor crowned. The stems are about a foot high, viscid at the middle; flowers small, yellowish. Sandy fields in the east of England.—Fl. July. Perennial.

5. *S. Anglica* (English Catchfly).—Whole plant hairy and viscid; *leaves* narrow; *flowers* lateral, alternate, erect, the lower ones when in fruit reflexed; *petals* crowned, slightly cloven. From 6–12 inches high or more, according to soil. The flowers are inconspicuous and of a pinkish white hue. Not uncommon in many parts of England.—Fl. all the summer. Annual.

6. *S. nutans* (Nottingham Catchfly).—*Flowers* all drooping one way; *branches* opposite, 3-forked; *calyx* swollen; *petals* deeply cloven, crowned. *Flowers* large, white or pink, expanding in the evening, when they are fragrant; height 1–2 feet. On limestone and chalk rocks, not common.—Fl. June, July. Perennial.

7. *S. conica* (Striated Corn Catchfly).—*Stem* erect, forked; *leaves* narrow, downy; *petals* cloven, crowned; *calyx* conical, with 30 furrows; height 6–12 inches; *flowers* small, pinkish. In sandy fields, very rare.—Fl. July. Annual.

8. *S. noctiflora* (Night-flowering Catchfly).—*Stem* erect, 1–2 feet high, repeatedly forked ; *calyx* with long teeth, oblong when in fruit, 10-ribbed ; plant hairy, viscid. The *flowers* are larger than the last, pale pink, and expand about sunset ; they close early in the morning, and are very fragrant during the night. Sandy, gravelly fields, not common.—Fl. July. Annual.

4. LYCHNIS *(Campion)*

1. *L. Flos-Cuculi* (Ragged Robin).—*Petals* deeply 4-cleft, the two centre lobes of each longer than the outer, crowned ; *capsule* 5-toothed ; *leaves* narrow ; *flowers* in a loose panicle. A pretty and well-known plant, with a purplish green, angular stem, the lower part of which is roughish with short bristly hairs, the upper parts slightly viscid ; flowers rose-coloured, with deeply-cut, narrow segments. Common in moist meadows and marshy places.—Fl. when the cuckoo is in full song, hence its Latin name, *Flos-Cuculi*. Perennial.

2. *L. vespertina* (Evening Campion). Height 1–2 feet ; *stems* branched ; plant slightly hairy and viscid ; *leaves* oblong, tapering ; *stamens* and *pistils* on different plants ; *petals* 2-cleft half-way down, crowned ; *capsule* conical, 10-toothed, the teeth erect ; *flowers* large, white, or sometimes pink, loosely panicled, opening in the evening, when they are fragrant. Waste places, common. —Fl. all the summer. Perennial.

3. *L. diurna* (Red Robin or Campion).—*Stamens* and *pistils* on different plants ; *petals* 2-cleft half-way down, crowned ; *capsule* nearly globose, 10-toothed, the teeth spreading or recurved ; *leaves* oblong, tapering, downy, as well as the stem. An ornamental hedge plant, 2–3 feet high, with rose-coloured flowers. Common. —Fl. all the summer. Perennial.

4. *L. Githago or Agrostemma Githago* (Corn Cockle).—*Calyx* much longer than the corolla ; *sepals* undivided, destitute of a crown. A common cornfield weed, with an upright downy stem, and large, handsome, purple-red flowers ; *seeds* large, and therefore troublesome when they become mixed with the corn during threshing.—Fl. June, July. Annual.

5. *L. Viscaria* (Red German Catchfly).—*Stems* 6–12 inches high, glabrous, viscid above ; *flowers* in compact heads, red ; *petals* slightly notched ; *capsules* 5-celled. Very rare, confined to a few places in Scotland and North Wales.—Fl. summer. Perennial.

6. *L. Alpina* (Red Alpine Campion).—A much smaller species, *stems* not more than 6 inches high, not viscid ; *flowers* red. Confined to a few mountain summits in Scotland and the north of England. —Fl. summer.

PLATE XII.

Greater Stitchwort   Campion   Evening Campion
Chickweed   Corn Cockle

5. SAGINA (*Pearl-wort*)

Sepals, stamens, and styles 4

1. *S. procumbens* (Procumbent Pearl-wort).—*Stems* prostrate, smooth ; *leaves* awl-shaped ; *petals* much shorter than the sepals ; *capsules* curved downwards before ripening. Well known to gardeners as a troublesome weed infesting the paths, and so prolific as to require repeated eradication. The flowers are at all times inconspicuous ; the stems are from 1–3 inches high.—Fl. all the summer. Annual or perennial.

SAGINA PROCUMBENS
(*Procumbent Pearl-wort*)

Three other British species occur, which are so nearly allied to the above as to be considered by some botanists mere varieties : *S. apetala* is small and slight, not branched, or only slightly so ; the *petals* very small or entirely wanting. *S. ciliata* is downy, the *sepals* lying close to the *capsule*. *S. maritima* (Sea Pearl-wort) has blunt fleshy leaves, and flowers destitute of petals.

Stamens 10 ; *sepals, petals, and styles* 5

2. *S. nodosa* (Knotted Pearl-wort).—*Leaves* opposite, growing together at the base, upper ones very short, growing in knots ; *flower-stalks* always erect ; *petals* longer than the calyx. A pretty little plant 2–4 inches high, with conspicuous white flowers 2 or 3 together, and tufted leaves. Wet sandy places, not uncommon.—Fl. summer. Perennial.

3. *S. Linnæi* (Alpine Pearl-wort).—In habit very nearly allied to *S. procumbens*, but it is perennial, and the corolla more conspicuous. Three forms occur :—

S. saxatalis, which is the common type, *stems* prostrate, *fruiting-stems* erect. A native of the Scotch mountains.

S. nivalis. A tufted variety with erect *flower-stalks.* Very rare ; found only on some mountain-tops in Scotland.

S. subulata (Awl-shaped Pearl-wort). Common in gravelly pastures.

6. MŒNCHIA

1. *M. erecta* (Upright Mœnchia).—A small upright plant 2–6 inches high, with narrow, rigid glaucous *leaves*, and white *flowers*, which are large in proportion to the rest of the plant ; the *sepals* are sharp-pointed, with a membranous edge ; the *petals* expand only in the sunshine.—Fl. May and June. Annual.

MŒNCHIA ERECTA
(*Upright Mœnchia*)

7. HOLOSTEUM (*Jagged Chickweed*)

1. *H. umbellatum* (Umbelliferous Jagged Chickweed).—A singular little plant, 4–5 inches high,
with leafy *stems*, which are smooth below and
hairy and viscid between the joints above. The
flowers grow in terminal umbrels about 5 together,
and are bent back after flowering, rising again
when the capsule ripens. *Petals* white. Very
rare ; found only on old walls, etc., in Norfolk
and Suffolk.—Fl. April. Annual.

8. STELLARIA (*Stitchwort*)

1. *S. aquatica* (Water Stellaria or Water Mouse-
ear Chickweed).—*Lower leaves* stalked ; *upper*
sessile, heart-shaped, tapering to a point, all
hairy at the margin ; *capsule* opening with 5
2 - cleft teeth. A much - branched, straggling
plant, with white flowers in the angles of the
stems, and in habit approaching *Stellaria
nemorum*. Wet places, but not general.—Fl. July,
August. Perennial.

HOLOSTEUM
UMBELLATUM
(*Umbelliferous
Jagged Chickweed*)

2. *S. nemorum* (Wood Starwort).—*Stems* ascending, 6–12 inches high ; *leaves* heart-shaped.
Flowers white, in loose cymes ; *petals* deeply cloven.—Damp
woods, chiefly in the north.—Fl. summer. Perennial.

3. *S. media* (Chickweed).—*Leaves* egg-shaped, with a short point ;
stems with a hairy *line* alternating from side to side ; *petals* deeply
2-cleft, not longer than the sepals ; *stamens* usually 10, sometimes 5.
Leaves succulent ; *flowers* small, white. Well distinguished by a
hairy line which runs up one side of the stem, and when it reaches
a pair of leaves is continued on the opposite side. Abundant as a
garden weed, in waste places and by roadsides.—Fl. all the year
round. Annual.

4. *S. uliginosa* (Bog Stitchwort).—*Stems* spreading, angular ;
leaves broadly lanceolate, with a stiff tip, smooth ; *flowers* panicled ;
petals deeply 2-cleft, shorter than the 3-nerved sepals, which are
united at the base. A slender plant 6–12 inches long, with very
small white flowers.—Fl. May, June. Annual.

5. *S. graminea* (Lesser Stitchwort).—*Stem* nearly erect, angular,
smooth ; *leaves* very narrow, acute, smooth-edged ; *flowers* in forked
panicles ; *petals* very deeply cleft, scarcely longer than the 3-nerved
sepals. Much smaller than the preceding in all its parts, and distinguished at once by the very deeply divided petals, which are
white but not so showy. Dry heathy places, roadsides, etc., common.—Fl. June, July. Perennial.

6. *S. palustris* (Glaucous Marsh Stitchwort).—*Stem* nearly erect, angular, smooth ; *leaves* narrow, tapering, entire, glaucous ; *flowers* solitary, on long axillary stalks ; *petals* very deeply 2-cleft, much longer than the 3-nerved sepals. Resembling the preceding in habit, 6–12 inches high, but with larger flowers. Marshy places. —Fl. June to August. Perennial.

7. *S. Holostea* (Greater Stitchwort, Satin-flower, or Adder's Meat). —*Stem* nearly erect, angular, rough-edged ; *leaves* narrow, tapering to a long point, minutely fringed ; *petals* deeply 2-cleft, twice as long as the *sepals*. Among the most ornamental of our early summer flowers, scarcely less conspicuous with its delicate green leaves than with its snow-white petals. The stems do not die down to the ground in winter, as is the case with most other herbaceous perennials ; but though dead to all appearance, they send out delicate green tufts very early in the year, so that the flowering stems, especially in bushy places, seem to have made unusually rapid growth.—Fl. April to June. Perennial.

9. SPERGULARIA (*Sand Spurrey*)

1. *S. rubra* (Common Spurrey).—*Leaves* linear, somewhat fleshy, pointed with a minute bristle ; *stipules* chaffy ; *stems* prostrate, branching, 3–6 inches. A small branching annual or biennial, with purple or sometimes almost white flowers, which vary much in size. Common in sandy fields.—Fl. June to August.

A variety called *S. maritima* occurs with fleshy semi-cylindrical *leaves* without points ; *stipules* chaffy ; *stems* prostrate. A stouter, larger plant, with larger flowers. Common on the seashore.—Fl. June to August.

10. SPERGULA (*Spurrey*)

1. *S. arvensis* (Corn Spurrey).—*Leaves* cylindrical, in whorls, with minute chaffy stipules at the base; *flowers* panicled, bent down when in fruit. A common weed in gravelly cornfields, 6–12 inches high, flowers white.—Fl. all the summer. Annual.

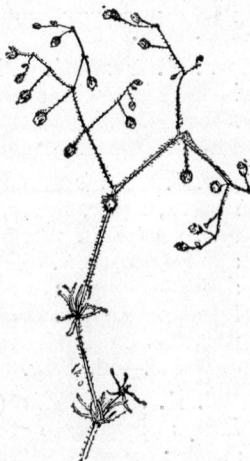

SPERGULA ARVENSIS
(*Corn Spurrey*)

11. POLYCARPON (*All Seed*)

1. *P. tetraphyllum* (Four-leaved All Seed).—A small plant, with prostrate, branched *stems*, 3–4 inches long, and many minute greenish white *flowers* with 3 stamens. The ovate leaves are oppo-

site, but the pairs are placed so close together as to give the appearance of 4-leaved whorls. Channel Isles and the south-west coast of England, but far from common.—Fl. May to August. Annual.

12. ARENARIA (*Sandwort*)

ARENARIA CHERLERI
(*Cyphel*)

1. *A. Cherleri* (Cyphel).—A mountain plant with long roots and numerous densely tufted *stems*, which scarcely rise above the ground, bearing crowded narrow *leaves* and solitary greenish *flowers*, which are generally without petals. Highland mountains.—Fl. June to August. Perennial.

2. *A. verna* (Vernal Sandwort).—A small tufted plant with awl-shaped *leaves ; stems* 2-4 inches high, bearing four or five comparatively large white *flowers* in loose cymes. Found in Scotland, the north of England, and in Cornwall, but uncommon.—Fl. early summer. Perennial.

3. *A. uliginosa* (Bog Sandwort).—A very rare form, resembling *A. verna*, but rather taller and with the *leaves* farther apart and thicker. Found only in a single locality in Durham.—Fl. summer. Perennial.

4. *A. tenuifolia* (Fine-leaved Sandwort).—A slender plant 3-4 inches high, with smooth, much-forked *stems* and finely awl-shaped *leaves*. *Petals* half the length or less of the calyx. Found in sandy fields in Eastern England.—Fl. summer. Annual.

5. *A. peploides* (Sea Purslane).—*Leaves* sessile, egg-shaped, acute, fleshy, smooth ; *sepals* obtuse. A low, succulent, marine plant, with creeping roots and forked stems. The flowers are small and white, and grow from the forks of the stem. The plant forms tangled masses on the seashore, and approaches in habit the Sea Milkwort. Not uncommon.—Fl. July. Perennial.

ARENARIA
PEPLOIDES
(*Sea Purslane*)

6. *A. serpyllifolia* (Thyme-leaved Sandwort).—*Leaves* broadly egg-shaped, pointed, roughish, sessile ; *stem* repeatedly forked, downy ; *sepals* tapering, hairy. A small shrublike herb 2-6 inches high, with inconspicuous white flowers, common on dry banks and walls. Varies much according to locality. Growing near the sea, the stems are less branched, and the leaves somewhat larger and more decidedly fringed.—Fl. June to August. Annual.

7. *A. ciliata* (Fringed Sandwort).—A small species 2-3 inches

high. The ovate *leaves* are fringed and slightly stalked ; *flowers* larger and with more conspicuous *petals* than in *A. serpyllifolia.* Rare, limestone district of Sligo, Ireland.—Fl. July. Perennial.

8. *A. trinervis* (Three-nerved Sandwort).—*Leaves* egg-shaped, acute, the lower ones stalked, 3–5 nerved, fringed : *flowers* solitary from the forks of the stem and axils ; *sepals* 3-nerved, the central nerve rough. A weak, straggling plant, about a foot long, approaching the chickweed (*Stellaria media*) in habit, from which, however, it may at once be distinguished by its undivided petals. —Fl. May, June. Annual.

13. CERASTIUM (*Mouse-ear Chickweed*)

1. *C. vulgatum* (Mouse-ear Chickweed).—A common annual weed, downy and generally viscid, with straggling branched *stems* 1–2 feet long, and inconspicuous *flowers*, of which the *petals* are usually shorter than the *calyx*, or occasionally wanting. The seed-vessels when ripening lengthen beyond the calyx and become curved. An indefinite number of very confusing varieties occur, which it is unnecessary to describe here.—Fl. all the summer.

CERASTIUM
VULGATUM
(*Mouse-ear Chick-
weed*)

2. *C. arvense* (Field Mouse-ear Chickweed).— An uncommon species, smaller than the foregoing, less downy and viscid ; *leaves* narrower, and with conspicuous white *flowers*, with *petals* twice as long as the *sepals*.—Fl. June, July. Perennial.

3. *C. Alpinum* (Alpine Mouse-ear Chickweed).—A short plant with ascending *stems ; leaves* broader than in the foregoing, and white with silky down ; *flowers* large and white. More or less frequent in the Highlands of Scotland, and occasional in the north of England.—Fl. summer. Perennial.

4. *C. trigynum* (Starwort Mouse-ear Chickweed).—A rare form found on the Breadalbane and other mountains in Scotland. *Stems* slender, ascending, about 6 inches long, with a line of hairs on alternate sides between each pair of leaves ; otherwise the plant is usually glabrous ; *leaves* narrow ; teeth of the *seed-vessel* twice as many as the styles ; *styles* usually 3, occasionally 4–6.—Fl. July, August.

NATURAL ORDER XV

LINACEÆ.—THE FLAX TRIBE

Sepals 3–5, overlapping when in bud, persistent ; *petals* equal in number to the sepals, twisted when in bud, falling off very soon after expansion; *stamens* equal in number to the petals, and alternate with them, united at the base into a ring with small teeth between them; *ovary* of about as many cells as there are sepals, and as many *styles*; *capsule* approaching a globular form, tipped with the hardened base of the styles, each cell incompletely divided by a partition extending from the back inwards; *seeds* one in each imperfect cell, pendulous. Herbaceous, rarely shrubby, plants, with undivided leaves and remarkably fugacious petals, principally, but not exclusively, confined to Europe and the north of Africa. The flowers are in many cases highly ornamental; but the most striking feature of the Flax tribe is the toughness of the fibre contained in their stems, and the mucilaginous qualities of their seeds, which also yield considerable quantities of oil. One species, *Linum usitatissimum*, has for ages supplied the valuable article of clothing which takes its name " Linen " from the plant which produces it; linseed oil is obtained from the seeds of the same plant, and the meal of the plant is valuable for poultices.

1 LINUM (Flax).—*Sepals* 5; *petals* 5; *capsule* 10-valved and 10-seeded. (Name from the Celtic, *Lin*, a thread.)

2. RADIOLA (Flax Seed).—*Sepals* 4, connected below, 3-cleft; *petals* 4; *capsule* 8-valved, 8-celled. (" Named from *radius*, a ray, I presume, in consequence of the raylike segments of the calyx."— Sir W. J. Hooker.)

1. LINUM (*Flax*)

Leaves alternate

1. *L. perenne* (Perennial Flax).—*Leaves* very narrow, tapering to a point; *sepals* inversely heart-shaped, obtuse, obscurely 5-ribbed. A slender plant with wiry stems, which are often procumbent; very narrow sessile leaves, and very elegant sky-blue flowers, which are so fugacious as scarcely to bear being gathered. The plant varies greatly in different localities. Chalky fields.— Fl. June, July. Perennial.

2. *L. angustifolium* (Narrow-leaved Flax. Pale F.).—*Leaves* very narrow, tapering to a point; *sepals* elliptical, pointed, 3-ribbed. Like the last, but distinctly marked by its sharp-pointed sepals and smaller, lighter blue flowers. Sandy pastures in the southern and western counties, common.— Fl. June, July. Annual or Perennial.

LINUM ANGUSTIFOLIUM
(*Narrow-leaved Flax*)

3. *L. usitatissimum* (Common Flax).— This is the flax of commerce, and, though a native plant, is not unfrequently found in cultivated ground. It

is distinguished from the preceding by its somewhat broader and more distant leaves, by its stems being mostly solitary, instead of several from the same root, by its notched petals, and by its larger size.—Fl. Summer. Annual.

Leaves opposite

4. *L. Catharticum* (Cathartic Flax).—*Leaves* oblong, lower ones broader ; *sepals* pointed. Very different in habit and size from any of the preceding ; stems slender, usually erect, rarely exceeding 6 inches in height, and bearing numerous small white flowers, which grow in loose panicles and droop before expansion. Dry pastures, abundant.—Fl. June, July. Annual.

2. RADIOLA (*Flax Seed*)

1. *R. millegrana* (All Seed, Thyme-leaved Flax Seed).—*Petals* 4, same length as *sepals ; leaves* minute, opposite. The only British species. One of the most minute of British flowering plants, never exceeding 3 inches in height. Stems repeatedly forked, and bearing a large number of small white flowers, which, as the plants generally grow many together, often prevent its being overlooked. Damp heaths, not uncommon.—Fl. July, August. Annual.

RADIOLA MILLEGRANA
(*All Seed, Thyme-leaved Flax Seed*)

NATURAL ORDER XVI

MALVACEÆ.—THE MALLOW TRIBE

Sepals 5, more or less united at the base, valvate in bud, often enclosed in an involucre of tracts which have the appearance of an outer calyx ; *petals* equalling in number the sepals, twisted when in bud ; *stamens* numerous, united by their filaments into a tube ; *ovary* formed of several carpels united in a radiate manner ; *styles* equal in number to the carpels, either distinct or united ; *capsules* (in all the British species) one-seeded, arranged in a whorl round the styles. A large and important family of herbaceous plants, shrubs, and trees, with divided alternate leaves, which are furnished with stipules and axillary flowers. They are most abundant in the tropical regions, where they form a large proportion of the vegetation, and gradually decrease towards the poles. According to Lindley, the number of species hitherto discovered amounts to about a thousand, all of which agree in containing a large quantity of mucilage, and being totally destitute of unwholesome qualities. In some species this mucilage, extracted by boiling the plant, especially the root, is employed medicinally in allaying irritation, both external and internal. Some few are used as food. The bark of others affords an excellent substitute for hemp. The cotton of commerce is obtained from the appendage of the seeds of several species of Gossypium, a family belonging to this Order. As ornamental garden flowers, Malope, several species of Hibiscus, and the Hollyhock are well known. The number of stove species in cultivation is very great.

1. MALVA (Mallow).—*Styles* numerous ; *bracts* of *involucre* enclosing calyx 3 ; the true *calyx* 5-cleft. (Name from the Greek, *malaché*, soft, from the emollient properties of the mucilage which it contains.)

2. LAVATERA (Tree Mallow).—*Styles* numerous ; *bracts* of *involucre* 3, joined at the base ; the true *calyx* 5-cleft. (Named in honour of the two *Lavaters*, friends of Tournefort.)

3. ALTHÆA (Marsh Mallow).—*Styles* numerous ; *involucre* with 6-9 *bracts*. (Name from the Greek, *altho*, to cure, from its healing properties.)

1. MALVA (*Mallow*)

1. *M. rotundifolia* (Dwarf Mallow).—*Stem* prostrate ; leaves roundish, heart-shaped, with 5 shallow lobes ; *fruit-stalks* bent down ; *fruit* downy ; distinguished by its prostrate stems and clusters of small, pale lilac axillary flowers. Waste places, not uncommon.—Fl. June to September. Annual.

2. *M. sylvestris* (Common Mallow).—*Stem* ascending or erect ; *root-leaves* kidney-shaped with 7 acute lobes ; *fruit-stalks* erect ; *fruit* not downy, wrinkled. A robust herbaceous plant 1–3 feet high, with large downy, lobed, but not deeply divided leaves, branched stems, and clusters of showy purple axillary flowers. When the flowers first expand the plant is handsome, but as the season advances the leaves lose their deep green hue and the stems put on a ragged appearance. Roadsides and waste ground, common.—Fl. June to August. Biennial.

3. *M. moschata* (Musk Mallow).—*Stem* erect, 12–18 inches high ; *root-leaves* kidney-shaped, deeply 5 or 7-lobed, and cut ; *stem-leaves* deeply 5-lobed, and variously cut into numerous narrow segments ; *bracts* of the *involucre* very narrow ; *fruit* hairy. Whole plant hairy, light green, with large handsome rose-coloured flowers, which are crowded towards the summit of the stem ; the foliage emits a faint musky odour, especially in hot weather ; a white variety is not uncommon in gardens. Hedges and borders of fields, not very common.—Fl. July, August. Perennial.

PLATE XIII.

Dwarf Mallow

Musk Mallow   Common Mallow

2. LAVATERA (*Tree Mallow*)

1. *L. arborea* (Tree Mallow).—A tall, handsome plant 2 or 3–12 feet high, with a thick, almost woody stem ; soft, downy, angular leaves, and abundance of purple flowers, resembling those of the Common Mallow, but somewhat smaller and of a deeper colour towards the centre. On sea-cliffs and insulated rocks on several parts of the south and west coast.—Fl. July to October. Biennial.

3. ALTHÆA (*Marsh Mallow*)

1. *A. officinalis* (Common Marsh Mallow).—*Leaves* 3–5-lobed, soft and downy on both sides. Readily distinguished from any others of the Mallow Tribe growing in Britain

LAVATERA ARBOREA (*Tree Mallow*)

by the numerous narrow bracts of the involucre, by the hoary down which thickly clothes the stems and foliage, and by the numerous, somewhat small, bluish-coloured flowers. Marshes, especially near the sea. —Fl. August, September. Perennial.

2. *A. hirsuta* (Hispid Marsh Mallow).—A rare species found near Cobham, Kent, and one or two other places, but not considered a native. Stems erect, slender, about a foot high, covered, like the leaves, with long hairs; the mauve-pink flowers solitary, in the axils of the upper leaves.—Fl. summer. Annual.

ALTHÆA OFFICINALIS
(*Common Marsh Mallow*)

NATURAL ORDER XVII

TILIACEÆ.—THE LIME TRIBE

Sepals 4 or 5, valvate when in bud ; *petals* equalling the sepals in number, often with a little pit at the base, sometimes wanting ; *stamens* numerous ; *ovary* of 2–10 united, rarely distinct *carpels ; style* 1, with as many *stigmas* as carpels ; *capsule* with one or more seeds in each cell.

The plants belonging to this Natural Order are mostly trees or shrubs. They all have a mucilaginous, wholesome juice, and many of them are remarkable for the toughness of the fibres of the inner bark. The East Indian genus *Corchorus* supplies jute ; whilst the Lime or Linden tree furnishes the material of which, in Russia, bast mats are made.

1. TILIA (Lime).—*Sepals* 5, soon falling off ; *petals* 5, with or without a scale at the base outside ; *ovary* 5-celled ; *style* 1 ; *capsule* 1-celled, not opening by valves, 2-seeded. (Name of uncertain origin.)

1. TILIA (*The Lime* or *Linden tree*)

1. *T. Europæa* (Common Lime).—*Leaves* obliquely heart-shaped, smooth except for small tufts of downy hair beneath ; *peduncles* springing from a leafy bract ; flowers very fragrant, of a grayish white colour ; *capsules* smooth. This is the common Lime of avenues and parks, and is a doubtful native. A more probable native is *T. parvifolia* (Small-leaved Lime), whose small leaves are glaucous on the under side, and the fruit downy and slightly ribbed. Another variety much planted, though probably not indigenous, is *T. grandifolia* (Large-leaved Lime). The leaves, which are much larger than in either of the foregoing, are downy beneath ; the young twigs are hairy, and the fruit downy and prominently ribbed.

TILIA PARVIFOLIA (*Small-leaved Lime-tree*)

NATURAL ORDER XVIII

HYPERICACEÆ.—THE ST. JOHN'S WORT TRIBE

Sepals 4 or 5, not falling off, unequal ; *petals* of the same number as the sepals, unequal-sided, twisted when in bud ; *stamens* numerous, united at the base into 3 or 5 sets ; *ovary* single ; *styles* 3-5 ; *fruit* a capsule or berry, of 3 or 5 valves and cells, the valves curved inwards ; *seeds* minute, numerous. Herbs, shrubs, or trees, with opposite leaves, generally marked with pellucid dots, and yellow flowers, inhabiting most parts of the world. Most of the species are aromatic and resinous, and some contain a yellow juice, which has been medicinally used for its astringent and tonic qualities. The only British genus is that which gives the Order its name—*Hypericum*.

1. HYPERICUM (St. John's Wort).—*Sepals* 5 ; *petals* 5 ; *stamens*

PLATE XIV.

Marsh St John's Wort

Large-flowered St John's Wort

Hairy St John's Wort

Perforated St John's Wort

Trailing St John's Wort

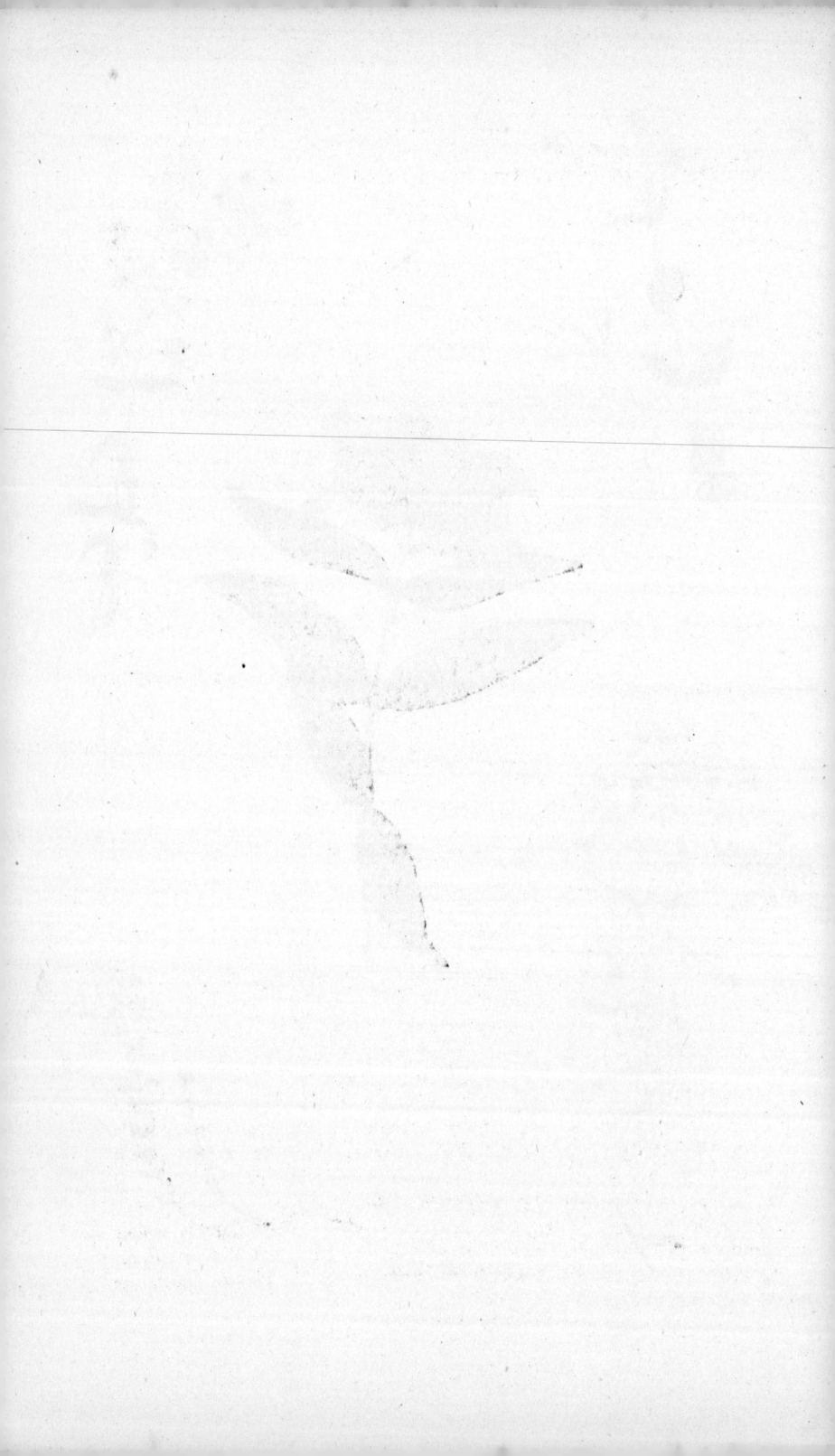

numerous ; *filaments* united into 3 or 5 sets ; *styles* 3 or rarely 5 ; *capsule* 3 or 5-celled. (Name from the Greek, *hypericon*, the name of the plant.)

1. HYPERICUM (*St. John's Wort*)

1. *H. calycinum* (Large-flowered St. John's Wort).—A low shrub about a foot high, with oblong, blunt *leaves*, and handsome yellow *flowers* 3-4 inches across ; *stamens* in 5 sets and very numerous ; *stems* usually not branched, but sometimes once branched low down. Common in gardens and shrubberies, and naturalized in several places.—Fl. July to September. Perennial.

2. *H. androsæmum* (Common Tutsan). — *Stem* shrubby, two-edged ; *leaves* egg-shaped, sessile ; *sepals* broad, unequal ; *styles* 3 ; *capsule* berry-like. A handsome shrubby plant, 2-3 feet high, conspicuous with clusters of largish yellow flowers, and afterwards with glossy, berry-like capsules. The leaves have a strong resinous smell, which they retain for some time after drying. Woods and hedges in the south and west of Great Britain, but not very common. —Fl. July. Perennial.

3. *H. perforatum* (Perforated St. John's Wort).—*Stem* herbaceous, erect, 2-edged, about 18 inches high ; *leaves* elliptic-oblong, copiously perforated with pellucid dots ; *sepals* erect, lanceolate, acute, with glandular dots ; *petals* marked with black dots ; *styles* 3. The yellow flowers in a terminal corymb. Woods and hedges, common.—Fl. July, August. Perennial.

4. *H. dubium* (Imperforate St. John's Wort).—*Stem* herbaceous, erect, 4-sided, with rounded angles ; *leaves* destitute of dots ; *sepals* reflexed, elliptical, blunt. Mountainous places ; very like the last, but not so common, and well distinguished by the above characters.—Fl. July, August. Perennial.

5. *H. quadrangulum* (Square-stalked St. John's Wort).—Best distinguished from the last two, which it much resembles, by the prominently 4-angled *stems*. *Leaves* oblong, egg-shaped, with pellucid dots ; *sepals* erect, lanceolate ; *stem* 1-2 feet high, erect, herbaceous, with flat panicles of pale yellow flowers. Wet places, common.—Fl. July, August. Perennial.

6. *H. humifusum* (Trailing St. John's Wort).—*Stems* prostrate ; *leaves* oblong, obtuse, perforated with pellucid dots ; *flowers* somewhat cymose, small, pale yellow ; *stamens* not numerous ; *petals* and *sepals* with a few black dots ; *stems* 3-9 inches long. Walls and gravelly banks, common.—Fl. July, August. Perennial.

7. *H. linarifolium* (Flax-leaved St. John's Wort).—A rare species, with slender erect *stems* 9 or 10 inches high ; very narrow *leaves*, marked with a few black dots beneath ; and corymbs of bright yellow *flowers*, larger than in *H. humifusum ; stamens* about 30.

Found only on the coasts of Devon and Cornwall.—Fl. summer. Perennial.

8. *H. pulchrum* (Slender St. John's Wort).—*Stem* erect, round, smooth, slender, 1–2 feet high; *leaves* heart-shaped, embracing the stem, marked with pellucid dots; *sepals* obtuse, fringed with black sessile glands. A slender plant, with scanty foliage, and golden yellow flowers, which, when in bud, are stained externally with red.—Fl. July, August. Perennial.

9. *H. hirsutum* (Hairy St. John's Wort).—*Stem* erect, nearly round, downy; *leaves* shortly stalked and downy beneath; *flowers* like *H. pulchrum*, but a lighter yellow, and the plant rather taller. Woods, especially in chalky or limestone soil, common. —Fl. July. Perennial.

10. *H. montanum* (Mountain St. John's Wort).—*Stem* erect, round, smooth; *leaves* oblong, sessile, smooth, with black dots near the margin on the under side; *sepals* acute, fringed with shortly-stalked glands; growing about 2 feet high, and at once distinguished from any of the preceding species by the black fringe of its sepals. Limestone hills, not common.—Fl. July. Perennial.

11. *H. Elodes* (Marsh St. John's Wort).—*Stem* creeping, 6–12 inches long; *branches* erect; *leaves* roundish, and, like the stems which they clasp, densely clothed with shaggy down; *flowers* few, pale yellow, remaining open but a short time. Spongy bogs; not uncommon in Western England.—Fl. July, August. Perennial.

NATURAL ORDER XIX
ACERACEÆ.—THE MAPLE TRIBE

Really a tribe of the Natural Order, Sapindaceæ, in another tribe of which occur the Horse-chestnut (*Hippocastaneæ*) and the *Litchi*. The Acers are trees with opposite, stalked *leaves*, which are veined in a palmate manner. *Calyx* divided into 5 parts (occasionally 4–9); *petals* of the same number; *stamens* about 8, inserted on a flattened ring beneath the ovary; *ovary* 2-lobed; *style* 1; *stigmas* 2; *fruit* 2-lobed, 2-celled, not bursting; *lobes* winged on the outside; *cells* 1–2-seeded. Found only in the temperate regions of the northern hemisphere; several species abound in a sweet juice, which in North America is manufactured into maple sugar.

1. ACER (Maple).—*Calyx* 5-cleft; *petals* 5; *capsules* 2, each furnished with a long wing. (Name from the Celtic, *ac*, a point, on account of the hardness of the wood, which was used for making spears and other sharp-pointed instruments.)

1. ACER (*Maple*)

1. *A. campestre* (Common Maple).—*Leaves* 5-lobed ; *lobes* bluntish, scarcely cut ; *clusters* of flowers erect. Woods and hedges ; a small tree, with very rugged corky bark, full of deep cracks.—Fl. May, June. Tree.

2. *A. pseudo-platanus* (Greater Maple or Sycamore).—*Leaves* 5-lobed ; *lobes* unequally serrated ; *clusters* of flowers drooping. A large and handsome tree, introduced into England before the fourteenth century, and now completely naturalized. The name Sycamore was given to it by the older botanists, who erroneously believed it to be identical with the *Sycamore* or *Mulberry-fig* of Palestine, which it somewhat resembles in the size and form of its leaves.—Fl. May. Tree.

ACER CAMPESTRE
(*Common Maple*)

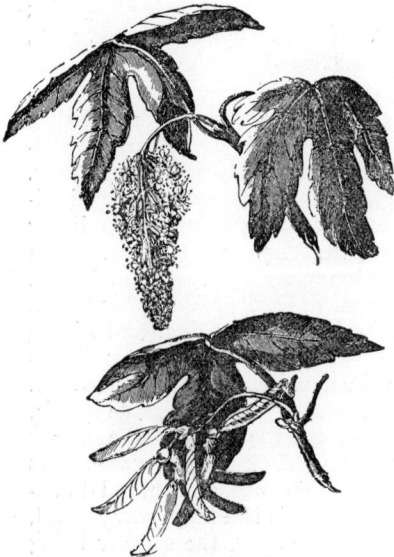

ACER PSEUDO-PLATANUS (*Great Maple or Sycamore*)

NATURAL ORDER XX

GERANIACEÆ.—GERANIUM TRIBE

Flowers regular in all the British genera except Impatiens ; *sepals* 5, overlapping when in bud ; *petals* 5, twisted when in bud ; *stamens* 5–10, generally united by their filaments ; *ovary* of 5 carpels placed round a long awl-shaped *beak* ; *stigmas* 5 ; *fruit* beaked, tapering into 5 *capsules*, each of which is 1 or more seeded, and terminates in the hardened style, which finally separates at the base and curls up, carrying the capsule with it. *For characteristics of the irregular flowers, see Impatiens.* An extensive Order of annual or perennial herbs and shrubs, in which some botanists have included the nearly allied *Balsams, Oxalis,* and *Tropæolums.* To the genus *Pelargonium* belong the innumerable varieties of handsome flowering plants, which, under the name of *Geraniums,* are so ornamental as greenhouse or window flowers. These greenhouse Geraniums were chiefly derived from South Africa, but have mostly been cultivated out of all recognition of the original forms.   There are very many species of the *Oxalis* tribe in South Africa, which are chiefly notice-able for the great beauty of their flowers and the oxalic acid con-tained in their leaves.   A few of them are cultivated as greenhouse and window plants, the most popular being that known as the *Bermuda Buttercup*, which has yellow flowers.   The tubers of some of them are edible.

1. GERANIUM (Crane's-bill).—*Stamens* 10, 5 of which are alter-nately larger, and have glands at the base ; *fruit* beaked, separat-ing into 5 carpels, each with a long *awn*, which is naked (not bearded on the inside).   (Name from the Greek, *geranos*, a crane, to the beak of which bird the fruit bears a fancied resemblance.)

2. ERODIUM (Stork's-bill).—*Stamens* 10, 5 of which are imper-fect ; *glands* 5, at the base of the perfect stamens ; *fruit* beaked, separating into 5 *carpels*, each with a long spiral *awn*, which is bearded on the inside.   (Name from the Greek, *eródion*, a heron, to the beak of which bird the fruit bears a fancied resemblance.)

3. OXALIS (Wood Sorrel).—*Sepals* 5, united below; *petals* 5, often united below ; *stamens* united by the base of their filaments ; *styles* 5 ; *capsules* 5-celled, angular.   (Name from the Greek, *oxys*, sharp or acid, from the acidity of the leaves.)

4. IMPATIENS (Balsam).—The flowers of this genus are so irregu-lar that it is almost impossible to define the characters without employing terms which would be out of place in a work which pro-fesses to give merely a popular description of British wild flowers. The following description, however, of the only species really indi-genous to Britain will serve to identify any others which are likely to fall in the reader's way.   An annual succulent plant, much swollen at the joints, with a solitary branched stem, and egg-shaped, deeply serrated leaves.   From the axil of each of the upper leaves proceeds a flower-stalk, taking a horizontal direction, and hiding itself beneath the leaf.   Each flower-stalk bears about four droop-ing flowers, which expand one at a time, and last a very little while. The calyx consists of two coloured, nearly round, concave sepals, with an oblique point ; within these, on the side of the flower nearest the stem, is inserted a horn-like petal or sepal—for botanists are undecided which to call it—wide at the mouth, and curved down-wards at the extremity ; on each side of this is a large wavy petal, unequally lobed, the largest lobe next the spur, the smaller being easily separable, and having the appearance of a distinct petal. Opposite the stem is a very broad, wavy petal, and at its base are five stamens with short filaments united just beneath the anthers into a ring, and enclosing a 5-celled ovary.   The sepals and petals soon fall off, when the ovary enlarges to a 5-celled, 5-valved capsule, externally resembling a cylindrical, strongly ribbed pod.   As the

PLATE XV.

Bloody Crane's-bill
Meadow Crane's-bill

Dove's-foot Crane's-bill
Dusky Crane's-bill

seeds approach maturity the valves of the capsule acquire an extraordinary elastic power, and if touched, instantaneously curl into a spiral form, and spring with considerable force many feet from the plant, dropping the seeds by the way.

1. GERANIUM (*Crane's-bill*)

1. *G. sanguineum* (Bloody Crane's-bill). — *Root-leaves* nearly round, with 7 deeply cut *lobes*, each of which is 3-cleft; *stem-leaves* 5 or 3-lobed. An exceedingly handsome plant, with hairy stems about a foot high, abundant foliage, and large bright purple flowers, borne singly on slender peduncles. Limestone and magnesian rocks, not common.—Fl. July to September. Perennial.

2. *G. phæum* (Dusky Crane's-bill).—*Stem* erect; *flowers* panicled; *sepals* slightly pointed; *petals* not notched as they are in the foregoing species, very spreading; *capsules* keeled, hairy below, wrinkled above. In woods and thickets, rare, and said to be only really wild in Yorkshire and Westmoreland, but not an uncommon garden plant; remarkable for the dingy, almost black hue of its flowers.—Fl. May, June. Perennial.

3. *G. sylvaticum* (Wood Crane's-bill).—*Stem* erect, 1–2 feet or more high, forked, with a corymbose *panicle* of purple flowers; 2 *flowers* on each peduncle; *leaves* palmate, 7-lobed; *lobes* cut and serrated; *stamens* awl-shaped, fringed; *fruit-stalks* erect. Woods and pastures, chiefly in the north, rare.—Fl. June, July. Perennial.

4. *G. pratense* (Meadow Crane's-bill).—*Stem* erect; *leaves* palmate, 7-lobed; *lobes* cut and serrated; *stamens* smooth, tapering from a broad base; *capsules* hairy all over; *fruit-stalks* bent down. The largest British species, growing in moist pastures; about 2 feet high, with large and handsome purplish blue flowers.— Fl. June to August. Perennial.

5. *G. pyrenaicum* (Mountain Crane's-bill). — *Stem* spreading, downy; *root-leaves* kidney-shaped, 5 to 7-lobed; *lobes* oblong, obtuse, 3-cleft, and toothed at the end; *petals* notched, twice as long as the pointed sepals; 2–3 feet high. Well distinguished by the thick down on its stems and leaves, and by its numerous, rather small, purple flowers, with cleft petals. Roadsides and meadows, not common.—Fl. June, July. Perennial.

6. *G. Robertianum* (Herb-Robert).—*Stem* spreading, 6–12 inches high; *leaves* ternate or quinate; *leaflets* deeply cut, the segments with minute points; *sepals* angular, hairy, pointed; *capsules* wrinkled and hairy. One of the most generally diffused and best known species, well distinguished by its red, hairy, succulent stems, and leaves which towards autumn acquire the same hue, and by its small, elegantly veined, bright reddish purple flowers. The scent

of the whole plant is strong and unpleasant. Road-sides and hedges, very common.—Fl. all the summer. Annual.

7. *G. Lucidum* (Shining Crane's-bill). — Smooth and glossy. *Leaves* nearly round, 5-lobed ; *sepals* angular and wrinkled. A beautiful little species, a few inches high, with small rose-coloured flowers, and shining stems and leaves which are generally tinged with bright red. Old walls and stony places, common.—Fl. all the summer. Annual.

8. *G. molle* (Dove's-foot Crane's-bill).—Downy with soft hair. *Leaves* roundish, lobed, and cut ; *petals* notched, little longer than the obtuse sepals ; *flowers* 2 on each peduncle ; *capsules* wrinkled ; *seeds* smooth ; *stems* spreading, and seldom a foot long. Easily distinguished from any of the preceding by its prostrate habit, downy herbage, and small light purple flowers. Fields and waste places, common.—Fl. all the summer. Annual.

9. *G. pusillum* (Small-flowered Crane's-bill).—Downy with soft hair. *Leaves* roundish, lobed, but not so deeply as in *G. molle*, the lobes cut ; *petals* notched ; *stamens* 10, 5 of which are usually without anthers ; *capsules* keeled, downy, not wrinkled ; *seeds* smooth. Resembling *G. molle* in habit, but smaller. Waste ground, common.—Fl. all the summer. Annual.

10. *G. rotundifolium* (Round-leaved Crane's-bill).—Downy with soft hair. *Leaves* roundish, lobed, but not so deeply as in *G. molle*, and cut ; *petals* entire ; *capsules* hairy, not wrinkled ; *seeds* dotted. Fields and waste places, not common, but perhaps often confounded with the last, which it much resembles in size and habit.—Fl. June to August. Annual.

11. *G. dissectum* (Jagged-leaved Crane's-bill).—*Stems* spreading, hairy ; *leaves* roundish, more or less hairy ; variously divided into numerous jagged, narrow segments ; *sepals* with long points ; *petals* notched ; *capsules* scarcely wrinkled, hairy ; *seeds* dotted ; *flowers* purple. Distinguished by its deeply cut, hairy, not downy leaves, and the exceedingly short pedicles. Fields and waste ground.—Fl. all the summer. Annual.

12. *G. columbinum* (Long-stalked Crane's-bill).—*Stems* decumbent, roughish, with short hairs ; *leaves* deeply 5-lobed, the lobes cut into many long, narrow, acute segments ; *flower-stalks* very long ; *sepals* with long points ; *capsules* smooth. Distinguished from the last by its larger bluish rose-coloured flowers, which grow on very long and slender stalks, and by its smooth capsules. Waste ground, not so common as the last.—Fl. June to August. Annual.

N.B.—Particular care should be taken when comparing specimens with the above descriptions to examine the *root*-leaves ; for the *stem*-leaves vary, even on the same plant, to such a degree as to defy description.

PLATE XVI.

Herb Robert

Mountain Crane's-bill   Jagged-leaved Crane's-bill

2. ERODIUM (*Stork's-bill*)

1. *E. cicutarium* (Hemlock Stork's-bill). — *Stems* prostrate, hairy ; *stalks* many-flowered ; *leaves* pinnate ; *leaflets* sessile, pinnatifid, cut. A straggling plant, with much the habit of the preceding genus, but distinguished at first sight by its *pinnate* leaves and *umbels* of lilac (sometimes white) flowers, the petals of which soon fall off. Waste places, especially near the sea ; common.—Fl. all the summer. Annual, though occasionally biennial.

2. *E. moschatum* (Musk Stork's-bill).—*Stems* prostrate, hairy ; *stalks* many flowered ; *leaves* pinnate ; *leaflets* nearly sessile, unequally cut ; perfect *stamens,* toothed at the base. The whole plant much shorter than the last, of a deeper green, somewhat clammy to the touch, and emitting, when handled, a strong scent of musk. Flowers bright magenta. Waste places, especially near the sea.—Fl. all the summer. Annual.

3. *E. maritimum* (Sea Stork's-bill).—*Stems* prostrate, hairy ; *stalks* 1 to 3-flowered ; *leaves* oblong, heart-shaped, variously lobed and notched ; *petals* minute or wanting. Whole plant roughish with minute hairs, and sending out several leafy stems, which lie remarkably close to the ground ; the leaves are not pinnate as in the other British species, and the flowers are rarely found with petals. Warm places near the sea, not uncommon in the west of England. Like many other seaside plants it is not unfrequently met with in inland mountainous districts, occurring plentifully on Dartmoor, in Devonshire, many miles from the sea.—Fl. all the summer. Perennial.

The beaks attached to the capsules of the stork's-bills become spirally twisted when ripe, often springing to a considerable distance from the parent plant. They are furnished on the inner side with long elastic bristles, and, being hygrometric, uncurl when moistened. The combined action of the beak and bristles thus gives to the seed the power of locomotion at every change in the moisture of the atmosphere. A twisted capsule, if moistened and laid on a sheet of paper, will, in its effort to straighten itself, soon crawl an inch or more away from the spot on which it was laid.

3. OXALIS (*Wood Sorrel*)

1. *O. Acetosella* (Common Wood Sorrel).—*Leaves* radicle, ternate, hairy ; *scape* with two bracts about the middle, single flowered ; *root* creeping, scaly. An elegant little plant, with delicate drooping clover-like *leaves*, and white or lilac-veined *flowers*, growing abundantly in woods and shady places. The leaves, though not so sensitive as some foreign species, fold together at night. This plant is supposed by many to be the true shamrock which was used

by St. Patrick to illustrate familiarly the doctrine of the Trinity, though at the present day *Trifolium repens* is generally used for that purpose.—Fl. May, June.   Perennial.

2. *O. corniculata* (Yellow Wood Sorrel).—*Stem* prostrate ; *flowers* yellow, smaller than *O. Acetosella*, and borne in an umbel of 2–5 on a slender axillary peduncle.   Perhaps truly wild in some parts of the south of England, and not un-frequent as a garden escape elsewhere. —Fl. all the summer.   Annual.

4. IMPATIENS (*Balsam*)

1. *I. noli-me-tangere* (Yellow Balsam, Touch-me-not).—Characters described above. The name, signifying *impatient*, was given from the sudden curling of the valves of the capsule when touched. It is an elegant plant, 1–2 feet high, with large flowers of a delicate yellow, beautifully spotted with orange colour. It grows in moist, shady woods, and on the stony banks of rivers in Yorkshire and Westmoreland.—Fl. July, August.   Annual.

A variety with orange-coloured flowers, spotted with red-brown, has been called *I. fulva.*

IMPATIENS NOLI-ME-TANGERE
(*Yellow Balsam, Touch-me-not*)

SUB-CLASS II

CALYCIFLORÆ

Sepals distinct or united ; *petals* distinct ; stamens inserted on the *calyx*, or close to its base.

NATURAL ORDER XXI

CELASTRACEÆ.—SPINDLE-TREE TRIBE

Sepals 4–5, imbricated when in bud, inserted on a fleshy disk ; *petals* and *stamens* equal in number to the sepals ; stamens alternate with the petals ; *ovary* sunk in the disk, 2–5-celled ; *fruit* either a capsule of 2–5 cells opening with valves, or berry-like ; *seeds* often wrapped in a covering distinct from the capsule (called an *arillus*.) A rather large number of plants are included in this Order, but not many of great interest. They are natives of the warmer parts of Europe, North America, and Asia, and a great number inhabit

PLATE XVII.

Long-stalked Crane's-bill
Musk Stork's-bill   Hemlock Stork's-bill
Wood Sorrel
Shining Crane's-bill.

the Cape of Good Hope. A few also occur in Chili, Peru, and New Holland. Many of them possess an acrid, stimulant principle. The green leaves of one species are said to be eaten by the Arabs to produce watchfulness, and a sprig of it is believed to be, to the person who carries it, a protection from the plague. The only British species, the Spindle Tree, is most remarkable for its pink-lobed seed-vessels, which in autumn render the tree a conspicuous object. The English name, *Spindle Tree*, is derived from the use made of its very compact wood.

1. EUONYMUS (Spindle Tree). — *Capsule* 3-5-angled, with 3-5 *cells* and *valves ; seeds* solitary in each cell, coated with a fleshy *arillus*. (Name from *Euonyme*, the mother of the Furies, in allusion to the injurious properties.)

1. EUONYMUS (*Spindle Tree*)

1. *E. Europæus* (Common Spindle Tree).— *Petals* usually 4, oblong, acute ; *stamens* usually 4 ; *branches* angular, smooth ; *leaves* broadly lanceolate, minutely serrated. A hedge and wood shrub, well marked by its clusters of small greenish *flowers*, glossy *leaves*, green *bark*, and above all by its deeply lobed *seed-vessels*, which when ripe are rose-coloured, and on opening disclose the *seeds* curiously wrapped in the scarlet *arillus*. The wood, like that of the wild cornel and guelder rose, is much used for making skewers. —Fl. May. Shrub.

EUONYMUS EUROPÆUS
(*Common Spindle Tree*)

NATURAL ORDER XXII

RHAMNACEÆ.—BUCKTHORN TRIBE

Calyx 4–5-cleft, valvate when in bud ; *petals* minute, inserted into the throat of the calyx ; *stamens* 4–5, opposite the petals ; *ovary* superior, or half superior, 2 to 4-celled, surrounded by a fleshy disk ; *fruit* either fleshy and not bursting, or dry, and separating into 3 divisions ; *seeds* several. Trees or shrubs, with simple alternate *leaves*, minute *stipules*, and small greenish *flowers*. Some species of *Zizyphus* produce the jujube, well known in this country as a sweet-meat. *Z. lotus* is famous for being the plant which afforded food to the ancient Lotophagi, or Lotus-eaters. Homer states that it was so delicious, that whatever stranger once tasted it immediately forgot his friends and native country and desired only to dwell within reach of it.

Only two plants of this tribe are indigenous to Britain, and belong to the genus *Rhamnus ;* their berries are medicinal, but too violent in their effects to be used with safety.

1. RHAMNUS (Buckthorn). — *Calyx* vase-like, 4 to 5-cleft ; *petals* 4–5 (sometimes wanting) ; *stamens* 4–5, inserted with the petals into the throat of the calyx ; *berry* 2 to 4-celled. (Name from the Greek, *rhamnos,* a branch.)

1. RHAMNUS (*Buckthorn*)

1. *R. catharticus* (Common Buckthorn).—*Branches* terminating in thorns; *flowers* 4-cleft, diœcious (stamens and pistils on separate plants) ; *leaves* egg-shaped, sharply serrated ; *berry* 4-seeded. A spreading shrub with dense clusters of small green flowers in the axils of the leaves. Berries black. These are powerfully cathartic. If gathered before they are ripe they yield a yellow dye ; when ripe they form, if mixed with gum arabic and lime-water, the green colour known under the name of Bladder-green. Woods and thickets, not uncommon.—Fl. May. Shrub.

RHAMNUS CATHARTICUS
(*Common Buckthorn*)

2. *R. Frangula* (Alder Buckthorn). — *Branches* without thorns ; *flowers* 5-cleft ; *stamens* and *pistils* on the same flower ; *leaves* entire, smooth ; *berry* 2-seeded. A rather slender shrub, 6–10 feet high, with smooth, blackish branches, deep green leaves, and small greenish flowers, which are not so densely tufted as in the last. Woods and thickets, commoner than the last. —Fl. May. Shrub.

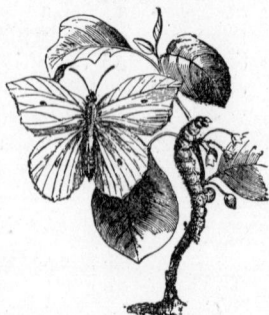

RHAMNUS FRANGULA (*Alder Buckthorn*)

NATURAL ORDER XXIII

LEGUMINOSÆ.—PEA AND BEAN TRIBE

Calyx 5-cleft, with the odd lobe in front ; *petals* 5, the upper one called the *standard* enclosing the other four when in bud ; the two side ones called the *wings* enclose the two lowest ones of all, which are joined along their lower margin, and form what is called the

PLATE XVIII.

Spindle-tree   Furze

keel ; stamens 10, their filaments either united into a tube or forming two sets of 9 and 1 ; *ovary, style,* and *stigma* single ; *seed-vessel*
a 2-valved, sometimes imperfectly jointed *pod,* or *legume ; seeds*
on the upper seam of the pod-valves. A highly interesting order
of plants, containing as many as 6500 species, which vary in size
from minute herbs to vast trees with trunks upwards of 80 feet
in circumference. In structure, properties, colour of flowers, and
range of growth they vary scarcely less than in dimensions ; they
are found in all parts of the known world, except St. Helena and
another remote island. Many species, under the general name of
pulse, afford most nutritious food—for example, Peas, Beans, and
Lentils ; others supply valuable fodder for cattle, as Clover, Vetches,
and Lucerne ; Rosewood, Logwood, and Acacia offer examples of
timber ; Gum Arabic, Catechu, Senna, Kino, Liquorice, Balsam of
Tolu, and Tamarinds are the products of other species ; Tonka,
Bean, and Balsam of Peru are well-known perfumes ; several
species of *Indigofera* afford the valuable article of commerce Indigo ;
and in Persia and Bokhara a tree called Camel's Thorn produces
abundance of *Manna,* which in those countries is an important
article of food. Other species possess medicinal properties of
various kinds ; not a few are poisonous ; and it is worthy of remark that some, the seeds of which are eminently nutritious, have
properties of an opposite nature residing in other parts of the plant.
The roots of the Kidney Bean, for instance, are dangerously narcotic. Many plants belonging to the *Mimosa* group display peculiar
irritability in their pinnate leaves. This is particularly the case
with *M. sensitiva* and *M. pudica,* which are commonly called sensitive plants. Almost all the plants of the Order which have compound leaves fold them together at night. In some foreign species
of Leguminosæ the legume loses its characteristic form and assumes
the appearance of a drupe, the papilionaceous form of the flower remaining ; in others the petals lose the papilionaceous arrangement,
but the seed-vessel retains the form of a legume. All the British
species, however, are decidedly papilionaceous, and the principal
varieties of form in the pod are those of the Bird's-foot and others,
where it is imperfectly jointed ; and in Medick, where it is often
spirally twisted, so as to resemble a snail-shell. The number of
British species amounts to nearly seventy, of which two species of
Furze, three of *Genista,* and one of Broom are shrubs ; the rest
are herbaceous.

1. ULEX (Furze).—*Calyx* of 2 sepals, with 2 minute *bracts* at the
base ; *legume* swollen, few-seeded, scarcely longer than the calyx.
(Name from the Celtic, *ec* or *ac,* a prickle.)

2. GENISTA (Green - weed). — *Calyx* 2-lipped, the upper lip
2-cleft, the lower with 3 teeth ; *standard* oblong ; *style* awl-
shaped ; *legume* swollen or flat. (Name from the Celtic, *gen,* a

shrub; *Planta Genista* originated the distinctive name of the Plantagenet family.)

3. SAROTHAMNUS (Broom).—*Calyx* 2-lipped, the upper lip with 2, the lower with 3 teeth; *standard* broadly ovate; *style* thickened upwards; *legume flat*, many-seeded. (Name, the Greek name of the plant.)

4. ONONIS (Rest-harrow).—*Calyx* 5-cleft, its segments very narrow; *keel* beaked; *style* threadlike; *legume* swollen, few-seeded. (Name from the Greek, *onos*, an ass, by which animal the plant is eaten.)

5. MEDICAGO (Medick).—*Legume* sickle-shaped, or spirally twisted. (Name of Greek origin, and denoting that some plant of the family was introduced from Media.)

6. MELILOTUS (Melilot).—*Calyx* with 5 nearly equal teeth; *petals* distinct, soon falling off; *legume* of few seeds longer than the calyx. (Name from *Mel*, honey, and *lotus*, the plant so called.)

7. TRIGONELLA (Fenugreek).—*Calyx* with 5 nearly equal teeth; *petals* distinct; *keel* obtuse; *legume* straight or nearly so, many-seeded. (Name in Greek denoting three-angled, from the form of the corolla.)

8. TRIFOLIUM (Trefoil).—*Calyx* with 5 unequal teeth; *petals* combined by their claws, and persistent; *legume* of few seeds, concealed in the calyx. (Name from *tria*, three, and *folium*, a leaf, each leaf being composed of 3 leaflets.)

9. LOTUS (Bird's-foot Trefoil).—*Calyx* with 5 nearly equal teeth; *keel* beaked; *legume* cylindrical, many-seeded, and imperfectly many-celled. (Name from the Greek, *lotos*.)

10. ANTHYLLIS (Lady's Fingers).—*Stamens* all united by their filaments; *calyx* inflated, 5-toothed; *legume* enclosed in the calyx. (Name from the Greek, *anthos*, a flower, and *ioulos*, down, from the downy calyx.)

11. OXYTROPIS.—*Stamens* in two sets, 9 and 1; *keel* of the *corolla* pointed; *legume* more or less perfectly 2-celled. (Name from the Greek, *oxys*, sharp, and *tropis*, a keel.)

12. ASTRAGALUS (Milk Vetch).—*Stamens* in 2 sets, 9 and 1; *keel* of the *corolla* blunt; *legume* more or less perfectly 2-celled. (Name from the Greek, *astragalos*, a pastern bone, from the knotted form of the root of the plant to which the name was originally given.)

13. VICIA (Vetch).—*Calyx* 5-cleft; *style* thread-like, or angular, with a small ring of down near the extremity, or a tuft on the under side, or glabrous.

14. LATHYRUS (Vetchling).—*Calyx* 5-cleft; *style* flattened on the upper side, downy beneath the stigma. (Name from the Greek, *lathyros*, a plant so called.)

15. ORNITHOPUS (Bird's-foot).—*Legume* curved, divided into many equal-sided joints, each of which contains a seed ; *keel* small, obtuse. (Name from the Greek, *ornis*, a bird, and *pous*, a foot, to which the tufts of seed-vessels bear a singular resemblance.)

16. HIPPOCREPIS (Horse-shoe Vetch).—*Legume* composed of numerous crescent-shaped joints, so that each legume has many deep notches on one side ; *keel* narrowed into a beak. (Name from the Greek, *hippos*, a horse, and *crepis*, a shoe, from the form of the joints of the seed-vessels.)

17. ONOBRYCHIS (Saint-foin).—*Legume* straight, 1-celled, 1-seeded, not opening, the lower edge fringed or winged. (Name from the Greek, *onos*, an ass, and *brycho*, to bray, it being supposed that the smell excites braying.)

1. ULEX (*Furze*)

1. *U. Europæus* (Common Furze, Gorse, or Whin).—*Bracts* ovate, not adhering closely to the calyx ; *branches* copiously beset with branched thorns. A much-branched, spreading shrub, almost leafless, except in its seedling state, when the leaves are composed of 3 narrow, soft leaflets. It attains maturity in about four years, but in sheltered places continues to grow until it reaches a height of from 12 to 18 feet. Its natural habit is, however, to grow on dry, exposed commons, which, in its flowering season, it covers with a gorgeous sheet of golden blossoms, entirely concealing its somewhat unsightly branches. Perhaps no plant is so broadly characteristic of English scenery and the English climate as " Yellow Whin." It does not thrive in hot countries, and if removed to a much colder climate pines and dies ; it is rare even in the Highlands of Scotland. The seed-vessels burst elastically in hot weather with a crackling noise, scattering the seeds on all sides. The calyx-teeth of this species are so closely united as to be scarcely visible.—Fl. February to June. Shrub.

A variety has been found in Ireland which does not flower freely, and also differs from the common form in having a soft and succulent instead of a rigid habit. This variety has been cultivated with success as fodder for sheep and oxen. A double-flowered variety is common in gardens.

2. *U. nanus* (Dwarf Furze).—*Calyx-teeth* spreading ; *bracts* very minute, closely pressed to the calyx. A very distinct species from the last, with which, however, it is sometimes confounded. It may readily be distinguished by the above characters, by its being smaller in all its parts, by the spreading wings of its orange-golden flowers, which, moreover, usually appear at the same season with the heath, a plant with which it loves to intertwine its branches. —Fl. August to November. Shrub.

F

2. Genista (*Green-weed*)

1. *G. Anglica* (Needle Green-weed, or Petty Whin).—*Stems* thorny and leafless below ; *leaves* narrow, smooth ; *legumes* smooth, inflated. A low shrub, about a foot high, with reclining tough stems, which are armed at intervals with groups of slender, very sharp thorns. The upper branches are destitute of thorns, and produce leafy clusters of yellow flowers, which are remarkable for turning green in drying.—Fl. May, June. Shrub.

2. *G. tinctoria* (Dyer's Green-weed, Woad-waxen).—Thornless ; *leaves* narrow, acute, nearly smooth ; *flowers* forming short racemes, each springing from the axil of a bract ; *legumes* flattened, smooth. A low shrub about a foot high, with tough stems, bright green foliage, and yellow flowers on short stalks. It grows in heathy places and fields, varying considerably in luxuriance according to situation, and is used to dye yarn a yellow colour.—Fl. July, August. Shrub.

3. *G. pilosa* (Hairy Green-weed).—Thornless ; *leaves* narrow, obtuse, the lower ones often inversely heart-shaped, silky beneath ; *flowers* axillary, on short stalks ; *legumes* downy. A low shrub, with prostrate stems, which are gnarled and much branched, and small yellow flowers. Heathy places, rare.—Fl. May, and again in the autumn. Shrub.

3. Sarothamnus (*Broom*)

1. *S. scoparius* (Common Broom).—The only British species, well distinguished by its slender, erect, angled branches, with small, scattered leaves, the lower ones stalked and occurring in threes, the upper ones sessile and usually single. Flowers large, yellow, 1 or 2 together in the leaf axils. Legumes when ripe nearly black, and hairy at the margin.—Fl. June. Shrub. Also known as *Cytisus scoparius*.

4. Ononis (*Rest-harrow*)

1. *O. arvensis* (Common Rest-harrow).—*Stem* shrubby, hairy ; *leaflets* oblong ; *flowers* axillary ; *calyx* much shorter than the corolla. A very variable plant, sometimes spreading on the ground and rooting at the joints ; at other times forming a small leafy bush. The roots are tough and very long, hence the English name. The branches often terminate in thorns ; the leaves are viscid ; the flowers of a bright rose-colour, and handsome. Barren, sandy places, common, especially near the sea.—Fl. all the summer. Perennial.

Several more or less distinct forms occur which have been variously classed as species and varieties, but they scarcely come within the scope of the present work.

PLATE XIX.

Broom

Dyer's Greenweed   Black Medick

2. *O. reclinata* (Small Spreading Rest-harrow).—A small herbaceous species, with pendulous, pale pink flowers, found only on the coast of Devonshire, near Tarbert, Galloway, and on the south-west coast of Scotland.—Fl. early summer. Annual.

5. MEDICAGO (*Medick*)

1. *M. falcata* (Sickle Medick).—A rare species found only in the eastern counties of England. *Stem* prostrate, 1–2 feet long; *leaflets* oblong and toothed; *flowers* large, yellow; *legumes* sickle-shaped.—Fl. June, July.

2. *M. sativa* (Lucerne).—Like the above, but more upright; *flowers* usually blue or violet; *legumes* spirally twisted. Largely cultivated as a fodder plant, and frequently found as an escape. —Fl. June, July. Perennial.

3. *M. lupulina* (Black Medick, or Nonsuch).—*Leaflets* inversely egg-shaped, finely toothed; *stipules* scarcely notched; *flowers* small, yellow, in dense oblong heads; *legumes* rugged, 1-seeded, kidney-shaped. A herbaceous plant with branching stems 12–18 inches long, sparsely covered with soft hairs; resembling in habit some of the smaller clovers, but distinguished from them by its legumes not being enclosed within the calyx. Legumes black, not spirally curved.—Fl. June to August. Annual.

4. *M. denticulata* (Toothed Medick).—*Stems* spreading; *leaflets* inversely heart-shaped, smooth; *stipules* jagged; *flowers* small, yellow, 2–5 in a head; *legumes* loosely spiral, edged with hooked prickles. Very rare.—Fl. April to June. Annual.

5. *M. maculata* (Spotted Medick). — Much like the last; *leaflets* inversely heart-shaped, with a purple spot in the centre of each; *stipules* toothed; *flowers* small, yellow, 2–4 together; *legumes* with hooked prickles, and twisted spirally into a ball. In Cornwall this plant, under the name of Spotted Clover, is considered very injurious to pasturage.—Fl. June to September. Annual.

MEDICAGO MACULATA
(*Spotted Medick*)

6. *M. minima* (Little Bur-Medick).— *Leaflets* inversely heart-shaped, downy; *stipules* scarcely toothed; *flowers* 2–4 together; *legumes* spirally twisted into a prickly ball; *prickles* hooked. Sandy places, rare. —Fl. June, July. Annual.

6. MELILOTUS (*Melilot*)

1. *M. officinalis* (Common Yellow Melilot).—*Stem* erect ; *leaflets* narrow, egg-shaped, serrated ; *flowers* in one-sided clusters ; *petals* equal in length ; *legumes* 2-seeded, wrinkled. A branched herbaceous plant, 2–3 feet high, with light green foliage and small yellow flowers ; not uncommon in waste places.—Fl. June to August. Annual or biennial.

2. *M. alba* (White Melilot).—A much less common plant than the last, probably not truly indigenous, and differs from the last in being usually taller and having white flowers, in which the standard is longer than the wings and keel.

7. TRIGONELLA (*Fenugreek*)

1. *T. ornithopodioides* (Bird's-foot Fenugreek).—A small plant with spreading, prostrate *branches* 2 or 3 inches long and small *flowers* of a whitish colour, growing 1–3 together in the axils of the leaves ; *legumes* 6 to 8-seeded, curved, glabrous, twice as long as the calyx. Dry sandy places, not common.—Fl. June to August. Annual.

8. TRIFOLIUM (*Trefoil*)

1. *T. incarnatum* (Crimson Clover).—Erect, 1–2 feet high, downy ; *flower-heads* oblong or cylindrical, crimson ; *stipules* membranous ; *leaves* composed of three obovate or inversely heart-shaped leaflets ; *calyx* with soft hairs, toothed. Much cultivated for fodder, and occurs as an escape. There is also a variety with pale yellow flowers. Fl. early summer. Annual.

2. *T. arvense* (Hare's-foot Clover).—*Flowers* in terminal oblong heads, which are soft with downy hair ; *calyx-teeth* hairy, much longer than the corolla ; *stem* branched, erect. A very distinct species, common in sandy places, especially near the sea. The peculiarly soft heads, which are nearly cylindrical, and in which the pale pink flowers are nearly concealed, at once distinguish this from any other British species.—Fl. July to September. Annual.

3. *T. stellatum* (Starry Clover). — A low, softly hairy form, with globular heads of pale yellow flowers. It occurs only on the coast near Shoreham, in Sussex, and is probably only a chance introduction. It is distinguished by the remarkably large calyx of the fruit, which spreads in a star-like manner.—Fl. early summer. Annual.

4. *T. ochroleucum* (Sulphur-coloured Trefoil).—*Flowers* in dense, stalked, terminal heads, which are at first hemispherical, afterwards egg-shaped ; *calyx-teeth* awl-shaped, the lower one much the longest ; *lower leaflets* heart-shaped, upper oblong. The whole plant is

PLATE XX.

Common Yellow Melilot

Common Rest Harrow   Common Bird's-foot Trefoil

downy; the flowers are cream-coloured, turning brown as they fade. Found only in some of the eastern counties of England; rare, dry pastures.—Fl. July, August. Perennial.

5. *T. pratense* (Purple Clover).—*Stem* decumbent or erect, 1–2 feet high; *flowers* in dense, roundish oblong heads, purplish red, sweet scented; *calyx* hairy, its bristle-like divisions half as long as the corolla; *stipules* broad, terminating abruptly in a bristle point; *leaflets* broad, obovate, or inversely heart-shaped, notched or entire. The common Clover of meadows, where it forms a valuable part of the hay crop. The long tubes of the corolla abound in honey, on which account they are often called by children Honeysuckles.—Fl. all the summer. Perennial.

6. *T. medium* (Zigzag Clover).—Not unlike the last, but distinguished by its slenderer and more erect habit, the zigzag growth of its *stems*, and especially by its narrower *leaflets*, and tapering, not abrupt *stipules*. Dry pastures and bushy places, common. It thrives better than the preceding in dry soils.—Fl. July, August. Perennial.

7. *T. maritimum* (Teazel-headed Trefoil). — *Stem* spreading, slender, pubescent; *flowers* in terminal roundish heads; *calyx-teeth* broad, pointed, and rigid, shorter than the corolla, finally becoming enlarged and spreading; *stipules* awl-shaped, very long; *flowers* small, pink. Salt marshes, not common. — Fl. June, July. Annual.

8. *T. striatum* (Soft Knotted Trefoil).—*Stems* spreading; the whole plant covered more or less with silky hairs; *flowers* light purple, in downy, terminal heads; *calyx* rigid, furrowed with straight, unequal, awl-shaped teeth, and swollen when in fruit. Barren places, especially near the sea.—Fl. June, July. Annual.

9. *T. Bocconi* (Boccone's Clover).—A small, erect species, 2–6 inches high, with roundish heads of small pale pink flowers, the heads usually growing in pairs. Found only near the Lizard in Cornwall; dry places.—Fl. July. Annual.

10. *T. scabrum* (Rigid Trefoil).—*Flowers* in dense prickly heads, which are both terminal and axillary; *calyx-teeth* unequal, very rigid, finally spreading; *stems* prostrate. A small plant, with inconspicuous whitish flowers, and remarkable only for its prickly calyces, especially when in fruit. Barren places, especially near the sea.—Fl. June, July. Annual.

11. *T. strictum* (Upright Clover).—*Stems* upright, about 6 inches high; *flower-heads* globular, 1–3 on a stem; *flowers* small, whitish; *leaflets* narrow, toothed; *legume* 1 or 2-seeded, bulged near the summit, longer than the calyx. Found only in the Channel Islands and at the Lizard in Cornwall.—Fl. May and June. Annual.

12. *T. glomeratum* (Smooth Round-headed Trefoil).—*Flowers* in

round prickly heads, which are both terminal and axillary ; *calyx-teeth* broad, very acute, reflexed ; *corollas* small, bright pink ; *stems* prostrate. Gravelly places near the sea, in the south and east of England ; not common.—Fl. June. Annual.

13. *T. suffocatum* (Suffocated Clover).—A minute, procumbent plant, with tiny ovid heads of whitish flowers, which are sessile. *Leaves* stalked ; *leaflets* obovate, glabrous ; *calyx-teeth* narrow and recurved. Sandy places near the sea ; rare.—Fl. June, July. Annual.

14. *T. resupinatum* (Reversed Clover)—*Stems* branched, leafy below, about a foot long ; *flower-heads* small, axillary, on short stalks ; the *corollas* are small and pink, with the standards curving outwards instead of inwards. Not a native, but is sometimes found in the south of England.—Fl. June, July. Annual.

15. *T. subterraneum* (Subterranean Trefoil).—*Flowers* 3-5 to-gether, in axillary heads, at first erect, in fruit abruptly bent down, and sending out branched fibres, which penetrate into the ground. A curious little plant, a few inches long, with prostrate, branched stems and white or pink flowers, which are remarkable for the above-named character of bending down and, by the help of the altered calyx, burying the seed in the ground while yet attached to the plant. Dry banks ; not uncommon.—Fl. May, June. Annual.

16. *T. fragiferum* (Strawberry-headed Trefoil).—*Stem* creeping ; *flower-heads* globose, on long stalks ; *calyx*, after flowering, mem-branaceous and remarkably inflated. This plant has somewhat of the habit of *T. repens*, but the flowers are light purple, and the heads of inflated calyces, which are often tinged with pink, are not unlike the fruit from which the plant receives its name. Dry meadows and pastures, not uncommon. — Fl. July, August. Perennial.

17. *T. repens* (White or Dutch Clover).—*Stem* creeping, taking root at the nodes ; *flowers* in roundish heads, stalked, finally bent back ; *legumes* 2 to 4-seeded ; the flowers are white, sometimes tinged with pink, and fragrant ; *leaflets* toothed, frequently having a mark in the centre. Abundant in meadows, where it forms excellent pasture.—Fl. through the summer. Perennial.

In a variety commonly cultivated in gardens under the name of Shamrock, nearly the whole of the centre of each leaflet is tinged with dark purple. The real Shamrock is this species, and, perhaps, any other " 3-leaved grass " which grows in similar situations. Much discussion about the identity of Shamrock might have been saved by recollecting that St. Patrick's day falls at a season (17 March) when the botanical characters of the trefoils are scarcely developed and that the devotees of that saint can hardly be expected

PLATE XXI.

Common Bird's-foot   Alsike Clover   Hare's-foot Clover
Subterranean trefoil.

to have possessed much botanical knowledge. Some antiquarians contend that, as Ireland was a well-wooded country in St. Patrick's time, the saint very probably selected a leaf of Wood Sorrel (*Oxalis acetosella*) to illustrate the doctrine of the Trinity.

18. *T. hybridum* (Alsike Clover).—Much like *T. repens ; stems* usually ascending, 1–2 feet high, never rooting at the nodes ; *flowers* like *T. repens,* and bending back with age in the same manner, but the corollas are of a decided pink colour. Established as a cultivated pasture plant, but not a native.—Fl. summer. Perennial.

19. *T. procumbens* (Hop Clover).—*Stems* slender, procumbent, 6–12 inches long ; *flower-stalks* rather long, axillary, bearing globular heads of small yellow flowers ; *leaves* stalked ; *legume* 1-seeded. Not unlike *Medicago lupulina* in habit, but at once distinguished when in fruit by the hop-like heads of withered flowers. Specimens occur near the sea, with scanty foliage and comparatively large flowers.—Fl. June, July. Annual.

20. *T. minus* (Lesser Clover).—A small variety of *T. procumbens ; stems* more procumbent ; *flowers* smaller, 4–20 on a head, pale yellow. Both this and *T. procumbens* are common in dry pastures.—Fl. summer. Annual.

21. *T. filiforma* (Slender Clover).—Smaller than *T. minus ; stems* slender, prostrate ; *flowers* yellow, very small, 2–6 or 7 in a head. Rare.—Fl. June, July. Annual.

9. LOTUS *(Bird's-foot Trefoil)*

1. *L. corniculatus* (Bird's-foot Trefoil).—*Stems* prostrate or ascending ; *flowers* in umbels, 4 or 5–12 together ; *calyx-teeth* straight in the bud. A pretty flower, known among children by the name of " Shoes-and-Stockings." The foliage is usually smooth, with a few scattered hairs, or more rarely covered with long soft hairs. The flowers on the same plant, and even in the same umbel, vary from bright yellow to deep brownish orange.—Fl. July, August. Perennial. A most variable species, some of its forms are so distinct and constant that they have been classed as species, and of these the most important are—

(i) *L. uliginosus* (Greater Bird's-foot Trefoil).—*Flowers* 5–12 in an umbel, rich yellow ; *calyx-teeth* while in bud spreading like a star ; *stems* nearly erect, tubular, 1–3 feet high, weak, and usually supported by the plants among which it grows ; whole plant more or less covered with soft hair. In damp bushy places ; common. —Fl. July, August. Perennial.

(ii) *L. crassifolius.*—A low-growing form with large flowers, 4–6 in an umbel, and glabrous, sometimes glaucous, leaves. Dry pastures.

(iii) *L. villosus.*—A form resembling the common type, but covered with spreading hairs and confined to Kent and Devonshire.

(iv) *L. tenuis.*—Distinguished by its very slender, branched *stems*, narrow *leaflets*, and smaller *flowers*. Rare.

2. *L. angustissimus* (Slender Bird's-foot Trefoil).—*Stems* slender and branched ; *leaflets* small ; whole plant clothed with soft hairs ; *flowers* small, 1 or 2 or occasionally 3 or 4 in an umbel ; *calyx-teeth* very long ; *legume* about an inch long. South coast of England ; rare.—Annual.

10. ANTHYLLIS (*Lady's Fingers*)

ANTHYLLIS VULNERARIA
(*Common Lady's Fingers*)

1. *A. vulneraria* (Common Lady's Fingers, or Kidney Vetch).—The only British species. A handsome, herbaceous plant, with pinnate *leaves* clothed with silky hairs (the terminal leaflet largest) and yellow *flowers*, with pale inflated *calyces*. The dense heads of flowers grow two together at the end of each stalk. Varieties with crimson, purple, cream-coloured, and white flowers occur.—Fl. June to August. Perennial.

11. OXYTROPIS

1. *O. Uralensis* (Purple or Hairy Mountain Oxytropis).—*Leaves* and *flowers* rising directly from the roots ; *flower-stalks* longer than the leaves, silky like the rest of the plant ; *legume* 2-celled ; *flowers* in heads, bright purple. Dry mountain pastures in Scotland.—Fl. June, July. Perennial.

2. *O. campestris* (Yellow Oxytropis).—*Leaves* and *flower-stalks* about equal in length ; *flowers* yellowish, tinged with purple ; *legume* imperfectly 2-celled. Found only among the Clova hills in Scotland.—Fl. June, July. Perennial.

12. ASTRAGALUS (*Milk Vetch*)

1. *A. glycyphyllus* (Sweet Milk Vetch).—*Stem* prostrate, 2–3 feet long ; *legumes* erect, curved, smooth, 2-celled ; *flowers* dull yellow, in short dense racemes ; *leaves* consisting of 5 or 6 pairs of leaflets.

PLATE XXII.

Bush Vetch

Slender Vetch   Spring Vetch

Thickets, or on gravelly or chalky soil; uncommon.—Fl. June, July. Perennial.

2. *A. danicus* (Purple Milk Vetch).—*Stem* prostrate, only a few inches long; *flower-stalks* longer than the leaves; *legumes* erect, hairy; *flowers* purplish (sometimes white), in short spikes. Chalky and gravelly places.—Fl. June, July. Perennial.

3. *A. Alpinus* (Alpine Milk Vetch).—*Stems* branching, prostrate; *leaflets* 8–12 pairs, with a terminal odd one; *flowers* drooping, bluish or white, tipped with purple; *legumes* pendulous, clothed with black hairs. Mountainous pastures, Perthshire, Braemar, and Clova in Scotland; rare.—Fl. July. Perennial.

13. VICIA (*Vetch*)

1. *V. hirsuta* (Hairy Vetch, or Tare).—
A slender, much-branched plant, forming tangled masses of stems and leaves; *leaves* consisting of 6–8 pairs of leaflets; *flowers* about 6 together, minute and bluish white; *legumes* hairy, 2-seeded. This, though a mischievous weed, is not the Tare of the Holy Scriptures, which is supposed to be the Darnel (*Lolium temulentum*). Fields and hedges; very common.—Fl. all summer. Annual.

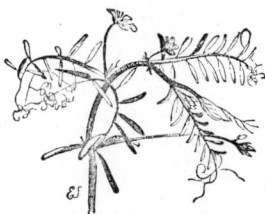

VICIA HIRSUTA (*Hairy Vetch, or Tare*)

2. *V. tetrasperma* (Slender Vetch).—*Flowers* 1–7 together, on a slender stalk, light purple; *legumes* smooth, usually 4-seeded; whole plant much slenderer and less branched than the last. Found in similar situations, but less common.—Fl. all summer. Annual.

3. *V. gracilis* (Slender Vetch), is by some botanists considered a distinct species, others make it a variety of the last. The *flowers* grow 1–4 together, and are larger than in *V. tetrasperma ;* *legumes* 6–8-seeded. Found in the south of England.—Fl. all summer. Annual.

4. *V. cracca* (Tufted Vetch).—*Leaflets* in about 10 pairs, narrow, pointed, silky, with tendrils; *stipules* half arrow-shaped, scarcely toothed; *flowers* crowded in one-sided spikes. One of the most ornamental of British plants, climbing along the tops of hedges, and adorning them with its slender spikes of blue and purple flowers. Bushy places; frequent.—Fl. July, August. Perennial.

5. *V. sylvatica* (Wood Vetch).—*Leaflets* in about 8 pairs, elliptical, abrupt, with a short point; *stipules* crescent-shaped, deeply toothed at the base; *legume* an inch long, smooth, 4–6-seeded. A large and beautiful species, with a long stem 3–6 feet high, climbing by means of its branched tendrils. *Flowers* numerous, in

drooping racemes, cream-coloured, with bluish veins. Mountainous woods ; not common.—Fl. June to August. Perennial.

6. *V. orobus* (Wood-bitter Vetch).—*Leaflets* in 7–10 pairs, oblong, acute, without tendrils ; *stipules* half arrow-shaped, slightly toothed. A branched, herbaceous plant, with many prostrate stems and one-sided racemes of large purplish white flowers. Rocky woods in the north.—Fl. May, June. Perennial.

7. *V. sepium* (Bush Vetch).—*Flowers* in axillary clusters of from 4–6 ; *legumes* smooth ; *leaflets* egg-shaped, obtuse, in 4–6 pairs, gradually decreasing in size towards the end of the leaf-stalk. Very common in woods and shady hedges, and distinguished by its clusters of bluish purple flowers, which grow on short stalks in the axils of leaves.—Fl. May, June. Perennial.

8. *V. lutea* (Yellow Vetch).—*Stems* prostrate or ascending, about 2 feet long ; *flowers* solitary, sessile, rather large, pale yellow ; *legumes* hairy. Sea coast ; rare.—Fl. June, July. Perennial.

9. *V. sativa* (Common Vetch).—*Flowers* solitary or in pairs, with very short stalks ; *leaflets* from obcordate to narrow in 5–7 pairs ; *stipules* half arrow-shaped, toothed at the base, marked with a dark spot ; *tendrils* usually branched. This species being extensively cultivated for fodder for cattle varies considerably in luxuriance according to soil. It usually grows about 2 feet high, and bears blue and purple or red flowers.—Fl. June, July. Annual.

A small variety, *V. angustifolia* (Narrow-leaved Vetch).—By some botanists considered a distinct species, has very narrow leaves and crimson flowers.

10. *V. lathyroides* (Spring Vetch).—Nearly allied to the last, but very much smaller ; *stems* low and spreading, rarely exceeding 6 inches ; *flowers* solitary, sessile, rich purple ; *legumes* smooth ; *leaflets* in 2–3 pairs ; *stipules* entire, not marked with a dark spot ; *seeds* nearly cubical, roughish. Dry places, but not very common. —Fl. April, May. Annual.

11. *V. Bithynica* (Bithynian Vetch).—*Stems* angular, 1–2 feet long ; leaflets 2 or 4 together with branched *tendrils ; flowers* rather large, purple, with whitish wings, 1 or 2 together on a stalk. Bushy places on a gravelly soil near the sea ; not common. —Fl. May to August. Annual.

14. LATHYRUS (*Vetchling*)

1. *L. nissolia* (Crimson Vetchling).—*Leaves* simple, very narrow, destitute of tendrils ; *flower-stalks* long, bearing 1 or 2 small bright crimson flowers ; whole plant about 1 foot high. Grassy places ; rare.—Fl. June, July. Annual.

2. *L. aphaca* (Yellow Vetchling) —A pretty little plant with

PLATE XXIII.

Meadow Vetchling   Tufted Vetch

small yellow flowers, 1 or 2 on a stalk, and remarkable for being entirely destitute of leaves, the place of which is supplied by a pair of stipules at the base of each tendril ; *stipules* large, leaflike, half arrow-shaped ; plant smooth, branching, about a foot long. A rare cornfield weed.—Fl. June to August. Annual.

3. *L. hirsutus* (Rough-podded Vetchling).—*Stems* weak, branched, about a foot long; *flowers* borne singly or in pairs on long stalks, the standards crimson, the rest pale blue ; *legumes* hairy. A rare species, found in Yorkshire, Essex, Kent, Surrey, and Somersetshire.—Fl. June, July. Annual.

4. *L. pratensis* (Meadow Pea).—A weak climbing plant 2–3 feet long ; *leaf* of 2 narrow leaflets ; *stipules* arrow-shaped, as large as the leaflets ; *flowers* yellow, all turning one way. Grassy places ; common.—Fl. July, August. Perennial.

5. *L. tuberosus* (Earth-nut Pea).—*Root* tuberous ; *stems* weak, angled, branched ; *leaf-tendrils* branched ; *leaflets* ovate ; *stipules* half arrow-shaped ; *flower-stalks* 3–6 inches in length, bearing a number of red flowers. Very rare ; found only as a cornfield weed at Fyfield in Essex.—Fl. June to August. Perennial.

6. *L. sylvestris* (Everlasting Pea).—The *stems* climb to the height of 3–6 feet, winged ; *leaf* of two long sword-shaped *leaflets* ; *flowers* large, greenish yellow, tinged with purple, but not so handsome as those of the garden species. Woods and thickets ; not very common.—Fl. July, August. Perennial.

7. *L. palustris* (Blue Marsh Vetchling).—A climbing plant, smaller than the last ; *leaf* of 2–4 pairs of very narrow acute leaflets ; *tendrils* generally branched ; *stems* winged ; *flowers* bluish purple, 2–8 together. Boggy meadows ; rare.—Fl. July, August. Perennial.

8. *L. maritimus* (Sea Pea).—*Stems* prostrate, 6–12 inches long, angled ; *leaves* of 3–8 pairs of egg-shaped leaflets ; *flower-stalks* shorter than the leaves, 6–8 flowered ; *flowers* purple, variegated with crimson and blue. Pebbly seashores ; rare.—Fl. July, August. Perennial.

9. *L. macrorrhizus* (Tuberous Bitter Vetch).—*Leaves* of 2–4 pairs of oblong leaflets, which are glaucous beneath ; *stipules* half arrow-shaped ; *stem* simple, winged, 6–12 inches high. A pretty spring Vetch, with clusters of blue and purple flowers in the angles of the leaves, growing in similar situations with the Wood Anemone, but appearing somewhat later. It may at once be distinguished from any of the true Vetches by its being destitute of tendrils, in place of which there are soft bristle-like points. The roots are tuberous, and are " eaten by Highlanders, under the name of Cormeille," a very small quantity being said to allay and prevent

hunger."—Sir W. J. Hooker. Woods ; not uncommon, especially in the west of England.—Fl. May, June. Perennial.

10. *L. Niger* (Black Bitter Vetch).—*Stem* branched, erect, 1–2 feet high, angular, but not winged ; *stipules* very narrow ; *root* not tuberous ; *flowers* 6–8 together ; the plant turns black in dying. A very rare Scottish species.—Fl. June to August. Perennial.

15. ORNITHOPUS (*Bird's-foot*)

1. *O. perpusillus* (Common Bird's-foot).—A minute and very beautiful plant, with spreading, prostrate *stem ;* downy *leaves* of 6–12 pairs of leaflets and an odd one ; heads of 2 or 3 exceedingly small cream-coloured *flowers*, veined with crimson, with a leaf at the base of each head ; and jointed *legumes*, which become curved as they ripen, and bear a resemblance to a bird's foot. Sandy heaths ; common.—Fl. July, August. Perennial.

2. *O. ebracteatus* (Sand Bird's-foot).—In many respects similar to the last ; the flowers are larger, the plant smooth and glaucous, and there is no leaf below the flower-head. Found in the Channel and Scilly Islands.—Fl. June to August. Annual.

ORNITHOPUS PER-
PUSILLUS (*Common
Bird's-foot*)

16. HIPPOCREPIS (*Horse-shoe Vetch*)

1. *H. comosa* (Tufted Horse-shoe Vetch).— The only British species. A low, tufted plant, with much-branched *stems*, which are woody at the base, and elegant *leaves*, composed of 6–12 narrow leaflets. The *umbels* of yellow *flowers* might be mistaken for those of *Lotus corniculatus*, but for the curious structure of the *seed-vessels*, which are shaped like a series of horse-shoes, united by their extremities. The plant may also be distinguished by its pinnate *leaves*. Common on chalky banks. —Fl. May to August. Perennial.

17. ONOBRYCHIS (*Saint-foin*)

1. *O. sativa* (Common Saint-foin).—The only British species. A handsome plant, often cultivated as fodder in dry, chalky, and gravelly soils. The *stems* are ascending, 1–2 feet long ; the *leaves* are composed of 8–12 pairs of oblong

HIPPOCREPIS COMOSA
(*Tufted Horse-shoe Vetch*)

PLATE XXIV.

Grass Vetchling   Tuberous Bitter Vetch

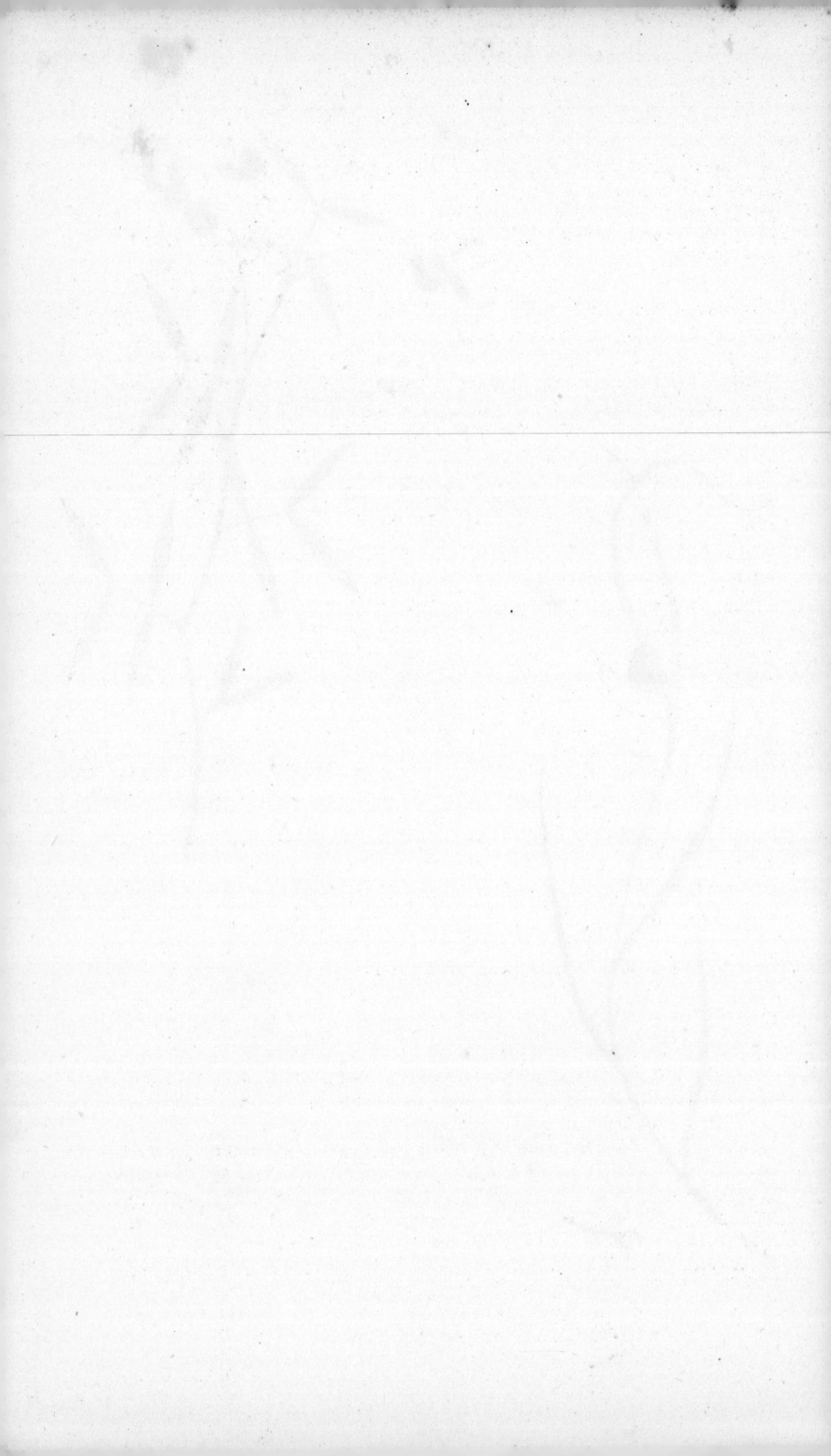

leaflets, with an odd one; and the *flowers* which grow in clusters, or rather spikes, are crimson, variegated with pink and white. Chalky and limestone hills.—Fl. June, July. Perennial.

NATURAL ORDER XXIV

ROSACEÆ.—THE ROSE TRIBE

Calyx most frequently 5-lobed, sometimes 4, 8, or 10-lobed; *petals* 5, inserted on the calyx, regular; *stamens* indefinite, generally more than 12, inserted on the calyx curved inwards before the expansion of the petals; *carpels* many or solitary, either distinct, or combined with each other and with the calyx; *styles* distinct, often lateral; *fruit* either a *drupe* (cherry or plum)— an assemblage of erect capsules opening at one side—a number of nut-like seeds inserted into a fleshy receptacle (Strawberry, Blackberry)—en-closed in the fleshy tube of the calyx (hip of the Rose)—or a *pome* (apple). A large and important Order, con-taining about a thousand species, many of which, either in a wild or cultivated state, produce excellent fruit—Cherries, Plums, Almonds, Peaches, Nectarines, Apricots, Strawberries, Raspberries, Blackberries, Apples, Pears, and Quinces, all belong to this Order. It is to be noted, however, that valuable as these fruits are, the leaves, bark, flowers, and seeds of many abound in a deadly poison, called hydrocyanic or prussic acid. The variety of form displayed by the fruit of the Rose Tribe has afforded a facility for sub-dividing the Order into several Sub-orders, or Groups, the characters of which are subjoined.

ONOBRYCHIS SATIVA
(*Common Saint-Join*)

Sub-order I.—AMYGDALEÆ.—*The Almond Group*

In plants belonging to this division the pistil is solitary, and the fruit when ripe is a *drupe*, that is, a single seed enclosed in a hard case, which is itself surrounded by a fleshy or juicy pulp, with an external rind or cuticle; the bark often yields gum, and prussic acid is generally abundant in the leaves and seeds. They are shrubs or trees, and inhabit the cold and temperate regions of the northern hemisphere. Examples of the deadly properties residing in these plants are afforded by the leaves of the common Laurel, *Prunus Lauro-cerasus*, even the vapour of which is destructive to insect life. The oil of Bitter Almonds is extremely poisonous, and many in-stances are recorded of its fatal effects. But notwithstanding the presence of this destructive principle in the leaves and other parts

of the trees belonging to this division, the fruit is, with the
exception of the Laurel, harmless, or even a nourishing food.
Amygdalus communis, the Almond Tree,
grows naturally in Barbary and in
Asia, from Syria to Afghanistan, and
is extensively cultivated in the south
of Europe. There are two varieties
of the tree, one yielding the sweet, the
other the bitter Almond. Jordan Almonds, which are considered the best,
are brought from Malaga; bitter Almonds are imported from Mogadore.
The varieties of *Amygdalus Persica* produce the Peach, Nectarine, and Apricot.
Prunus domestica and its varieties afford
Plums of many kinds. *P. Lusitanica*
is well known by the name of Portugal
Laurel.

AMYGDALEÆ
(*The Almond Group*)

1. PRUNUS (Plum and Cherry).—*Nut*
of the *drupe* smooth, or slightly seamed.
(Name from the Greek, *prouné*, a plum. *Cerasus*, a name sometimes given to one division of this genus, is derived from *Cerasus*,
a city of Pontus, whence the Roman general Lucullus introduced
a superior kind, B.C. 67.)

Sub-order II.—SPIREIDÆ.—*Meadow-sweet Group*

This division contains a limited number of herbaceous or shrubby
plants, which bear their seeds in dry, erect capsules, opening at the
side, termed *follicles*. Several species of *spiræa* are ornamental
shrubs, and are commonly cultivated in gardens.

2. SPIRÆA (Meadow-sweet, Dropwort).—*Calyx* 5-cleft; *stamens*
numerous; *follicles* 3–12, bearing few seeds. (Name of Greek
origin.)

Sub-order III.—POTENTILLIDÆ.—*The Strawberry Group*

In this division the form of the fruit varies much more than in
either of the preceding; but in every case the calyx is permanent
and contains a number of nut-like seeds, with or without tails,
placed on a pulpy, spongy, or dry receptacle; in the Bramble, each
seed is enveloped in pulp, the fruit being an assemblage of small
drupes; in Agrimony alone there are but two seeds, which are
enclosed in a bristly, hardened calyx. The plants of this division
are mostly herbaceous, but some few are shrubs. None of them are
injurious; the roots and leaves of some are astringent or tonic.

The fruit of the Strawberry, Raspberry, and Bramble is too well known to need any description.

3. DRYAS (Mountain Avens).—*Calyx* in 8–10 equal divisions, which are all in one row ; *petals* 8–10 ; *styles* finally becoming feathery tails, not hooked at the extremity. (Name from the Greek, *drys*, an Oak, from a fancied resemblance between the leaves.)

4. GEUM (Avens).—*Calyx* 10-cleft, in two rows, the outer division smaller ; *petals* 5 ; *styles* finally becoming jointed, awns hooked at the extremity. (Name from the Greek, *geyo*, to taste.)

5. POTENTILLA (Cinquefoil).—*Calyx* 8 or 10-cleft, in two rows ; *petals* 4 or 5 ; *seeds* without awns. (Name from the Latin, *potens*, powerful, from the powerful properties supposed to reside in some species.)

6. FRAGARIA (Strawberry).—*Calyx* 10-cleft, in 2 rows ; the outer divisions smaller ; *petals* 5 ; *seeds* without awns, on an enlarged, fleshy receptacle. (Name from the Latin, *fragum*, a strawberry, and that from *fragrans*, fragrant.)

7. RUBUS (Bramble).—*Calyx* 5-cleft ; *petals* 5 ; *fruit* an assemblage of small drupes, arranged on and round a spongy receptacle. (Name from the Latin, *ruber*, red.)

8. AGRIMONIA (Agrimony).—*Calyx* 5-cleft, top-shaped, covered with hooked bristles ; *petals* 5 ; *stamens* about 15 ; *seeds* 2, enclosed in the tube of the hardened calyx. (Name of Greek origin.)

Sub-order IV.—SANGUISORBIDÆ.—*The Burnet Group*

The plants of this group would seem at first sight to be scarcely connected with those already described. It will, however, be found, on close examination, that in many important respects they agree with the characters given in the description of the Order ROSACEÆ, though in others scarcely less important they appear to differ ; these are the absence of petals, and the hardened calyx of the fruit containing 1 or 2 nut-like seeds. The calyx is 3 to 8-cleft, and the stamens are usually few in number. The plants are either herbaceous or shrubby, and, like those of the last group, their properties are astringent or tonic. In some species the flowers grow in round or oblong heads.

9. ALCHEMILLA (Lady's Mantle).—*Calyx* 8-cleft, in 2 rows, the outer divisions smaller ; *petals* 0 ; *stamens* 1–4, opposite the smaller divisions of the calyx ; *seeds* 1 or 2, enclosed in the hardened calyx. (Name from its pretended value in Alchemy.)

10. SANGUISORBA (Burnet).—*Calyx* 4-cleft, coloured (not green), with 2-4 scale-like bracts at the base ; *petals* 0 ; *stamens* 4 ; *seeds*

1 or 2, enclosed in the tube of the hardened calyx. (Name from the Latin, *sanguis*, blood, and *sorbeo*, to staunch, from the supposed virtues of the plant.)

11. POTERIUM (Burnet Saxifrage).—*Stamens* and *pistils* in separate flowers ; *flowers* in heads ; *calyx* 4-cleft, coloured, with 3 scale-like bracts at the base ; *petals* 0 ; *stamens* numerous ; *stigma* tufted. (Name from the Greek, *potérion*, a drinking-cup, the plant being used in the preparation of *Cool-tankard*.)

Sub-order V.—ROSIDÆ.—*The Rose Group*

This division contains the genus from which both the Order and Sub-order take their names.   Here also the fruit furnishes the main characteristic ; it consists of a number of nut-like, hairy seeds, enclosed within the fleshy tube of the calyx, which is contracted at the top.   The Roses are shrubs more or less prickly (not thorny), with pinnate leaves.   The number of species is very great, of varieties incalculable, the beauty and fragrance of the flowers having rendered them favourite objects of cultivation from a very early period.   From the petals of *R. centifolia* and *R. Damascena* are made Rose-water and Attar of Roses.   It is stated that 100,000 Roses, the produce of 10,000 bushels, yield only nine drams of Attar. From the pulp of the fruit, called a hip, is made a conserve, which is used in the preparation of various medicines.

12. ROSA (Rose).—*Calyx* urn-shaped, contracted at the mouth, and terminating in 5, often leaf-like, divisions ; *petals* 5 ; *stamens* numerous ; *seeds* numerous.   (Name from the Latin, *rosa*, and that from the Greek, *rhodon*, its ancient names.)

Sub-order VI.—POMEÆ.—*The Apple Group*

In the plants of this division the fruit is what is called a *pome ;* that is, the tube of the calyx enlarges and becomes a fleshy or mealy fruit, enclosing 1–5 cells, which are either horny, as in the Apple, or bony, as in the Medlar.   The Apple Group contains well-known fruit trees, namely, the Apple, Pear, Quince, Medlar, Service, Mountain Ash, and Hawthorn.   The seeds, and occasionally the flower and bark of some, yield prussic acid.   All the cultivated varieties of Apple are derived from the Wild Apple, or Crab, *Pyrus Malus ;* the garden Pears from a thorny tree, with hard astringent fruit, *Pyrus communis*.   The wood of the Pear is very close-grained, and is sometimes used by wood-engravers.   The fruit of the Mountain Ash and some other species yields malic acid, and the leaves prussic acid, in as great abundance as the Laurel.   All the plants of this division are either trees or shrubs.

13. PYRUS (Pear, Apple, Service, and Mountain Ash).—*Calyx*

5-cleft ; *petals* 5 ; *styles* 2–5 ; *fruit* fleshy or juicy, with 5 horny, 2-seeded cells. (Name from the Latin, *pyrus*, a pear.)

14. MESPILUS (Medlar).—*Calyx* 5-cleft, divisions leaflike ; *petals* 5 ; *styles* 2–5 ; *fruit* fleshy, top-shaped, terminating abruptly, with the ends of the bony cells exposed. (Name from the Greek, *mespile*, a medlar.)

15. CRATÆGUS (Hawthorn).—*Calyx* 5-cleft, divisions acute ; *petals* 5 ; *styles* 1–5 ; *fruit* oval or round, concealing the ends of the bony cells. (Name from the Greek, *cratos*, strength, in allusion to the hardness of the wood.)

16. COTONEASTER (Cotoneaster).—Small trees or shrubs with small and usually entire *leaves ; flowers* small and generally solitary ; *sepals* 5 ; *petals* 5 ; *stamens* indefinite ; *carpels* 2–5, not joined to each other, but inserted by their backs on the calyx tube ; *fruit* 2 to 5-chambered. (Name of classical origin.)

1. PRUNUS (*Plum and Cherry*)

Fruit covered with bloom ; young leaf with halves rolled together

1. *P. spinosa* (Sloe, Blackthorn).— *Branches* very thorny ; *leaves* narrow, elliptical, smooth above, slightly downy near the midrib below ; *flowers* mostly solitary. A well-known thorny bush, which probably derived its name Black-thorn from the hue of its bark, which is much darker than that of the Haw-thorn. The flowers appear in March and April, and usually before the leaves have begun to expand. The latter are used to adulterate tea. The fruit is small, nearly round, and so austere that a single drop placed on the tongue will produce a roughness on the throat and palate which is perceptible for a long time. It enters largely into

PRUNUS SPINOSA
(*Sloe or Blackthorn*)

the composition of spurious port wine, and sloe gin is a most comforting beverage. Woods and hedges ; abundant.—Fl. March to May. Shrub.

2. *P. insititia* (Bullace).—*Branches* ending in a thorn ; *leaves* elliptical, downy beneath ; *flowers* in pairs. Larger than the last, and producing a larger and more palatable black or yellow fruit. The leaves and flowers expand about the same time. This is by some botanists considered merely a variety of the preceding. *P. domestica* (Wild Plum) appears to be as closely connected with the Bullace as that is with the Sloe ; the branches are thornless and

G

the fruit oblong. From one or other of these three all the cultivated varieties of Plum are supposed to have originated.—Fl. April, May. Small tree.

Fruit without bloom ; young leaf with the halves folded together

Prunus Padus (*Bird-Cherry*)

3. *P. Padus* (Bird-Cherry).—*Flowers* in pendulous racemes ; *leaves* narrow, egg-shaped ; *fruit* ovid, black, bitter ; *stone* rugged. A handsome shrub, or small tree, not uncommon in the north of England in a wild state, and common in gardens and shrubberies elsewhere. The racemes of flowers and drupes are not unlike those of the Portugal Laurel, to which the plant is nearly allied, but the leaves are not ever-green.—Fl. white, May. Small tree.

4. *P. avium* (Wild Cherry).—*Flowers* in umbels ; *leaves* drooping, suddenly pointed, downy beneath ; *calyx-tube* contracted above ; *fruit* heart-shaped, small, bitter, black or red, and is greedily devoured by birds as soon as ripe. A highly orna-mental tree, not only on account of its elegant white flowers in spring, but even more so in autumn, when its leaves assume a bright crimson hue.—Fl. May. A lofty tree without suckers.

5. *P. cerasus* (Red Cherry).—*Flowers* in umbels ; *leaves* not drooping, smooth on both sides ; *calyx-tube* not contracted ; *fruit* round, juicy, acid, always red. This species is distinguished from the pre-ceding by the characters given above and by its lower stature, which is said not to exceed 8 feet, while the other attains a height of 30–40 feet ; it also sends up numerous suckers from the roots. Some botanists, however, consider them mere varieties of the same tree. From one or other all the cultivated kinds of cherry are derived. Woods and hedges ; not so common.—Fl. May. Shrub.

2. SPIRÆA (*Meadow-sweet*)

1. *S. ulmaria* (Meadow-sweet, Queen of the Meadows).—A handsome herbaceous

Spiræa Ulmaria (*Meadow-Sweet, Queen of the Meadows*)

PLATE XXV.

Blackberry

Stone Bramble

Water Avens

Dewberry

plant 2–4 feet high ; *leaves* pinnate, the alternate leaflets smaller, downy beneath, the terminal leaflet large and 3-lobed ; *flowers* yellowish white, crowded into compound erect cymes, very fragrant. Moist meadows ; common.—Fl. July, August. Perennial.

2. *S. Filipendula* (Dropwort).—An erect herbaceous plant 1–2 feet high ; *leaves* pinnate, with the alternate leaflets smaller, all deeply cut into narrow, serrated segments ; *flowers* in a panicled cyme, less crowded than in the last, the *petals* pink externally before they expand, and when open white and scentless ; the *rootlets* have swollen nodes or tubers. Dry pastures, especially on limestone soil. A variety with double flowers is common in gardens.—Fl. July to September. Perennial.

3. *S. salicifolia* (Willow-leaved Spirea).—A shrubby species 4–5 feet high, with spike-like clusters of rose-coloured flowers and simple (not pinnated) leaves. It is occasionally found in damp situations in the north, but is not indigenous.—Fl. July, August. Perennial.

3. DRYAS (*Mountain Avens*)

1. *D. octopetala* (Mountain Avens).—The only British species. *Stems* hard and thick, creeping ; *leaves* oblong, deeply cut, white with woolly down beneath ; *flowers* white, large, and handsome, borne singly on erect simple stalks 2–3 inches high ; *petals* usually 8. Not uncommon in the mountainous parts of England, Scotland, and Ireland, and easily distinguished by its handsome white flowers, which are an inch or more in diameter.—Fl. June, July. Perennial.

DRYAS OCTOPETALA
(*Mountain Avens*)

4. GEUM (*Avens*)

1. *G. urbanum* (Common Avens, Herb Bennet).—An erect, somewhat slender, little branched plant, 1–2 feet high ; *root-leaves* pinnate, with smaller leaflets at the base ; *stem-leaves* ternate ; *flowers* erect, yellow ; *awns* rigid, hooked at the end ; *stipules* large, rounded, and cut. Hedges and thickets ; common.—Fl. June to August. Perennial.

GEUM URBANUM (*Common Avens, Herb Bennet*)

2. *G. rivale* (Water Avens).—Not so tall as the last, and stouter, the *flowers* drooping, not so spreading ; *root-leaves* pinnate, with the alternate leaflets and those at the base smaller ; *stem-leaves* ternate ; the *calyx* is deeply tinged

with a dull purplish hue with darker veins ; the *petals* are of a purplish pink colour tinged with an orange shade.—Fl. June, July. Perennial.

A variety (*G. intermedium*) is sometimes found which partakes of the characters of both the above species. It is probably a natural hybrid between the two.

5. POTENTILLA (*Cinquefoil*)

1. *P. Fragariastrum* (Strawberry-leaved Cinquefoil).—*Stem* prostrate ; *leaves* 3 on a stalk ; *leaflets* inversely egg-shaped, cut, silky on both sides ; *petals* equalling or sometimes longer than the calyx. One of the earliest spring flowers, often confounded by young botanists with the Wild Strawberry (*Fragaria vesca*). It may, however, be always distinguished by its prostrate mode of growth and short, notched petals ; the flower-stalks of the Strawberry being erect, and the petals entire. Banks and hedges ; abundant.— Fl. January to May. Perennial.

2. *P. reptans* (Creeping Cinquefoil).—*Stem* creeping, rooting at the joints ; *leaves* stalked ; *leaflets* inversely egg-shaped, tapering at the base, serrated ; *flower-stalks* solitary ; *flowers* handsome, yellow, on long stalks. Meadows and waysides ; common.— Fl. June to August. Perennial.

POTENTILLA
TORMENTILLA
(*Tormentil*)

3. *P. Tormentilla* (Tormentil).—*Leaves* of 3 leaflets, ternate, sessile ; *root-leaves* of 5 leaflets (pinnate), stalked ; *leaflets* narrow, acute, cut ; *stem* ascending ; *petals* generally 3. A small plant, with bright yellow flowers and very woody roots. Banks and woods ; common. Specimens are not uncommon in which the stem is prostrate and the flowers rather larger ; this by some botanists is considered a distinct species, and is called *Tormentilla reptans* (Creeping Tormentil), or *P. procumbeus*.—Fl. all the summer. Perennial.

4. *P. argentea* (Hoary Cinquefoil).—*Stem* prostrate ; *leaves* pinnate ; *leaflets* inversely egg-shaped, cut, white and downy beneath, their edges rolled back ; *flowers* yellow, small, several together at the ends of the stems. Pastures and roadsides, on gravelly soil ; not common. —Fl. June. Perennial.

5. *P. verna* (Spring Cinquefoil).—*Stem* prostrate ; *leaflets* sometimes 7 on the root ; *leaves* inversely egg-shaped, serrated towards the end, hairy on the edge and ribs beneath, not downy. A small woody plant, about 5 inches long, with yellow

PLATE XXVI.

Silverweed
Strawberry-leaved Cinquefoil
Wild Strawberry

Shrubby Cinquefoil

flowers 2-3 together at the ends of the stems. Dry pastures in various parts of England, but not common.—Fl. April to June. Perennial.

6. *P. alpestris* (Alpine Cinquefoil).—Closely allied to the last ; the *stem* is more upright and the *flowers* larger and sometimes spotted. Rocky places in the north ; rare.—Fl. June, July. Perennial.

7. *P. Sibbaldi* (Sibbaldia).—A small prostrate plant, with ternate, hairy *leaves*, and small *flowers ; calyx* green ; *petals* minute or wanting ; the number of *stamens* and *pistils* is very variable ; *leaflets* wedge-shaped, ending in three points. Found only on some of the Highland mountains, but sometimes very abundant there.—Fl. June, July. Perennial.

8. *P. fruticosa* (Shrubby Cinquefoil). —*Leaves* pinnate ; a bushy species 2-3 feet high, with hairy *leaves* and large yellow *flowers*, which last grow several together at the end of the stems. Bushy places in the north of England and west of Ireland ; rare.— Fl. June, July. Perennial.

POTENTILLA SIBBALDI (*Sibbaldia'*

9.—*P. anserina* (Silver-weed, Goose-grass).—*Leaves* pinnate, the alternate leaflets smaller ; *leaflets* sharply cut, silky on both sides, especially beneath ; *flower-stalks* solitary, axillary. Well marked by its creeping stem, which roots at the joints, its elegantly cut silky foliage, and showy yellow flowers. Waste ground ; common.— Fl. June, July. Perennial.

10. *P. rupestris* (Rock Cinquefoil).—A shrubby species with a woody perennial stem and annual, herbaceous, flowering stems, which bear loose corymbs of large white flowers. Found only on the Breidden Hill, Montgomeryshire.—Fl. May, June. Perennial.

11. *P. palustris* (Marsh Cinquefoil).—A herbaceous bog-plant, growing about a foot high. The lower *leaves* are usually of 7 long, cut leaflets, the upper of 5 or 3 ; and each *stem* bears several leaves and a number of large dingy purple *flowers*. —Fl. July. Perennial.

6. FRAGARIA (*Strawberry*)

1. *F. vesca* (Wood Strawberry).—*Calyx* of the fruit bent back ; *hairs* on the general flower-stalk widely spreading, on the partial

CALYCIFLORÆ

flower-stalks close pressed, silky. A well-known plant, with bright green hairy leaves, rooting stems, and erect flower-stalks. By these last two characters, as well as by the drooping fruit, this plant may be distinguished from *Potentilla Fragariastrum* (Strawberry-leaved Cinquefoil), which is often mistaken for it by young botanists. The Strawberry probably derives its name from the custom of laying straw between the rows of plants in gardens. Woods and thickets; common.—Fl. May to July. Perennial.

A variety, *F. elatior* (the Hautboy Strawberry), which is taller, more hairy, produces less runners, and being often unisexual, produces no fruit, is not really wild, though it often occurs as a garden escape.

7. RUBUS (*Bramble*)

1. *R. Idæus* (Raspberry).—*Root-stock* creeping; *stem* nearly erect, round, downy, and prickly; *leaves* pinnate, of 3-5 leaflets, which are white and very downy beneath; *flowers* drooping; *fruit* hoary, scarlet, or yellow in some cultivated varieties, and of an agreeable flavour. The origin of all the garden varieties, from which it differs in little but the size of the fruit. Rocky woods; not uncommon. —Fl. May, June. Shrub.

2. *R. fruticosus* (Common Bramble, or Blackberry).—*Root-stock* not sending out suckers; *stem* arched, angular, prickly, often rooting at the extremities, which arch down and touch the ground, in this way producing fresh plants; *leaves* of 3-5 leaflets; *leaflets* ovate, toothed, the midribs and leaflets often thorny; *flowers* white or pink, erect, in compound panicles; *calyx* of the fruit spreading or bent back; *fruit* black or sometimes reddish. This description includes a large number of species and varieties to which names have been severally given; but it is not here thought necessary to describe the characters at length, the genus being confessedly a difficult one, and likely to be of interest to a specialist only. Common everywhere. Most of the species flower from July to August, and ripen their fruit in September and October. Shrub.

3. *R. cæsius* (Dewberry).—*Stem* prostrate, nearly round, prickly below, bristly above; *leaves* of 3-5 leaflets; *panicle* simple; *calyx* clasping the fruit. In this species the fruit, which consists of a few large drupes, is half enclosed in the calyx, and is covered with a grey bloom. Thickets and borders of fields; not uncommon.—Fl. June to August. Shrub.

4. *R. saxitilis* (Stone Bramble).—Stem herbaceous, about 1 foot high, rooting; *prickles* few or none; *leaves* of 3 leaflets; *flowers* few together, greenish yellow; *fruit* scarlet, consisting of 1-4 large drupes. Stony, mountainous places, especially in the north.— Fl. July, August. Perennial.

PLATE XXVII.

Marsh Cinquefoil   Creeping Cinquefoil.

5. *R. Chamæmorus* (Cloudberry).—*Root-stock* a creeping rhizome ; *stem* herbaceous, about 6 inches high, without prickles ; *leaves* simple, 5–7-lobed ; *flowers* solitary, large, white, and with the *stamens* and *pistils* on different plants. The fruit is orange-red and of a pleasant flavour. A very distinct species, growing in peaty mountainous situations in the north of Great Britain and Ireland. Known in Scotland as *avrons,* and in Norway as möltebeere.— Fl. June, July. Perennial.

8. AGRIMONIA (*Agrimony*)

1. *A. Eupatoria* (Common Agrimony).—The only British species. A slender herbaceous plant 1–2 feet high, very different in habit from any of the preceding. The *leaves* are pinnate, with the alter-nate leaflets smaller, and all are deeply cut. The *flowers* are yellow, and grow in long tapering spikes. The whole plant is covered with soft hairs, and when bruised emits a slightly aromatic scent. Its properties are said to be tonic, and on this account it is often col-lected by village herbalists and made into tea. Common in waste ground.—Fl. July, August. Perennial.

9. ALCHEMILLA (*Lady's Mantle*)

1. *A. vulgaris* (Common Lady's Mantle).—*Leaves* kidney-shaped, 7–9-lobed ; *lobes* blunt, serrated ; *flowers* in loose panicles. A herbaceous plant about 6 inches high, with large and handsome soft leaves and numerous small yellowish green flowers. Hilly pas-tures ; not uncommon.—Fl. June to August. Perennial.

2. *A. Alpina* (Alpine Lady's Mantle).—*Leaf* of 5–7 oblong, blunt leaflets, serrated at the end, white and satiny beneath. A very beautiful plant, re-markable for the lustrous, almost metallic hue of the underside of its leaves. Mountains in Scotland and the north of England. — Fl. July, August. Perennial.

3. *A. arvensis* (Field Lady's Mantle, or Parsley Piert).—*Leaves* 3-cleft, wedge-shaped, downy ; *lobes* deeply cut ; *flowers* tufted, sessile in the axils of the leaves. A small inconspicuous weed, 3–6 inches long, with minute greenish flowers, which are almost concealed by the leaves and their large stipules. Common everywhere.—Fl. May to August. Annual.

ALCHEMILLA ARVENSIS (*Field Lady's Mantle*)

10. Sanguisorba (*Burnet*)

1. *S. officinalis* (Great Burnet).—The only British species. A tall, elegant plant, with pinnate *leaves*; *stems* 2-3 feet high, sparely clothed with leaves below, branched into 3 or 4 terminal flower-stalks, each bearing an oblong head of small, crowded, purple-brown *flowers*. Moist pastures; not uncommon.—Fl. June to September. Perennial.

Sanguisorba Officinalis   Poterium Sanguisorba
(*Great Burnet*)   (*Salad Burnet*)

11. Poterium (*Salad Burnet*)

1. *P. sanguisorba* (Salad Burnet).—The only British species. Not unlike the last, but smaller, about 1 foot high, and the flower-heads more globular. The *leaves* are pinnate, with serrate leaflets, and have the taste and smell of cucumber. The *flowers* grow in small round heads, and are greenish, sometimes tinged with purple. The upper flowers in each head bear crimson tufted *pistils*, the lower ones 30-40 *stamens*, with very long drooping *filaments*. Common in dry pastures, especially on chalk and limestone.—Fl. July, August. Perennial.

12. Rosa (*Rose*)

1. *R. spinosissima* (Burnet, or Scotch Rose).—*Leaflets* small, simply serrated, smooth; *calyx* simple; *fruit* nearly round. A thick, very prickly bush 2-4 feet high, the prickles nearly straight

PLATE XXVIII.

Common Agrimony   Common Lady's Mantle

and intermixed with bristles. The foliage is small, leaves with 7–9 leaflets; flowers solitary, white, very fragrant; fruit dark purple. Waste places, especially near the sea. The origin of the garden varieties of Scotch Rose.—Fl. May, June. Shrub.

2. *R. tomentosa* (Downy-leaved Rose). —*Leaflets* doubly serrated, and glandular; *calyx* pinnate. Distinguished by its stout, long *shoots*, downy, almost hoary *leaves*, large white or pale pink *flowers*, 1–3 together, and oblong *fruit*, covered more or less with small prickles and usually crowned with the copiously pinnate *calyx-leaves*. Hedges and thickets, particularly in the north; common.—Fl. June, July. Shrub.

ROSA SPINOSISSIMA (*Burnet-leaved Rose*)

3. *R. rubiginosa* (Sweet Brier).—*Leaflet* doubly serrated, hairy, glandular beneath, mostly rounded at the base; *calyx* pinnate, remaining attached to the ripe fruit; *fruit* pear-shaped when young, and becoming globose, red, and usually smooth; larger *prickles* hooked, the smaller ones straight, mixed with bristles. The Eglantine of the poets, but not of Milton, whose " twisted Eglantine " is the Woodbine or Honeysuckle. A favourite garden plant, deservedly cultivated for the sake of its deliciously fragrant foliage. Bushy places, especially on chalk.—Fl. June, July. Shrub.

4. *R. canina* (Dog Rose).—*Leaves* smooth, or slightly hairy; *calyx* pinnate, not remaining attached to the fruit; *styles* distinct; *prickles* hooked; flowering *stems* usually smooth, and bearing solitary flowers or 3 or 4 together. This is the Common Hedge Rose, a flower belonging exclusively to summer, and welcomed at its first appearance scarcely less warmly than the early Primrose of spring. The colour of the flower varies from white to a deep blush, and the leaves also differ considerably; but the above characters will be found to include all the principal varieties. Hedges and bushy places; abundant.—Fl. June, July. Shrub.

5. *R. arvensis* (Trailing Dog Rose).—*Prickles* small, hooked; *leaves* smooth; *calyx* slightly pinnate, not remaining attached to the fruit; *styles* united; *stigmas* forming a round head. Distinguished from all other British species of Rose by its slender, trailing stems. The flowers are white and scentless, and there are fewer prickles than in most other species. Woods and hedges; common in the south of England.—Fl. June to August. Shrub. Botanists describe no less than nineteen species of native Roses, but, as many

PYRUS COMMUNIS (*Wild Pear*)

of these are rare and the characters of others are difficult to discriminate, it has been thought best to describe here only those which are of common occurrence, or otherwise remarkable.

13. PYRUS (*Pear, Apple, Service,* and *Mountain Ash*)

1. *P. communis* (Wild Pear).—*Leaves* simple, egg-shaped, serrated; *flowers* white, in bunches on spurs of the previous year's formation; *fruit* tapering at the base. A small upright tree, often bearing thorns at the extremities of its branches. The seed-vessel, in a wild state, is woody, austere, and worthless, yet is the origin of the countless luscious varieties of our gardens and orchards. Woods and hedges.—Fl. April, May. Tree.

2. *P. malus* (Crab Apple).—*Leaves* simple, egg-shaped, serrated; *flowers* in a sessile umbel; *styles* combined below; *fruit* hollow beneath. A small, spreading tree, with thornless branches, umbels of white flowers delicately shaded with pink, and nearly round fruit, which is intensely acid. It was formerly much used in making verjuice and in the preparation of pomatum, so called from *pomum*, an apple. Woods and hedges.—Fl. May. Tree.

PYRUS MALUS (*Crab Apple*)

3. *P. torminalis* (Wild Service Tree). — *Leaves* egg-shaped, with several deep, sharp lobes; *flowers* in corymbs. A small tree, with leaves shaped somewhat like those of the Hawthorn, but larger, and with white flowers, which are succeeded by brownish, spotted, berry-like fruit. Woods and hedges in the south of England.—Fl. May. Tree.

PYRUS TORMINALIS (*Wild Service Tree*)

PLATE XXIX.

Dog Rose

Common May

4. *P. aucuparia* (Fowler's Service, Mountain Ash, Quicken, or Rowan Tree).—*Leaves* pinnate, serrated ; *flowers* in corymbs ; *fruit* nearly round.   One of the most elegant of British trees, conspicuous in the flowering season by its delicate green foliage and large corymbs of small white flowers, and in autumn by its clusters of berry-like pomes, which are greedily eaten by birds, and often used as a lure by the bird-catcher or fowler—*auceps*.   Mountainous woods.— Fl. May.   Tree.

PYRUS ARIA (*White Beam Tree*)

PYRUS AUCUPARIA (*Fowler's Service Tree*)

5. *P. Aria* (White Beam Tree).— *Leaves* egg-shaped, deeply and irregularly serrated, white below ; *flowers* in corymbs ; *fruit* nearly round.   A small tree, well distinguished by its very large leaves, which are remarkably white and silky beneath, especially when beginning to expand. Woods, especially in chalky or limestone soils.—Fl. June.   Tree.

14. MESPILUS (*Medlar*)

1. *M. Germanica* (Common Medlar).—A tree well known in a cultivated state, and although found apparently wild in the south of England, it is probably not a true

MESPILUS GERMANICA (*Common Medlar*)

native. The *flowers* are white and very large, and the *fruit* is remarkably flattened at the top, exposing the upper ends of the long seed-cells.—Fl. May.　Tree.

15. CRATÆGUS (*Hawthorn*)

1. *C. oxyacantha* (Hawthorn, White-thorn, or May).—A branching, thorny shrub or small tree, which, though it varies considerably in its mode of growth, shape of its leaves, and colour of its flowers and fruit, is so well known as to need no description. The *leaves* are wedge-shaped, divided into 3–5-toothed lobes, and expand before the flowers ; the *flowers* white or pink, and fragrant ; *fruit* red, containing 1–3 hard carpels. The name Hawthorn is supposed to be a corruption of the Dutch *hæg*, or hedge ; although, therefore, the fruit is generally called a *haw*, that name is derived from the tree which produces it, and the tree does not, as is frequently supposed, take its name from the fruit which it bears.—Fl. May, and in the mountains till late in June.　Tree.

16. COTONEASTER (*Cotoneaster*)

1. *C. vulgaris* (Common Cotoneaster).—A small shrub with entire, ovate *leaves*, glabrous above and cottony on the under side ; *flowers* small, pinkish, solitary or several together ; *fruit* a small reddish berry. In Britain found only in one station, viz. the limestone cliffs of Great Orme's Head, Caernarvonshire.—Fl. May, June. Perennial.

NATURAL ORDER XXV

ONAGRACEÆ.—THE WILLOW HERB TRIBE

Calyx of 4, sometimes 2 lobes, which in bud are attached to each other by their edges ; the *calyx-tube* more or less united to the ovary ; *petals* as many as the lobes of the calyx, twisted while in bud ; *stamens* 4 or 8, rarely 2, springing from the mouth of the calyx ; *ovary* of 2 or 4 cells, often crowned by a disk ; *stigma* knobbed, or 4-lobed ; *fruit* a berry, or 4-celled capsule. Herbaceous plants or shrubs, principally inhabiting the temperate parts of the globe, especially America and Europe. In this Order we find the elegant American genus *Fuchsia*, with its coloured 4-cleft calyx and often edible fruit. Many species of *Œnothera* are cultivated as garden plants, some bearing flowers 3 or 4 inches in diameter ; those with yellow or white flowers, which open only in the evening, are called Evening Primroses. The properties of the plants which compose this Order are unimportant. The wood of the *Fuchsia* is said to be used as a dye, and the roots of *Œnothera biennis*, the Common

Evening Primrose, are eatable. In all, the number 4 predominates in the arrangement of the parts.

1. EPILOBIUM (Willow Herb).—*Calyx* 4-parted, the lobes not combined after expansion ; *petals* 4 ; *stamens* 8 ; *capsule* long, 4-sided, 4-celled, 4-valved ; *seeds* numerous, tufted with down. (Name from the Greek, *epi*, upon, and *lobos*, a pod, the flowers being placed on the top of the pod-like seed-vessel.)

2. ŒNOTHERA (Evening Primrose).—*Calyx* 4-parted, the lobes more or less combined after expansion, and bent back ; *stamens* 8 ; *capsule* 4-celled, 4-valved ; *seeds* numerous, not bearded. (Name in Greek signifying *catching the flavour of the wine*.)

3. ISNARDIA.—*Calyx* 4-parted ; *petals* 4 or none ; *stamens* 4 ; *capsule* inversely egg-shaped, 4-angled, 4-celled, 4-valved, crowned with the calyx. (Named after a French botanist of the eighteenth century, *Antoine d'Isnard*.)

4. CIRCÆA (Enchanter's Nightshade).—*Calyx* 2-parted ; *petals* 2 ; *stamens* 2 ; *capsule* 2-celled, each cell containing a seed. (Name from *Circe*, the enchantress so celebrated in Greek Mythology.)

1. EPILOBIUM (*Willow Herb*)

1. *E. angustifolium* (Rose Bay, or Flowering Willow).—*Leaves* narrow pointed, smooth, or hoary. A tall, handsome species 2–4 feet high, not often met with in a wild state, but common in gardens, where it is cultivated for the sake of its long racemes of handsome rose-coloured flowers. Caution should be used in introducing it into a small garden, as its roots creep extensively, and are very difficult to eradicate. Damp woods ; rare, except as an escape. —Fl. July. Perennial.

2. *E. hirsutum* (Great Hairy Willow Herb, Codlins-and-cream).— A handsome species 4–6 feet high, with large rose-coloured *flowers ; petals* all equal ; *stamens* erect ; *stigma* 4-cleft ; whole plant woolly ; *leaves* clasping the stem, narrow oblong, serrated ; *stem* much branched ; *root* creeping. Well marked by its very downy stems and leaves and creeping roots. Wet places by streams and ditches ; common.—Fl. July, August. Perennial.

3. *E. parviflorum* (Small-flowered Hairy Willow herb).—Downy ; *leaves* sessile, narrow, toothed ; *stem* 1–2 feet high, nearly simple ; *root* fibrous ; *flowers* pink. Distinguished from the last by its smaller size, unbranched mode of growth, and fibrous roots. Wet places ; common.—Fl. July, August. Perennial.

4. *E. montanum* (Broad Smooth-leaved Willow Herb).—A small species about a foot high. *Leaves* egg-shaped, acute, smooth, toothed, the lower ones shortly stalked ; *stem* round, slightly downy ;

flowers rose-coloured, the buds usually drooping. It may often be detected when in seed by its capsules, the valves of which open lengthwise, and disclose the numerous seeds bearded with cottony down. Dry places; common.—Fl. July, August. Perennial.

5. *E. roseum* (Pale Smooth-leaved Willow Herb).—*Stem* erect, branched, 1–2 feet high, imperfectly 4-angled, and bearing a panicle of small rose-coloured *flowers; leaves* ovate, smooth, toothed, on longish stalks. Damp places, mostly in the south.

6. *E. tetragonum* (Square-stalked Willow Herb).—*Stem* branched, 4-angled, nearly smooth, 1–2 feet high; *leaves* narrow, sessile, toothed; *flowers* small, pink; buds erect. Wet places; common. —Fl. July, August. Perennial.

7. *E. palustre* (Narrow-leaved Marsh Willow Herb).—*Leaves* narrow, wedge-shaped at the base, slightly toothed, sessile; *stem* round, nearly smooth. From 1–2 feet high, with very narrow, nearly entire leaves, small flowers, which droop while in bud, and a round stem, which often has 2 downy lines on opposite sides. Wet places; not common.—Fl. July, August. Perennial.

8. *E. alsinifolium* (Chickweed-leaved Willow Herb).—A mountainous species about 6 inches high and branched; *leaves* very thin, egg-shaped, pointed, toothed, shortly stalked; *flowers* pink, rather large. Moist mountainous places in the north.—Fl. July, August. Perennial.

9. *E. Alpinum* (Alpine Willow Herb). —Also a mountain species, with a branched *stem* 3 or 4 inches high, bearing 1 or 2 pink *flowers*, drooping while in bud. *Leaves* obtuse, shortly stalked. Moist mountainous places in the north. —Fl. July. Perennial.

2. ŒNOTHERA (*Evening Primrose*)

1. *Œ. biennis* (Common Evening Primrose).—A stout herbaceous plant 2–3 feet high, with lanceolate, light green, smooth *leaves*, and spikes of large, pale yellow, fragrant *flowers*, which open in the evening and wither towards the middle of the next day. It is common in gardens, and in a few places appears to be naturalised.— Fl. July to September. Biennial.

ŒNOTHERA BIENNIS
(*Common Evening Primrose*)

PLATE XXX.

Great Hairy Willow-Herb   Common Enchanter's Nightshade

Purple Loosestrife   Hoary Willow-Herb   Rose Bay

3. Isnardia

1. *I. palustris* (Marsh Isnardia).—The only British species. A small, herbaceous plant, 6–8 inches long, with prostrate rooting *stems ; leaves* ovate, smooth, stalked, and opposite ; and small axillary sessile *flowers*, which are destitute of petals. Very rare. Has been found only at Buxstead in Sussex, and in the New Forest. —Fl. July. Annual.

4. Circæa (*Enchanter's Nightshade*)

1. *C lutetiana* (Common Enchanter's Nightshade).—A slender, herbaceous plant 1–2 feet high, with a branched, downy *stem ;* egg-shaped *leaves*, toothed and pointed, and hairy *calyx.* The roots are creeping, the flowers small, white, with pink stamens, and are borne in graceful branched racemes, and are succeeded by 2-lobed, hairy seed-vessels. Damp shady places; common ; often a troublesome weed in damp gardens.—Fl. July, August. Perennial.

2. *C. Alpina* (Alpine Enchanter's Nightshade).—*Stem* nearly smooth ; *leaves* heart-shaped, toothed, shining. Closely resembling the last, but smaller and less branched ; 5–8 inches high ; the *fruit* is not so bristly, and is usually 1-seeded. The leaves are remarkable for their delicate texture, and when dried are nearly transparent. Mountainous woods in the north.—Fl. July, August. Perennial.

Natural Order XXVI

HALORAGACEÆ.—The Mare's-tail Tribe

Calyx adhering to the ovary, and either expanding into 3 or 4 minute lobes, or reduced to a mere rim ; *petals* either minute and placed on the mouth of the calyx, or wanting ; *stamens* either equalling the petals in number, twice as many, or, when petals are absent, 1 or 2 ; *ovary* with one or more cells ; *stigmas* equal in number to the cells of the ovary ; *capsule* not opening ; *seeds* solitary, pendulous. An unimportant Order, comprising about eighty species of plants, scattered over most parts of the globe, none of which have any economic use. They are for the most part herbaceous aquatics, with inconspicuous flowers often destitute of petals, and in one genus, *Hippuris* (Mare's-tail), composed of a minute *calyx*, a solitary *stamen*, and a single *seed*. In several species the *stamens* and *pistils* are in separate flowers.

1. Hippuris (Mare's-tail).—*Calyx* forming a minute, indistinctly 2-lobed rim for the ovary ; *petals* 0 ; *stamen* 1 ; *style* 1 ; *seed* 1 ;

nut-like. From the Greek words, *hippos* and *oura*, meaning a horse's tail.)

2. MYRIOPHYLLUM (Water Milfoil).—*Stamens* and *pistils* in separate flowers, but on the same plant (monœcious); *calyx* 4-parted; *petals* 4; *stamens* usually 8; *styles* 4; *fruit* of 4 nut-like seeds. (Name from the Greek, *murios*, countless, and *phyllon*, a leaf, from its numerous leaves.)

1. HIPPURIS (*Mare's-tail*)

1. *H. vulgaris* (Common Mare's-tail).—The only British species, not uncommon in stagnant water. A singular plant, with erect, jointed *stems*, which are un-branched, except at the base, and taper to a point, bearing whorls of 8–12 very narrow leaves with hard tips. The inconspicuous *flowers* are sessile in the axils of the upper leaves, and are often without stamens. Not to be confounded with the genus, *Equisetum* (Horse-tail), a plant allied to the ferns, which has a jointed stem and rigid leaves, but bears its fructifica-tion in terminal heads.—Fl. June, July. Perennial.

HIPPURIS
VULGARIS
(*Common
Mare's-tail*)

2. MYRIOPHYLLUM (*Water Milfoil*)

1. *M. spicatum* (Spiked Water Mil-foil).—An aquatic plant, rooting in the mud of stagnant waters, and form-ing a tangled mass of slender, much branched stems; *leaves* 4 in a whorl, finely divided into numerous hair-like segments, the whole plant being sub-merged, except the leafless, slender spikes of inconspicuous greenish flowers, arranged in whorls, which rise a few inches above the surface. Common. —Fl. July, August. Perennial.

MYRIOPHYLLUM SPICATUM
(*Spiked Water Milfoil*)

2. *M. verticillatum* (Whorled Water Milfoil).—Differs from the preceding in having the *flowers* in whorls at the base of the leaves. *M. alterniflorum* (Alter-nate Flowered Water Milfoil) has barren flowers, alternately arranged in a short, leafless spike, with the fertile flowers, about 3 together, in the axils of the leaves at its base. The last two are rare.

Natural Order XXVII

CERATOPHYLLACEÆ.—The Horn-wort Tribe

Stamens and *pistils* in separate flowers, but on the same plant (monœcious) ; *calyx* many-parted ; *corolla* none ; *stamens* 10–20, without filaments ; *anthers* 2-pointed ; *ovary* 1-celled ; *style* curved ; *seed-vessel* nut-like, 1-seeded, not opening.   In the present volume the original arrangement of the earlier editions of the book has been kept, viz. *Ceratophylleæ* contains but one genus, the Horn-worts, and follows the Mare's-tail Tribe.   Some botanists place the Horn-worts and Water Spear-worts, as two genera forming one Order, after the Spurges ; others place Water Star-wort among the Mare's-tail Tribe, and Horn-wort as an Order by itself, following the Spurges.   The Horn-worts are an unimportant family of aquatic plants, very distinct in structure from any other known plants, with rigid whorled *leaves*, which are repeatedly forked, and inconspicuous *flowers*.   (Name in Greek, signifying *horn-leaved*.)

CERATOPHYLLUM DEMERSUM (*Common Horn-wort.*

   1. *C. demersum* (Common Horn-wort). — *Fruit* armed with 2 thorns near the base, and terminated by the curved *style*.   An aquatic plant growing entirely under water, with long, slender *stems* ;   whorled, bristle-like *leaves*, which are 2–4 times forked, and often inflated and jointed ; the *flowers* also are whorled, and grow in the axils of the leaves.   Slow streams and ditches ;   frequent. — Fl. July. Perennial.

   C. submersum scarcely differs from the preceding, except in having fruit without thorns ; and the plant is a paler green.

Natural Order XXVIII

LYTHRACEÆ.—Loosestrife Tribe

Calyx tubular, many-parted, often with intermediate teeth : *petals* inserted between the outer divisions of the calyx, soon falling off ; *stamens* springing from the tube of the calyx, within the petals, and either equalling them in number, or twice, thrice, or four times as many ; *ovary* 2 to 4-celled ; *style* single ; *capsule* many-seeded, covered by the calyx, but not united to it.   A large Order containing both herbaceous and shrubby species, and represented in most parts of the Old and New World.   Known by the

H

above characteristics and their mostly having opposite, entire leaves without stipules, and four-cornered stems. Many of the plants of this tribe possess astringent properties, and some are used for dyeing. *Lawsonia inermis* is a plant from which the Henna of Egypt is obtained. It is used by the women of that country to stain their nails an orange colour, and is also employed for dyeing morocco leather reddish-yellow.

1. LYTHRUM (Purple Loosestrife).—*Calyx* cylindrical, with 12 divisions, alternately smaller; *petals* 6; *stamens* 6 or 12; *style* long. (Name from the Greek, *lythron*, blood, from the colour of the flowers.)

2. PEPLIS (Water Purslane).—*Calyx* bell-shaped, with 12 divisions, alternately smaller; *petals* 6, minute, soon falling off, or absent; *stamens* 6; *style* very short. (Name from the Greek, *peplion*, purslane, anciently the name of another genus.)

1. LYTHRUM (*Purple Loosestrife*)

1. *L. salicaria* (Purple Loosestrife or Willowstrife).—*Leaves* opposite, long, and narrow, heart-shaped at the base; *flowers* whorled, in leafy spikes; *stamens* 12. An exceedingly handsome plant, 2–4 feet high, generally growing on river banks, among sedges and rushes, and sending up tall tapering spikes of purple flowers, which, seen from a distance, might be mistaken for Foxgloves. The stamens are arranged in two whorls, those of each whorl of a different length to the style; the style in some instances being longer than the stamens, in others shorter, and in others of a length between that of the stamens of the two whorls. Watery places; abundant.—Fl. July, August. Perennial.

2. *L. hyssopifolia* (Hyssop-leaved Purple Loosestrife).—A much smaller plant, 4–8 inches high; lower *leaves* opposite, upper alternate; *flowers* small, purple, solitary, sessile in the upper leaf axils; *stamens* 6. It grows in moist places in the south of England, but is far from common.

PEPLIS PORTULA
(*Water Purslane*)

2. PEPLIS (*Water Purslane*)

1. *P. Portula* (Water Purslane).—A humble, creeping, aquatic plant, with opposite, smooth *leaves*, 4-angled *stems*, and inconspicuous axillary *flowers*. The stems are usually more or less tinged with red; and when the plant grows in places from which the water has dried up the leaves acquire the same hue. Common.—Fl. July, August. Annual.

NATURAL ORDER XXIX
TAMARICACEÆ.—THE TAMARISK TRIBE

Calyx 4–5 parted, overlapping when in bud, remaining after the petals have withered ; *petals* 4–5, from the base of the calyx ; *stamens* equal in number to the petals or twice as many, distinct, or united by their filaments ; *ovary* not combined with the calyx ; *styles* 3 ; *capsule* 3-valved, 1-celled, containing many seeds, which are tufted with down at the extremity. Mostly shrubs with rod-like branches, and minute leaves which resemble scales. They are, with the exception of one Mexican genus, confined to the eastern half of the northern hemisphere, and are most numerous on the shores of the Mediterranean ; but though preferring the seaside, they are not infrequently found on the banks of rivers, and occur in the desert, especially where the soil is impregnated with salt, as in the neighbourhood of Mount Sinai, where a species of Tamarisk, very like the common one, produces a sugary substance called by the Arabs *Manna*. The bark is astringent, and several species are remarkable for the large quantity of sulphate of soda contained in their ashes, and for the galls which they bear on their branches. These are highly astringent, and are used both in medicine and dyeing.

1. TAMARIX (Tamarisk). — *Calyx* 5-parted ; *petals* 5 ; *stamens* 5 or 10 ; *stigmas* feathery. (Named from the *Tamaris*, a river in Spain, now called the *Tambra*, where the Tamarisk abounds.)

1. TAMARIX (*Tamarisk*)

1. *T. Gallica* (Common Tamarisk).—A handsome shrub or small tree, with long flexible *branches* and minute scale-like *leaves*, which are closely pressed to the twigs, and give the tree a light, feathery appearance. The *flowers*, which are rose-coloured, grow in spiked panicles. The plant is not a native, but has been largely planted on the south coast, where it appears to be well established.—Fl. July. Shrub.

TAMARIX GALLICA
(*Common Tamarisk*)

NATURAL ORDER XXX
CUCURBITACEÆ.—THE GOURD TRIBE

Stamens and *pistils* in separate flowers, either on the same plant (monœcious) or on different plants (diœcious) ; *calyx* 5-toothed, united with the corolla ; *corolla* often scarcely to be distinguished from the calyx; *stamens* 5, more or less united ; *anthers* twisted ; *ovary* imperfectly 3-celled ; *style* short ; *stigmas* short, thick, lobed, velvety ; *fruit* more or less juicy ; *seeds* flat, wrapped in a skin. A large and important Order, containing herbaceous plants, with juicy stems, and climbing by means of tendrils, which spring from the base of the leaf-stalks. The leaves are usually lobed and rough ; the flowers often large, white, red, or yellow ; the fruit juicy or fleshy. They inhabit principally the hot regions of the globe, but a few are found in temperate climates ; and a great number are cultivated in Europe, either for ornament or use. Their properties are in many instances exceedingly violent, of which the common drug *Colocynth* affords an example ; the Bottle Gourd is another, it being recorded that some sailors were poisoned by drinking beer that had been standing in a flask made of one of these gourds. The poisonous plant mentioned in 2 Kings IV. 39–40 is supposed to be a plant of this tribe, the *Wild*, or *Ass Cucumber*, which bears an oval fruit of a very bitter taste, and grows in sandy desert places. As this cucumber has very much the same appearance as that which is cultivated in gardens, but only somewhat smaller, and as even its leaves and tendrils are similar, it might easily happen that a man sent out by the disciples of the prophets took wild cucumbers for a harmless fruit and prepared a meal of them. But the bitterness of the boiled cucumber made those who tasted it fear that it was poisonous, the opinion being general with the Hebrews that a bitter taste indicated the presence of poison (see Rev. VIII. 10, 11). The only plant belonging to this tribe, which is a native of Britain, *Bryonia dioica* (White Bryony), partakes of the properties of Colocynth, and the root is said to be a valuable medicine. The Spirting Cucumber, so called from the force with which it expels the poisonous juice, together with the seeds, when ripe, is a very dangerous drug, a few grains of Elaterium, a prepared form of this juice, having been known to bring on symptoms of poisoning. A case is even recorded where a person was taken dangerously ill from having merely carried a specimen in his hat. Many species, however, produce edible fruit ; for instance, the numerous varieties of Melon and Cucumber, the Water Melon, so highly esteemed for the cool, refreshing juice of its ripe fruit, and one of our finest table vegetables, the Vegetable Marrow. It is said that the tender shoots of the White Bryony may be used with safety, having been boiled, and that they resemble Asparagus in flavour ; but it is highly pro-

PLATE XXXI.

White Bryony

bable that shoots of Black Bryony (*Tamus communis*), a plant belonging to a different Order, may have been used instead ; in either case the experiment is a dangerous one.

1. BRYONIA (Bryony).—*Stamens* 5, in 3 sets ; *style* 3-cleft; *fruit* a globose berry. (Name from the Greek, *bryo*, to shoot or bud, the rapid growth of the Gourd Tribe being proverbial.)

1. BRYONIA (*Bryony*)

1. *B. dioica* (White Bryony).—The only British species. An elegant climbing plant, with large light green, rough *leaves*, palmately divided into 5 lobes, having undivided *tendrils* at the base, and bunches of whitish *flowers*, with green veins. The *fertile flowers* may be distinguished at once from the *barren* by the presence of an ovary below the calyx. These develop into globular scarlet berries, which hang about the bushes after the stems and leaves have withered. The berries of Black Bryony (*Tamus communis*) are larger and elliptical in shape ; both should be avoided as injurious, if not poisonous. Frequent in England, except in the extreme western counties.—Fl. May to August. Perennial.

NATURAL ORDER XXXI
PORTULACEÆ.—THE PURSLANE TRIBE

Sepals 2, united at the base ; *petals* usually 5 ; *stamens* 3 or more ; *ovary* 1-celled, opening transversely or by 3 valves ; *seeds* usually more than 1. Herbs or shrubs, with juicy stems and leaves, and irregular flowers, which open only during sunshine. The most remarkable plant in this Order is the Common Purslane, which has been used from the earliest times as a pot-herb. Many species have large, showy flowers, but the few British representatives are insignificant plants with small white flowers.

1. CLAYTONIA.—*Petals* free ; *stamens* 5, springing from the base of the petals ; *stigmas* 3 ; *capsule* 3-valved and 3-seeded. (Name after *John Clayton*, a Virginian botanist.)

2. MONTIA (Water Blinks).—*Calyx* of 2 sepals ; *corolla* of 5 petals, 3 smaller than the others, and all united at the base ; *tube* of corolla split to the base ; *capsule* 3-valved, 3-seeded. (Named after *J. de Monti*, the Italian botanist.)

1. CLAYTONIA (*Claytonia*)

1. *C. perfoliata* (Perfoliate Claytonia).—A smooth, rather fleshy plant 4–12 inches high. *Root-leaves* roundish, borne singly on stalks, *flowers* small, white, in several small racemes, just below which is a roundish leaf, through the centre of which the stalk passes. Of

North American origin, but has become a plentiful and well-established weed in several parts of England.—Fl. April to July. Annual.

2. *C. Sibirica*, of the same origin as the above, has ovate *root-leaves*, tapering to a point ; roundish sessile *ste ı-leaves* ; and is about as common.

2. MONTIA (*Water Blinks*)

MONTIA FONTANA
(*Water Blinks*)

1. *M. fontana* (Water Blinks).—The only species. An unpretending little plant, with opposite or nearly opposite *leaves* and *minute flowers*, in solitary or in few-flowered, drooping, axillary racemes ; *calyx* 2-cleft ; *corolla* irregular, white, the corolla-tube split in front. Whole plant smooth and rather succulent. Common in wet places.—Fl. May to August. Annual.

NATURAL ORDER XXXII

PARONYCHIACEÆ.—THE KNOT-GRASS TRIBE

Sepals 5 ; *petals* 5, minute, inserted between the lobes of the calyx, sometimes wanting ; *stamens* varying in number, opposite the petals, if equalling them in number ; *ovary* not combined with the calyx ; *pistils* 2–5 ; *fruit* 1-celled, opening with 3 valves or not at all. Small, branching, herbaceous, or somewhat shrubby plants, with sessile, undivided leaves and minute flowers, principally confined to the south of Europe and north of Africa, where they grow in the most barren places, covering with a thick vegetation soil which is incapable of bearing anything else. A few only are found as far north as Great Britain, and nearly all of these are confined to the southern shores.

1. CORRIGIOLA (Strapwort).—*Sepals* 5 ; *petals* 5, as long as the calyx ; *stamens* 5 ; *stigmas* 3, sessile. (Name from *corrigia*, a strap, from the shape of the leaves.)

2. HERNIARIA (Rupture-wort).—*Sepals* 5 ; *petals* 5, resembling barren filaments ; *stamens* 5, inserted on a fleshy ring ; *stigmas* 2, nearly sessile. (Name from the disease for which the plant was formerly supposed to be a remedy.)

3. ILLECEBRUM (Knot-grass).—*Sepals* 5, coloured, thickened, ending in an awl-shaped point ; *petals* 0 or 5 ; *stigmas* 2. (Name from the Latin, *illecebra*, an attraction.)

1. CORRIGIOLA (*Strap-wort*)

1. C. littoralis (Sand Strap-wort).—A small but pretty plant, with slender, spreading *stems*, which lie quite prostrate, very narrow, strap-shaped, glaucous *leaves* and tufts of small white *flowers*. It grows in two or three places on the seashore of Devon, and is very abundant on the banks of the Loe Pool, near Helston, Cornwall. Very rare.— Fl. August to October. Annual.

CORRIGIOLA LITTORALIS
(*Sand Strap-wort*)

2. HERNIARIA (*Rupture-wort*)

1. H. glabra (Smooth Rupture-wort).—A small, prostrate plant, with much of the habit of Wild Thyme ; abundant in the neighbourhood of the Lizard Point, Cornwall, but very rare elsewhere. Though called *smooth*, the leaves are always more or less fringed at the edges. The flowers are green, and grow in sessile tufts in the axils of the leaves, or not unfrequently crowded into leafy spikes. A form with narrow, hairy leaves (*H. hirsuta*) is found at Christchurch, in Hampshire.—Fl. July to September. Perennial.

3. ILLECEBRUM (*Knot-grass*)

1. I. verticillatum (Whorled Knot-grass).—A pretty plant with slender, tangled *stems* of a red tint, glaucous, sessile *leaves*, and axillary whorls of white flowers, which are remarkable for their thickened calyx-leaves, terminating in a soft point. In boggy ground and standing water, among other aquatic plants ; only in Cornwall, Devonshire, and the Channel Islands.— Fl. July to September. Perennial.

ILLECEBRUM VERTICILLATUM
(*Whorled Knot-grass*)

NATURAL ORDER XXXIII

CRASSULACEÆ.—THE STONECROP TRIBE

Sepals 3–20, more or less united at the base ; *petals* equal in number to the sepals, inserted in the bottom of the calyx ; *stamens* the same or twice as many, in which latter case those opposite the

petals are shorter than the others ; *ovaries* as many as the petals,
1-celled, tapering into stigmas, often with a gland at the base of
each ; *fruit* consisting of several erect seed-vessels, which open
lengthwise ; *seeds* in a double row.   Herbs or shrubs, remarkable
for their thick, fleshy leaves and star-like flowers, inhabiting most
parts of the world, especially the south of Africa, and growing in
the driest situations, where not a blade of grass nor a particle of
moss can live ; on naked rocks, old walls, on sandy, hot plains, alternately exposed to the heaviest dews of night and the fiercest rays
of the noonday sun, having the power of laying in during the rainy
season a large store of moisture, which they obstinately retain, and
requiring no further nourishment, save what they derive from the
atmosphere.   A   common   British   species,   *Sedum   telephium*
(Orpine, Live-long), will grow for months, if suspended by a string
from the ceiling of a room, without once being supplied with water.
An African species, *Bryophyllum calycinum*, will not only grow if
similarly treated, but if its leaves be gathered and laid on the ground
they will send out from the notches on their margin young shoots,
in all respects resembling the parent plant.   The properties of the
tribe are in general acrid ; some few contain malic or tartaric acid,
and one or two are sometimes used in medicine for their astringent
properties.

   1. TILLÆA.—*Sepals, petals, stamens,* and *carpels* 3–5 each, the
latter 2-seeded.   (Named after *Michael Angelo Tilli,* an Italian
botanist.)

   2. COTYLEDON (Pennywort).—*Sepals* 5 ; *corolla* tubular, 5-cleft ;
carpels 5, with a scale at the base of each.   (Name from the Greek,
cotyle, a dish, from the shape of the leaves.)

   3. SEMPERVIVUM (House-leek).—*Sepals, petals,* and *carpels* 6–20 ;
stamens 12–40.   (Name from the Latin, *semper,* always, and *vivo,*
to live.)

   4. SEDUM (Stonecrop).—*Sepals, petals,* and *carpels* 4–6 ; *stamens*
8–12.   (Name from the Latin, *sedeo,* to sit, from the humble growth
of the plants.)

1. TILLÆA

   1. *T. muscosa* (Mossy Tillæa).—A minute plant, with small, opposite, blunt *leaves* and greenish white *flowers* tipped with red.   It has
somewhat of the habit of a *Sagina,* from which, however, it is very
distinct.   In sandy, waste places in the south and east of England.
—Fl. June, July.   Annual.

2. COTYLEDON (*Pennywort*)

   1. *C. umbilicus* (Wall Pennywort).—A remarkably succulent
plant, with circular, notched *leaves,* which are depressed above and

PLATE XXXII.

Rock Stonecrop
Wall Pennywort

Claytonia
Orpine or Live-long

are supported on their stalks by their centres, or *peltate*. The *flowers* are pendulous and grow in racemes ; 6–12 inches high, of a greenish yellow colour. The leaves are well known to children by the name " penny pies." Rocks and old walls in the south and west of England.— Fl. June to August. Perennial.

3. Sempervivum (*House-leek*)

1. *S. tectorum* (Common House-leek).— A common but scarcely indigenous plant growing on the roofs of cottages. The *leaves* are thick and juicy, fringed at the edges, and grow in compact, rose-like tufts. Each of the purple *flowers* contains 12 per- fect and 12 imperfect *stamens ;* the latter, which are arranged alternately with the petals, frequently bearing *anthers* contain- ing embryo seeds (ovules) like those found in the carpels, but they never attain ma- turity. The leaves contain malic acid. —Fl. July. Perennial.

SEMPERVIVUM TECTORUM
(*Common House-leek*)

SEDUM
RHODIOLA
(*Rose-root*)

4. Sedum (*Stonecrop*)

1. *S. Rhodiola* (Rose-root).—*Stamens* and *pistils* on separate plants, the pollen bearers having 8 stamens, the seed bearers 4 carpels. A succulent, broad-leafed plant, with the habit of *S. telephium*, but stouter. The *flowers* are greenish yellow, and grow in compact ter- minal *cymes* on simple *stems* 6–12 inches high ; *roots* thick and knotted, having the perfume of rose-water, whence its English name. Abundant on mountains in Scotland, Ireland, and the north of England, and found also on sea cliffs.—Fl. June. Perennial.

2. *S. Telephium* (Orpine, or Live-long).—*Leaves* oblong, egg-shaped, serrated ; *stems* erect, 1–2 feet high. The largest British species, and well distin- guished, not only by its corymbs of purple flowers, but its large, broad leaves. A common cottage- garden plant, frequently occurring as an escape.

3. *S. Anglicum* (English Stonecrop).—*Leaves* egg- shaped, fleshy, spurred at the base beneath, sessile ; *cymes* 2-cleft ; *petals* very sharp. A small plant 3–4 inches high, with stems which are at first prostrate and rooting, afterwards erect ; the leaves are mostly alternate, often tinged with red, small,

and very thick; the flowers conspicuous for their star-like form, their white petals spotted with red, and bright purple anthers. Rocky and sandy places, especially near the sea.—Fl. June, July. Annual.

4. *S. dasyphyllum* (Thick-leaved Stonecrop).—Very like the last; smaller, slightly viscid; *leaves* mostly opposite, globular, and fleshy; *flowers* white, tinged pink. Old walls in the south; an escape.

5. *S. album* (White Stonecrop).—Rather taller than *S. Anglicum*, and more slender. *Flowering-stems* 4-6 inches high; also barren, prostrate stems; *leaves* oblong, cylindrical, blunt, spreading, about half an inch long; *cyme* much branched, drooping when in bud. Rocks and old walls. Supposed to be indigenous in the Malvern Hills, and not uncommon as an escape.—Fl. July, August. Perennial.

6. *S. villosum* (Hairy Stonecrop).—A small species, with hairy, viscid stems and *leaves* and pinkish white *flowers*. Frequent in Scotland and the north of England.—Fl. June, July. Annual.

7. *S. acre* (Biting Stonecrop).—*Leaves* egg-shaped, fleshy, spurred at the base, sessile; *cymes* 3-cleft. Very like *S. Anglicum* in habit, but with yellow flowers, and growing in similar situations; it may, however, be distinguished, when not in flower, by its thicker and more crowded leaves, which are very acrid, and have gained for the plant the name of Wall-pepper. Walls, rocks, and sandy ground; frequent. —Fl. June, July. Perennial.

SEDUM ACRE
(*Biting Stonecrop*)

8. *S. sexangulare* (Tasteless Stonecrop). —Distinguished from the last by its longer and more slender *leaves*, 6 in a whorl. Old walls. Found in the Isle of Sheppey and elsewhere in the eastern counties, but not indigenous.—Fl. July. Perennial.

9. *S. rupestre* (Rock Stonecrop).—A species allied to *S. reflexum*, with slightly flattened *leaves*, which are spurred below, and terminal; *cymes* of large yellow flowers. Found on St. Vincent's Rocks and other limestone cliffs; rare.—Fl. June, July. Perennial.

10. *S. reflexum* (Recurved Yellow Stonecrop).—*Leaves* awl-shaped, spurred at the base, nearly cylindrical, the lowermost curved back. Easily distinguished from any of the preceding by its slender but tough *stems*, 6-10 inches high, clothed with spreading or reflexed *leaves*, which are cylindrical and pointed. Walls and dry banks; not uncommon, but probably not indigenous.—Fl. July, August. Perennial.

PLATE XXXIII.

Rue-leaved Saxifrage

Grass of Parnassus   White Meadow Saxifrage

Natural Order XXXIV

GROSSULARIACEÆ.—The Gooseberry and Currant Tribe

Calyx growing from the summit of the ovary, 4–5 cleft ; *petals* 4–5, small, inserted at the mouth of the calyx-tube, and alternating with the stamens ; *ovary* 1-celled, with the ovules arranged in 2 opposite rows ; *style* 2 to 4-cleft ; *berry* crowned with the withered flower, pulpy, containing many stalked seeds. Shrubs with or without thorns and having alternate lobed leaves, which are plaited when in bud. The flowers grow in clusters in the axils of the leaves, each flower with a bract at its base, and are succeeded by pulpy berries, which in several species are highly prized for their agreeable flavour. In other species the taste is mawkish or extremely acid. The plants of this tribe grow only in the temperate parts of the world, especially in North America and on the mountains of northern India. In Africa they are unknown.

1. RIBES (Currant and Gooseberry).—*Calyx* 5-cleft ; *petals* 5, inserted at the mouth of the calyx-tube ; *stamens* 5 ; *berry* many-seeded, crowned by the withered flower. (Name anciently given to a species of Rhubarb.)

1. RIBES (*Currant* and *Gooseberry*)

Flowers 1–3 together ; branches thorny

1. *R. Grossularia* (Gooseberry).—The common Gooseberry of gardens. Frequently met with in hedges and thickets and in wild rocky places in the north, but probably an escape. It is well distinguished by its sharp *thorns*, which grow either singly or 2–3 together, below the leaf-buds.—Fl. April, May. Shrub.

Flowers in clusters ; branches without thorns

2. *R. rubrum* (Red Currant).—*Flowers* in drooping racemes ; *bracts* at the base of each flower-stalk very small ; *calyx* smooth ; *leaves* bluntly 5-lobed. The Red and White Currant of gardens ; not uncommon in hedges near houses ; and in Scotland and the north of England supposed to be wild.—Fl. April, May. Shrub.

3. *R. nigrum* (Black Currant).—*Flower-clusters* loose, drooping, with a single stalked flower at the base of each ; *calyx* downy ; *leaves* sharply 3- to 5-lobed, dotted with glands beneath. The Black Currant of gardens ; occasionally wild in

RIBES NIGRUM (*Black Currant*)

damp woods. Easily distinguished, at all seasons, by the strong perfume of its buds and leaves.—Fl. April, May. Shrubs.

4. *R. Alpinum* (Tasteless Mountain Currant).—The *stamens* and *pistils* on separate plants ; the *flowers* grow in erect clusters, with very long *bracts* at the base of each. It grows in mountainous places ; is perhaps truly wild in the north of England, and is found also in Scotland ; rare.—Fl. April, May. Shrub.

Natural Order XXXV

SAXIFRAGACEÆ.—The Saxifrage Tribe

Sepals 5 or rarely 4, more or less united at the base ; *petals* equalling the sepals in number, inserted between the sepals, rarely 0 ; *stamens* equalling the petals or twice as many ; *ovary* 2 or 4-celled or 1-celled ; *styles* equalling in number or twice as many as the cells ; *seeds* numerous. This Order, though it contains some such shrubs as the Hydrangeas and Deutzias, is principally composed of herbaceous mountainous plants, with tufted foliage and glandular stems. They abound in temperate and cold climates, but are not found in tropical countries. The genus *Saxifraga* is an extensive one, and contributes greatly to the beauty of the vegetation high up in the mountains ; but some species grow on old walls, by the sides of rivulets, and in moist meadows. *Chrysosplenium* (Golden Saxifrage) has no petals. Few of the plants belonging to this tribe are applied to any use. Most of them have slight astringent properties, and some few are bitter and tonic.

1. SAXIFRAGA (Saxifrage).—*Calyx* in 5 divisions ; *petals* 5 ; *stamens* 10 ; *styles* 2 ; *capsule* 2-celled, 2-beaked, opening between the beaks ; *seeds* numerous. (Name in Latin signifying *rock-breaker*, many of the species growing in the crevices of rocks.)

2. CHRYSOSPLENIUM (Golden Saxifrage).—*Calyx* in 4 divisions ; *petals* 0 ; *stamens* 8 or rarely 10 ; *styles* 2 ; *capsule* 2-beaked. (Name from the Greek, *chrysos*, gold, and *splen*, the spleen, from some imaginary virtues of the plant.)

3. PARNASSIA (Grass of Parnassus).—*Calyx* deeply 5-cleft ; *petals* 5 ; *stamens* 5, with 5 fringed scales interposed ; *stigmas* 4 ; *capsule* 1-celled, with 4 valves. (Name from *Mount Parnassus*, but on what account is uncertain.)

1. SAXIFRAGA (*Saxifrage*)

1. *S. oppositifolia* (Purple Mountain Saxifrage).—*Stems* prostrate, branched, perennial, forming tufts ; *leaves* egg-shaped, opposite. A pretty plant, forming low tufts, seldom above an inch in height, and bearing in the early summer large, handsome, magenta-purple

flowers, which are often so crowded as to completely hide the stems and foliage. It grows on the mountains of Scotland, Wales, and Northern England.—Fl. April, May. Perennial.

2. *S. aizoides* (Yellow Mountain Saxifrage).—*Leaves* very narrow, fleshy, fringed ; *flowers* in a leafy panicle. A handsome species about 6 inches high, with large bright yellow flowers spotted with scarlet. Damp situations by mountain streams, etc., in the north of England, Scotland, and in Ireland.—Fl. June to September. Perennial.

3. *S. Hirculus* (Yellow Marsh Saxifrage).—A rare mountain species, with narrow, undivided, alternate *leaves* and rather large yellow *flowers*, borne singly on 6-inch stems. Wet situations in the north.—Fl. August. Perennial.

4. *S. hypnoides* (Cut-leaved or Mossy Saxifrage).—*Root-leaves* 3 to 5-cleft ; those on the creeping shoots 3-cleft or entire ; *lobes* of the leaves all very narrow, acute, bristle-pointed, and fringed. Distinguished by its dense tufts of finely divided leaves and loose panicles of 1–8 rather large white flowers. Mountainous places, especially in the north ; very frequent in gardens.—Fl. May to July. Perennial.

5. *S. cæspitosa* (Tufted Alpine Saxifrage).—Closely allied to the preceding, but distinguished by broader *leaves*, which are more obtuse and more cut ; the *calyces* also are blunter. The *flowers* are smaller, and are borne singly or in twos on rather downy stems 2 or 3 inches high. High mountains in the north ; very rare.—Fl. May to August. Perennial.

6. *S. granulata* (Meadow Saxifrage).—*Root-leaves* kidney-shaped with rounded lobes ; *stem-leaves* nearly sessile, sharply lobed ; *flowers* panicled ; *roots* granulated. A pretty plant, with slender, leafy stems, 6–12 inches high, and rather large, pure white flowers. The roots are remarkable for producing numerous downy, bulb-like tubers. A double variety is common in gardens. Gravelly meadows; not uncommon.—Fl. May, June. Perennial.

7. *S. cernua* (Drooping Saxifrage).—Somewhat like the last ; *stems* erect, slender, unbranched ; *leaves* kidney-shaped, lobed, the upper ones with bulbs in the axils ; *flowers* 1–3, somewhat drooping, and in Britain often absent. Found only at the summit of Ben Lawers.—Fl. June to August. Perennial.

8. *S. rivularis* (Alpine Brook Saxifrage).—A small glabrous species, with stalked, deeply divided *root-leaves;* and very small white *flowers*, borne 2 or 3 together on weak, almost leafless *stems*. Very rare ; only found on the summits of one or two Highland mountains.—Fl. July, August. Perennial.

9. *S. tridactylites* (Rue-leaved Saxifrage).—Whole plant viscid,

with glandular hairs ; *leaves* wedge-shaped, 3 to 5-cleft ; *stem* much branched; *flowers* terminal, on separate pedicles. A small species, rarely more than 3 inches high, with very hairy and viscid stems and small white flowers. The whole plant has usually a red tinge. On the tops of walls and roofs of cottages; common.—Fl. May, June. Annual.

10. *S. nivalis* (Alpine Saxifrage).—*Leaves* all from the root, inversely egg-shaped, sharply crenate ; *calyx* half inferior ; *flowers* in a crowded head. An Alpine plant 3–6 inches high, with rather large white flowers, which grow in a compact head. Mountains in the north; rare.—Fl. July, August. Perennial.

11. *S. stellaris* (Starry Saxifrage).—A mountain plant 3–5 inches high, with oblong, wedge-shaped, coarsely toothed, scarcely stalked *leaves ;* and panicles of rather large white *flowers*, with two yellow spots at the base of each petal. Wet rocks and the sides of mountain rivulets in Scotland, Ireland, and the north of England.—Fl. June, July. Perennial.

12. *S. umbrosa* (London Pride, or St. Patrick's Cabbage).—A well-known plant, with roselike tufts of roundish, egg-shaped, fleshy *leaves* with white notches, tapering at the base into flat *stalks*, and panicles of small white *flowers* dotted with pink. It grows wild in the south and west of Ireland, is naturalized in many parts of England, and is very common in gardens. Though growing naturally on mountains, there is scarcely any situation where it will not make itself at home, even in the smoky gardens of London. Hence it varies considerably in form, and has been subdivided by some botanists into several species.—Fl. June. Perennial.

13. *S. Geum* (Kidney-shaped Saxifrage).—Very near *S. umbrosa*, and only distinguished by its kidney-shaped *leaves*, borne on long stalks, which are usually more hairy and less flattened than in that species. A form intermediate between the two has been called *S. hirsuta*. Both *S. Geum* and *S. hirsuta* are very rare, only occurring in Ireland.

CHRYSOSPLENIUM OPPOSITIFOLIUM (*Common Golden Saxifrage*)

2. CHRYSOSPLENIUM (*Golden Saxifrage*)

1. *C. oppositifolium* (Common Golden Saxifrage).—*Leaves* opposite, roundish heart-shaped. A small aquatic plant about 6 inches high, with abundance of bright green, tender foliage and terminal flat clusters of yellowish green flowers. Sides of shady rivulets and wet woods ; common.—Fl. April, May. Perennial.

2. *C. alternifolium* (Alternate-leaved Golden Saxifrage).—*Leaves* alternate, lower ones kidney-shaped, on long stalks. Very like the

last, and growing in similar situations, but rare. The flowers in this species are of a deeper yellow; in both the number of stamens is usually 8.—Fl. April, May. Perennial.

3. PARNASSIA (*Grass of Parnassus*)

1. *P. palustris* (Common Grass of Parnassus).—The only British species. An exceedingly elegant plant 8–10 inches high, with solitary cream-coloured *flowers*, beautifully veined. The nectaries are fan-like scales, fringed with white hairs, and terminating in yellow wax-like glands. Bogs; principally in the north.—Fl. August to October. Perennial.

NATURAL ORDER XXXVI

UMBELLIFERÆ.—THE UMBELLIFEROUS TRIBE

Calyx superior, 5-toothed, often reduced to a mere margin; *petals* 5, usually ending in a point, which is bent inwards; *stamens* 5, alternate with the petals, curved inwards when in bud; *ovary* inferior, 2-celled, crowned by a fleshy disk, which bears the petals and stamens; *styles* 2; *stigmas* small; *fruit* composed of 2 carpels, which adhere by their faces to a central stalk, from which, as they ripen, they separate below, and finally are attached to the upper extremity only; each *carpel* is marked by 5 vertical ridges, with 4 intermediate ones; these ridges are separated by channels, in which are often found, imbedded in the substance of the fruit, narrow cells (called vittæ) containing a coloured, oily matter; *seeds* 1 in each carpel, attached by their upper extremity, and containing a large horny *albumen*; the flowers are usually small and situated on the extremities of little stalks, which are united at the base and form an *umbel*. When several of these smaller umbels proceed in like manner from a common stalk the umbel is said to be *compound*; the larger being called a *general umbel*, the smaller *partial*. The small leaves which commonly accompany the flowers of this tribe are called *general* or *partial bracts*, according to their position; each collection of bracts is sometimes termed an *involucre*. All the British plants belonging to this Order are herbaceous, with tubular, or solid, jointed stems. With two exceptions, *Eryngium* and *Hydrocotyle*, they have compound umbels. By far the larger number have also divided leaves, more or less sheathing at the base, and white flowers. Though it is easy at a glance to decide to what Order they are to be assigned, no such facility exists in distinguishing the *families* of the Umbelliferæ. Indeed, were it not for the large number of species (about 1500) which are known to exist, it is probable that they would have been brought together by botanists, so as to form but a few genera, whereas they have been

divided into some 152 ; and as all these agree in the more important parts of fructification, the distinction of the genera are
necessarily founded on differences so minute that, in the case of
other plants, they would perhaps be considered sufficient to do no
more than distinguish species. To the young botanist, therefore,
the study of the Umbelliferæ is unusually difficult ; all the more
important distinctions being founded on the ripe fruit—namely, the
number, position, and shape of the *ridges*, the presence or absence
of *vittæ*, and the form of the *albumen*. As it would be absurd in a
work professing to be a popular description of British Wild Flowers
to attend solely, or even in any great degree, to these characters,
it has been thought desirable to limit the number of species described to those which are of most common occurrence, and to notice
any peculiarity in growth, which, though not strictly admissible
into a systematic description, may assist the student in discovering
the names of the plants he may meet with.

Among the large number of species of which this tribe is con-
stituted one would naturally expect to find plants varying greatly
in their properties. And such is the case to a certain extent ; the
roots, leaves, and seeds are variously employed—some as food and
condiments, others as medicine ; while others are highly poisonous.
Yet when considered with reference to their properties they may
be conveniently arranged into four groups, all members of each
group being remarkably similar. The first comprises plants which
abound in an acrid, watery juice, which is more or less narcotic in
its effects on the animal frame, and which, therefore, when properly
administered in minute doses, is a valuable medicine. Among these
the most important is *Conium* (Hemlock) ; every part of this plant,
especially the fresh leaves and green fruit, contain a volatile, oily
alkali, called *Conia*, which is so poisonous that a few drops soon
prove fatal to a small animal. It acts on the nervous system, and
is a valuable medicine in cancerous and nervous diseases. Several
other British species are poisonous, especially *Œnanthe, Cicuta*, and
Æthusa, described below. The second group comprises those which
abound in a resinous gum, of a fetid odour, which is supposed to be
owing to the presence of sulphur in combination with the peculiar
essential oil. Among these the first place is held by *Asafœtida*, the
hardened milky juice of various species of *Ferula*, inhabiting Persia
and the neighbouring countries. This drug was held in high repute
among the ancients for its medical virtues ; it was supposed to be
an antidote to poison, to restore sight to the blind, and youth to
the aged ; and was besides considered a certain specific against
various diseases. Gum Galbanum is the produce of other umbelliferous plants, natives of the East. The third group comprises
plants the seeds of which abound in a wholesome aromatic oil. The
principal of these are well known, under the names of *Caraway,
Coriander, Dill, Anise,* and *Cumin.* The fourth group comprises

plants which contain some of the above properties in a very slight degree, or so modified as to form wholesome, esculent vegetables. Among these *Carrots* and *Parsnips* occupy the first place; *Celery* and *Alexanders*, in their wild state, are too acrid to be used as food, but when blanched by artificial means become mild and agreeable; *Parsley, Fennel,* and *Chervil*, the last now nearly out of use, are well-known pot-herbs; *Samphire* affords the best of pickles; the root of *Eryngo* is sweet, aromatic, and tonic, and is commonly sold in a candied state; the root of *Angelica* (*Angelica Archangelica*) is fragrant and sweet when first used, but leaves a glowing heat in the mouth, and is commended by the Laplanders both as food and medicine: the candied stems form a favourite sweetmeat. Several species produce underground tubers, which, under the name of pig-nuts, or earth-nuts, are eaten by children and pigs; and others, common in the East, afford valuable pasturage for cattle. Of all the British umbelliferous plants, the most dangerous are the Water Dropworts (*Œnanthe*), the large tuberous roots of which, resembling Dahlia roots, are often exposed by the action of running water, near which they grow, and are thus easily got at by children and cattle. The following table contains a description of all the common British species; a list of the rarer ones and introduced species will be found at the end of the Order.

Umbels simple or irregular

1. HYDROCOTYLE (White-rot).—*Flowers* in simple umbels; *fruit* of two flattened, roundish lobes, united by the narrow edge; *leaves* round, peltate. (Name from the Greek, *hydor*, water, and *cotyle*, a platter, from the shape of the leaves and place of growth.)

2. SANICULA (Sanicle).—*Flowers* in panicled tufts, the outer without stamens, the inner without pistils; *fruit* egg-shaped, covered with hooked prickles. (Name from the Latin, *sano*, to heal, the plant being formerly supposed to have remarkable healing qualities.)

3. ERYNGIUM (Eryngo).—*Flowers* in a dense prickly head; *fruit* egg-shaped, covered with chaffy scales.

Umbels compound; fruit of two flattened lobes, which are united by the narrow edge, not prickly, nor beaked

4. CONIUM (Hemlock).—*Fruit* egg-shaped, each carpel with wavy ridges; *general bracts* few; *partial* 3, all on the outside. (Name from the Greek for the plant.)

5. SMYRNIUM (Alexanders).—*Fruit* of 2 kidney-shaped carpels, each having 3 prominent ridges; *bracts* 0. (Name from the Greek, *smyrna*, myrrh, from the scent of some of the species.)

6. CICUTA (Water Hemlock).—*Fruit* of 2 almost globose carpels, with 5 broad, flattened ridges; *general bracts* 1 or 2, very narrow,

I

often 0 ; *partial* several, unequal.   (Name from the Latin, *cicuta,*
a Hemlock stalk.)

7. APIUM (Celery).—*Fruit* roundish egg-shaped, of 2 almost distinct carpels, each with 5 slender ridges ; *bracts* 0.   (Name, the
Latin of this or some allied plant.)

8. PETROSELINUM (Parsley).—*Fruit* egg-shaped ; *carpels* each
with 5 slender ridges ; *general bracts* few ; *partial* many.   (Name
from the Greek, *petros,* a rock, and *selinon,* parsley.)

9. HELOSCIADIUM (Marsh-wort).—*Fruit* egg-shaped or oblong ;
carpels each with 5 slender, prominent ridges ; *general bracts* 0 ;
partial several.   (Name from the Greek, *helos,* a marsh, and *skiadion,*
an umbel.)

10. SISON (Stone Parsley).—*Fruit* egg-shaped ; *carpels* with 5
slender ridges ; *petals* broad, deeply notched, with an inflexed
point ; *bracts* both general and partial, several.   (Name, the Greek
for some allied plant.)

11. ÆGOPODIUM (Gout-weed).—*Fruit* oblong ; *carpels* with 5
slender ridges ; *bracts* 0.   (Name in Greek signifying *goat's-foot,*
from some fancied resemblance of the leaves.)

12. CARUM (Caraway).—*Fruit* oblong ; *carpels* with 5 slender
ridges ; *general bracts* 0, or rarely 1 ; *partial* 0.   (Name from *Caria,*
a country of Asia Minor.)

13. CONOPODIUM (Earth-nut).—*Fruit* oblong, crowned with the
conical base of the erect styles ; *carpels* with 5 slender, blunt ridges ;
general bracts 0 ; *partial* few.   (Name from the Greek, *konos,* a cone,
and *pous,* a foot.)

14. PIMPINELLA (Burnet Saxifrage).—*Fruit* oblong, crowned with
the swollen base of the reflexed styles ; *carpels* with 5 slender ridges,
and furrows between ; *general bracts* 0, or rarely 1 ; *partial* 0.   (Name
of doubtful origin.)

15. SIUM (Water Parsnip).—*Fruit* nearly globose ; *carpels* with
5 slender, blunt ridges ; *bracts,* general and partial, several.   ("Name,
according to Theis, from the Celtic word *siw,* water."—Sir W. J.
Hooker.)

16. BUPLEURUM (Hare's-ear).—*Fruit* oblong ; *carpels* with 5 prominent ridges, crowned at the flat base of the styles ; *partial bracts*
very large.   (Name from the Greek, *bous,* an ox, and *pleuron,* a rib,
from the ribbed leaves of some species.)

Umbels compound ; fruit not flattened, not prickly, nor beaked

17. ŒNANTHE (Water Dropwort).—*Fruit* egg-shaped, cylindrical,
crowned with the long straight *styles ; carpels* with 5 blunt, corky

ridges; *flowers* somewhat rayed, those of the centre only being
fertile. (Name from the Greek, *oinos*, wine, and *anthos*, a flower,
from the wine-like smell of the flowers.)

18. ÆTHUSA (Fool's Parsley).—*Fruit* nearly globose; *carpels*
with 5 sharply-keeled ridges, crowned with the reflexed *styles;*
partial bracts 3, all on one side, drooping. (Name from the Greek,
aitho, to burn, from its acrid properties.)

19. FŒNICULUM (Fennel).—*Fruit* elliptical; *carpels* with 5
bluntly-keeled ridges; *bracts* o. (Name from the Latin, *fœnum*,
hay, to which it has been compared in smell.)

20. LIGUSTICUM (Lovage).—*Fruit* elliptical; *carpels* with 5 sharp,
somewhat winged ridges; *bracts*, both general and partial, several.
(Name from *Liguria*, where the cultivated species abounds.)

21. SILAUS (Pepper Saxifrage).—*Fruit* egg-shaped; *carpels* with
5 sharp, somewhat winged ridges; *petals* scarcely notched (yellow);
general bracts 1 or 2; *partial* several. (Name given by the Romans
to some probably allied plant.)

22. MEUM (Spignel).—*Fruit* elliptical; *carpels* with 5 sharp,
winged ridges; *petals* tapering at both ends; *general bracts* few;
partial numerous. (Name, the Greek for this or some allied plant.)

23. CRITHMUM (Samphire).—*Fruit* elliptical; *carpels* spongy,
with 5 sharp, winged ridges; *bracts*, both *general* and *partial*,
numerous. (Name from the Greek, *crithe*, barley, to which grain
the fruit bears a fancied resemblance.)

*Umbels compound; fruit of two flattened carpels, which are united
by their faces, not prickly, nor beaked*

24. ANGELICA.—*Fruit* with three sharp ridges at the back of each
carpel, and two at the sides, the latter expanding into an even
border; *general bracts* few, or o; *partial* numerous. (Named
angelic, from its medicinal properties).

25. PASTINACA (Parsnip).—*Fruit* very flat, with a broad border;
carpels with 3 slender ridges on the back and 2 near the outer edge
of the margin; *general* and *partial bracts* rarely more than 1;
flowers yellow. (Name from the Latin, *pastus*, pasture.)

26. HERACLEUM (Cow Parsnip).—*Fruit* nearly the same as in
Pastinaca; flowers rayed; *general bracts* several, soon falling off;
partial numerous. (Name from *Hercules*, who is said to have
brought this, or some allied plant, into use.)

Umbels compound ; fruit prickly, not beaked

27. DAUCUS (Carrot).—*Fruit* slightly flattened ; *carpels* united by their faces, oblong ; *ridges* bristly, with a row of prickles between ; *general bracts* very long, often pinnatifid. (Name, the Greek name of the plant.)

28. CAUCALIS (Bur-parsley).—*Fruit* slightly flattened ; *carpels* united by thin narrow edges ; *ridges* bristly, with 1–3 rows of hooked prickles between. (Name, the Greek name of the plant.)

29. TORILIS (Hedge Parsley).—*Fruit* slightly contracted at the sides ; *ridges* of the *carpels* bristly, with numerous prickles between ; *partial bracts* numerous. (Name of doubtful origin.)

Umbels compound ; fruit more or less beaked

30. SCANDIX (Shepherd's Needle).—*Fruit* contracted at the sides, with a very long beak ; *carpels* with 5 blunt ridges ; *general bracts* 0 ; *partial* several, longer than the flowers. (Name, the Greek name of the plant.)

31. ANTHRISCUS (Beaked Parsley).—*Fruit* with a short beak ; *carpels* without ridges ; *general bracts* 0 ; *partial* several. (Name, the Greek name of this or some allied plant.)

32. CHÆROPHYLLUM (Chervil).—*Fruit* contracted at the sides, with a short beak ; *carpels* with 5 blunt ridges ; *partial bracts* several. (Name in Greek signifying *pleasant leaf*, from the agreeable perfume of some species.)

33. MYRRHIS (Cicely).—*Fruit* contracted at the sides, with a deep furrow between the carpels ; *carpels* with 5 sharply-keeled ridges ; *general bracts* 0 ; *partial* several. (Name from the Greek, *myrrha*, myrrh, from the fragrance of the leaves.)

1. HYDROCOTYLE (*White-rot*)

1. *H. vulgaris* (Common White-rot, Marsh Pennywort).—A small creeping plant, very unlike the rest of the Umbelliferous Tribe, with round, smooth, *crenate* leaves, 1–1½ inches across, and inconspicuous heads of about 5 minute reddish-white *flowers*, which never rise above the leaves, and require a close search to be detected at all. Each leaf is attached by its centre to the stalk, and resembles a little platter. The only British species ; common in marshes and bogs.—Fl. May June. Perennial.

Before long, you will receive
a bill from Spence Builders —
or drainage work in the
garden — I had to undertake
this work — on the behalf of
neighbour Mr Hunter
their difficulties ashstead
cross — I instructed the arguments
firm which employed by
— to send a detailed
account to you indicating
my share to you — before
paying it — please forward
it to me — that I may
decide whether the division has been fairly made —

PLATE XXXIV.

Wood Sanicle   Marsh Pennywort

2. SANICULA (*Sanicle*)

1. *S. Europæa* (Wood Sanicle).—A slender, smooth plant about 1½ feet high, with glossy *leaves*, which are 3 to 5-lobed and cut. The *flowers* are dull white, and grow in panicled heads rather than umbels, and are succeeded by roundish *seeds*, which are covered with hooked prickles. The only British species; common in woods. —Fl. June, July. Perennial.

3. ERYNGIUM (*Eryngo*)

1. *E. maritimum* (Sea Eryngo, Sea Holly).—A stout, prickly plant, with more of the habit of a Thistle than one of the Umbelliferous Tribe. The whole plant is remarkably rigid and glaucous. The *flowers* are blue, and grow in dense heads. The *roots* are large, fleshy, and brittle, and extend for a distance of many feet into the sand. When candied they form a well-known sweetmeat, which, however, is less popular than formerly. Sandy sea-coasts; frequent. —Fl. July, August. Perennial.

2. *E. campestre* (Field Eryngo).—A taller, more slender, more branched, and less glaucous species. Very rare, occurring only in one or two localities, and probably not indigenous.—Fl. July, August. Perennial.

4. CONIUM (*Hemlock*)

1. *C. maculatum* (Common Hemlock).—A tall, much branched, and gracefully growing plant, with elegantly cut foliage and white flowers. Country people are in the habit of calling by the name of Hemlock many species of umbelliferous plants. The real Hemlock may, however, be accurately distinguished by its slender growth, perfectly smooth *stem*, which is spotted with red, by its finely divided *leaves*, which are also smooth, and by the *bracts* at the base of the partial *umbels*, which only go half-way round. It usually grows from 2–4 feet high, but in sheltered situations it sometimes attains more than double that height. —Fl. June, July. Biennial.

CONIUM MACULATUM (*Common Hemlock*)

5. Smyrnium (*Alexanders*)

Smyrnium Olusatrum (*Common Alexanders*)

1. *S. Olusatrum* (Common Alexanders).—A tall and stout plant, growing in waste ground, especially near the sea. Well distinguished from any other plant of the tribe by its broad, bright green, glossy *leaves*, which grow in threes, and by its numerous large *umbels* of greenish yellow *flowers*. The *stem* is smooth, 3–4 feet high, furrowed, and hollow. The *seeds* are nearly black when ripe. The young shoots are sometimes boiled and eaten. —Fl. May, June. Biennial.

6. Cicuta (*Cowbane*)

1. *C. virosa* (Cowbane, Water Hemlock).—A poisonous, aquatic species 3–4 feet high ; distinguished by its very stout, hollow *stem*, pinnate and long-stalked *lower leaves*, twice ternate *upper leaves*, and stalked *umbels* of white *flowers*. The name Water Hemlock is often applied to several species of Œnanthe, which are also very poisonous. Ponds and ditches ; rare.—Fl. July, August. Perennial.

7. Apium (*Celery*)

1. *A. graveolens* (Celery, Smallage). —The origin of the garden Celery, and unmistakably distinguished by its strong flavour and odour, which in no respect differ from those of the garden plant. The *stem* is usually 1–2 feet high, branched, and leafy, but sometimes nearly prostrate. The *flowers* are small and white, and grow either in terminal or axillary *umbels*, which are often sessile and unequal. In its wild state the plant is not eatable, but when it has been cultivated on rich soil, and the leaf-stalks have been blanched by being " earthed up," and

Apium Graveolens (*Celery, Smallage*)

so deprived of light, it is a wholesome vegetable. Found mostly in moist places near the sea, but it also occurs as a probable escape in some inland districts.—Fl. June to September. Biennial.

8. Petroselinum (*Parsley*)

1. *P. segetum* (Corn Parsley).—Well distinguished by its slender, branched *stem*, which is remarkably tough and wiry, by its small pinnated *leaves* and *umbels* of small whitish *flowers*, and by the *rays* of the *umbel* being few and very unequal in length. The *root-leaves* wither early, and the few which grow on the stem are small and inconspicuous. Corn fields and waste places; not uncommon.—Fl. August, September. Biennial.

2. *P. sativum.* — Is the common Parsley of gardens, which, though often found seemingly wild, is not really indigenous.

PETROSELINUM SEGETUM
(*Corn Parsley*)

9. Helosciadium (*Marsh-wort*)

HELOSCIADIUM NODIFLORUM
(*Procumbent Marsh-wort*)

1. *H. nodiflorum* (Procumbent Marsh-wort). — *Stem* prostrate and rooting; *leaves* pinnate; *leaflets* egg-shaped, serrated; *umbels* on very short stalks, opposite the *leaves*. A plant with somewhat of the habit of Water-cresses, in company with which it often grows, and for which it is sometimes mistaken. It may be distinguished when out of flower by its serrated and somewhat pointed leaves and by its hollow stems. The flowers are small and white. In ditches and rivulets; abundant.—Fl. July, August. Perennial. *H. repens* is a smaller plant and has narrowed *leaves*, but is scarcely a distinct species.

2. *H. inundatum* (Least Marsh-wort) has the lower *leaves* finely divided into numerous hair-like segments. The *umbels* usually only 2 rays of small white *flowers*, and, with the upper leaves, are the only parts of the plant which rise out of the water. Ponds; a common plant often overlooked.—Fl. June, July. Perennial.

10. SISON (*Stone Parsley*)

1. *S. amomum* (Hedge Stone Parsley).—A slender plant 2–3 feet high, with a wiry, branched *stem* and pinnate, cut *leaves*, the leaflets of the upper ones being very narrow. The *general umbels* consist of about 4 *rays*, with 2–4 *bracts* at the base; the *partial umbels* are small, and have 4 *bracts* at the base of each; the *flowers* are cream-coloured and very small. The whole plant has a nauseous smell. The only British species. Damp, chalky places; common in the south of England, becoming rarer farther north. —Fl. August. Biennial.

11. ÆGOPODIUM (*Gout-weed*)

1. *Æ. podagraria* (Common Gout-weed).—A common and very trouble-some garden weed, with a creeping *root*, large, thrice ternate *leaves*, and white *flowers*. The *stems* grow about a foot high. The leaves are sometimes boiled and eaten, but have a strong and very disagreeable flavour.—Fl. May, June. Perennial.

ÆGOPODIUM PODAGRARIA
(*Common Gout-weed*)

12. CARUM (*Caraway*)

1. *C. carui* (Common Caraway).—*Root* spindle-shaped; *stem* much branched, about 2 feet high; the *leaves* twice pinnate, with leaflets cut into very narrow segments; the *flowers* are white, and grow in rather large *umbels*, with rarely more than 1 *bract*, and that at the base of the general umbel. Occurs in many places as an escape from cultivation. Produces the well-known caraway seeds.—Fl. June. Biennial.

2. *C. verticillatum* (Whorled Caraway).—Smaller than the last, with pinnate *leaves*, the leaflets of which are divided to the base into very numerous hair-like segments, and are so crowded as to appear whorled. Very rare, except in the west of Scotland.—Fl. July, August. Perennial.

3. *C. bulbocastanum* (Bulbous Caraway).—*Root* tuberous; *stem* 1–2 feet high; *leaves* twice or thrice pinnate; *bracts* of the partial and general umbel numerous; *flowers* white. A local plant, so abundant in the chalk district near Baldock, in Hertfordshire, that " the farmers turn their pigs upon the fallows to feed upon the roots."—Hooker and Arnott. Found in chalky fields in one or two other districts, but very local.—Fl. June, July. Perennial.

13. CONOPODIUM (*Earth-nut*)

1. *C. denudatum* (Earth-nut, Pig-nut).—A slender plant, about a foot high, bearing a few finely divided *leaves*, and terminal *umbels* of white *flowers*. The *root*, which is a roundish tuber and is covered with a thin skin easily removed, is eatable, but only fit for the food of the animal after which it is named. A much commoner plant than the last.—Fl. May, June. Perennial.

14. PIMPINELLA (*Burnet Saxifrage*)

1. *P. saxifraga* (Common Burnet Saxifrage).—A slender plant 1-2 feet high, with a thick though not tuberous *root*. The lower *leaves*, which are pinnate, with sharply cut leaflets, grow on long stalks; the upper ones are twice pinnate, and deeply cut into very narrow, sharp segments. Common in dry pastures.—Fl. July, August. Perennial.

2. *P. magna* (Greater Burnet Saxifrage).—Stouter and larger than the last, and has all the *leaves* pinnate, the terminal leaflet on each being 3-lobed; the *flowers* are white, or often pink. It grows in shady places, but is far from common.—Fl. July, August. Perennial.

PIMPINELLA SAXIFRAGA
(*Common Burnet Saxifrage*)

15. SIUM (*Water Parsnip*)

1. *S. latifolium* (Broad - leaved Water Parsnip).—*Leaves* pinnate; *leaflets* narrow, oblong, pointed, equally serrated; *umbels* terminal; *bracts*, both general and *partial*, pointed and narrow. A stout plant, with a creeping root-stock, an erect, furrowed stem 3-5 feet high, and pinnated leaves of 5-13 large and distinct leaflets, and long, flat umbels of white flowers. Watery places; not uncommon.—Fl. July, August. Perennial.

2. *S. angustifolium* (Narrow-leaved Water Parsnip). — *Leaves* pinnate; *leaflets* unequally cut, egg-shaped, the upper ones narrower; *umbels* opposite the leaves, stalked. Smaller

SIUM ANGUSTIFOLIUM
(*Narrow-leaved Water Parsnip*)

than the last, and resembling *Helosciadium nodiflorum*, from which it may be distinguished by its stalked *umbels*, and by its having general and partial *bracts*, which are reflexed and often cut. Watery places; not uncommon.—Fl. August. Perennial.

16. BUPLEURUM (*Thorow-wax*)

BUPLEURUM ROTUNDI-
FOLIUM (*Common
Thorow-wax, Hare's-ear*)

1. *B. rotundifolium* (Common Thorow-wax, or Hare's-ear).—*Stem* branched above; *leaves* roundish, egg-shaped, undivided, perfoliate; *general bracts* wanting; *partial* ones large, bristle-pointed, thrice as long as the flowers. A singular plant, well distinguished by its perfoliate leaves, which have a glaucous hue, and its large, greenish-yellow, partial bracts, which are far more conspicuous than the minute yellow flowers. Cornfields, on chalky soil.—Fl. July. Annual.

2. *B. tenuissimum* (Slender Hare's-ear).— Remarkable for its slender, wiry *stem*, about a foot high and usually ascending; and its very narrow, undivided *leaves*, and small *umbels* of very few minute yellowish *flowers*. It grows in salt marshes on the south and east coasts of England.—Fl. August, September. Annual.

3. *B. aristatum* (Narrow-leaved Hare's-ear). — A small plant 3–6 inches high, with pale, rigid *leaves*, inconspicuous greenish *flowers*, and large, sharp-pointed *bracts*. Found nowhere in Great Britain but at Torquay and Eastbourne, and in the Channel Islands. Sandy, waste places.—Fl. June, July. Annual.

4. *B. falcatum* (Sickle-leaved Hare's-ear).—A slender, erect species 1–3 feet high, with slightly branched, hollow *stems*, and narrow, entire *leaves*, pointed and curved, ribbed on the under side; *flowers* yellow, minute. Found near Ongar, in Essex, and in Hertfordshire. Probably not indigenous.—Fl. August, September. Perennial.

17. ŒNANTHE (*Water Dropwort*)

1. *Œ. fistulosa* (Tubular Water Dropwort).—*Root* sending out runners; *stem-leaves* pinnate, shorter than their tubular *stalks*. An erect, slightly branched plant 2–3 feet high, well marked by its tubular stems, leaves, and leaflets. The lower leaves are entirely submerged, and of these the leaflets are flat, but all the rest of the plant consists of a series of tubes. The *umbels* are of very few rays, which, when in fruit, are nearly globular. Watery places; not uncommon.—Fl. July, August. Perennial.

2. *Œ. crocata* (Hemlock Water Dropwort).—*Leaves* thrice pinnate; *leaflets* wedge - shaped, variously cut. A large, stout plant 3–5 feet high, with clustered, tuberous roots, somewhat like those of the Dahlia, spreading, glossy leaves, and large umbels of white flowers. The plant is popularly known by the name of *Water Hemlock*, and being very poisonous should not be allowed to grow in places where cattle are kept, as instances are numerous in which cows have been poisoned by eating the roots. Watery places; common.—Fl. July Perennial.

ŒNANTHE CROCATA
(Hemlock Water Dropwort)

3. *Œ. phellandrium* (Fine-leaved Water Dropwort, Horsebane).— *Stems* 2–3 feet high, very stout at the base ; *roots* fibrous ; *leaves* divided into very fine segments, the lower ones submerged ; *umbels* smaller than in the last, on short stalks, springing either from the forks of the branches or from opposite the leaves. Ditches and the sides of ponds ; common.—Fl. July to September. Biennial.

4. *Œ. pimpinelloides* (Parsley Water Dropwort).—*Roots* fibrous, often swollen into tubers ; *stems* 1–3 feet high, furrowed ; lower *leaves* bipinnate, segments broader than in the more finely divided upper leaves, which have long, narrow segments ; *umbels* compact, flat-topped ; *rays* rather short, and with usually an involucre of narrow bracts at the base. A variable plant. Found in meadows and in both salt and fresh marshes in the south ; not uncommon.—Fl. June to August. Perennial.

5. *Œ. Lachenalii.*—*Root-fibres* fleshy ; lobes of *lower leaves* blunt, *upper leaves* with narrow pointed segments ; *flowers* white, in lax umbels. Nearly allied to the last. Common in salt marshes.—Fl. July to September. Perennial.

18. ÆTHUSA (*Fool's Parsley*)

1. *Æ. cynapium* (Fool's Parsley).— A slender plant about a foot high, with dark green, doubly pinnate *leaves*, and terminal *umbels* of white *flowers*. It is a common garden weed, and in its young state somewhat resembles parsley ; but when in flower may readily be distinguished from that and all other

ÆTHUSA CYNAPIUM
(Fool's Parsley)

British umbelliferous plants by having no *general bracts*, but at the base of each *partial umbel* three very long and narrow *bracts*, which are all on the outer side, and point downwards. The plant is poisonous, and has a disagreeable smell when bruised.—Fl. July, August. Annual.

19. FŒNICULUM (*Fennel*)

1. *F. vulgare* (Common Fennel).—A well-known plant, with an erect rod-like *stem* 2–3 or more feet high, numerous *leaves*, which are deeply divided into soft, hair-like segments, and large terminal *umbels* of yellow *flowers*. The whole plant is aromatic, and the chopped leaves are often used as an ingredient in sauce for fish. Waste places, especially near the sea; common.—Fl. July, August. Perennial.

FŒNICULUM VULGARE
(*Common Fennel*)

20. LIGUSTICUM (*Lovage*)

1. *L. Scoticum* (Scottish Lovage).—From 1–2 feet high; *stem* slightly branched, tinged with red; *leaves* twice ternate, with large, broad, serrated *leaflets; umbels* with *general* and *partial bracts; flowers* reddish-white. Rocky seashore in Scotland and Northumberland.—Fl. July. Perennial.

21. SILAUS (*Pepper Saxifrage*)

1. *S. pratensis* (Meadow Pepper Saxifrage).—From 1–3 feet high; *leaves* thrice pinnate, with narrow opposite *leaflets*, and terminal *umbels* of dull, yellowish white flowers; *general bracts* 1–3; *partial* numerous. "The whole plant, being fetid when bruised, is supposed in some parts of Norfolk to give a bad flavour to milk and butter; but cattle do not eat it, except accidentally or in small quantities, though sufficient perhaps to have the effect in question."—Sir J. E. Smith. Meadows; not very general.—Fl. July to September. Perennial.

22. MEUM (*Spignel*)

1. *M. athamanticum* (Spignel, Meu, or Bald-money).—Well distinguished by its twice pinnate *leaves*, the leaflets of which are divided into numerous thread-like segments. The whole plant,

and especially the root, which is eaten by the Highlanders, is highly aromatic, with a flavour like Melilot, which it communicates to milk and butter from the cows feeding on its herbage in spring. "Bald, or Bald-money, is a corruption of *Balder*, the *Apollo* of the northern nations, to whom this plant was dedicated."—Sir W. J. Hooker. Dry mountainous pastures in the north.—Fl. June, July. Perennial.

MEUM ATHAMANTICUM
(*Spignel, Meu, or Bald-money*)

CRITHMUM MARITIMUM
(*Sea Samphire*)

23. CRITHMUM (*Samphire*)

1. *C. maritimum* (Sea Samphire).—Well distinguished by its long, glaucous, fleshy *leaflets* and yellow *flowers*. The whole plant is aromatic, and has a powerful scent. The young leaves, if gathered in May, sprinkled with salt, and preserved in vinegar, make one of the best of pickles. Rocks by the sea-coast; abundant. On those parts of the coast where Samphire does not abound, other plants, which resemble it in having fleshy leaves, are sometimes sold under the same name, but they are very inferior.—Fl. July, August. Perennial.

24. ANGELICA

1. *A. sylvestris* (Wild Angelica). —A stout and tall plant 2–4 feet high; the *stem* is furrowed, tinged with purple, and slightly downy, especially in its upper part; the

ANGELICA SYLVESTRIS (*Wild Angelica*)

leaves are twice pinnate ; the *laflets* egg-shaped and serrated ; the *umbels* are large and furnished with both *general* and *partial bracts ;* the *flowers* are white, tinged with pink. Wet places ; common.— Fl. July. Perennial.

A. Archangelica is a larger species, commonly cultivated for the sake of its aromatic *stems*, which when candied form a favourite sweetmeat. It is not indigenous.

25. PASTINACA (*Parsnip*)

1. *P. sativa* (Common Parsnip).— Well known in gardens as an agreeable and nutritive vegetable. In its wild state the plant, which is not uncommon in limestone and chalky pastures, closely resembles the cultivated variety, but has smaller roots and more downy leaves. The *flowers* are yellow, and grow in terminal *umbels*.—Fl. July, August. Biennial.

PASTINACA SATIVA
(*Common Parsnip*)

26. HERACLEUM (*Cow-parsnip*)

1. *H. sphondylium* (Common Cow-parsnip, Hog-weed).—A very tall and stout plant, with a channelled, hairy *stem*, 4–6 feet high, large, irregularly cut, rough *leaves*, and spreading *umbels* of conspicuous white *flowers*. In spring the plant is remarkable for the large oval tufts formed by the sheathing base of the stem-leaves, which contain the flower-buds. This, with many other umbelliferous plants, is often confounded by farmers with Hemlock, and great pains are taken to eradicate it ; but cattle eat it with impunity, and it is probably a wholesome and nutritive food. It is often very abundant in meadows.—Fl. July. Biennial.

HERACLEUM SPHONDYLIUM
(*Common Cow-Parsnip, Hog-weed*)

27. Daucus (*Carrot*)

1. *D. carota* (Wild Carrot).—A tough-stemmed, bristly plant 1–3 feet high, with a *tap-root*, much-cut *leaves*, and large *umbels* of dull white *flowers*. Well distinguished by having the central *flower*, or *partial umbel* of flowers, bright red or deep purple. In flavour and scent it resembles the garden Carrot.—Fl. July, August. Biennial.

A variety (*D. maritimus*) abundant on many parts of the sea-coast differs from the preceding in having somewhat fleshy *leaves*, and in being destitute of the central purple flower or umbel.

28. Caucalis (*Bur-parsley*)

1 *C. daucoides* (Small Bur-parsley).—*Leaves* repeatedly divided; *umbels* of about 3 rays, without bracts; *partial umbels* of few flowers, with about 3 bracts. A somewhat bushy plant, nearly smooth, with a stem which is deeply furrowed, and hairy at the joints. The flowers, which are pinkish white, grow in lateral and terminal umbels, and are succeeded by large prickly seeds. Chalky fields; not common.—Fl. June. Annual.

2. *C. latifolia* (Great Bur-parsley).—*Stem* 1–2 feet high; *leaves* pinnate; the *leaflets* lanceolate and serrate; *general umbels* 2 to 4-rayed; *partial* 4 to 6-rayed. Distinguished from the above, and from all other British plants of the tribe, by its handsome large rose-coloured flowers. Occurs occasionally as a cornfield weed on calcareous soils, but is very rare, and is not indigenous.—Fl. July. Annual.

29. Torilis (*Hedge Parsley*)

1. *T. anthriscus* (Upright Hedge Parsley).—*Leaves* twice pinnate; *leaflets* narrow, sharply cut; *umbels* stalked; *general* and *partial bracts* several. A tall, slender plant 2–3 feet high, with a solid rough stem, hairy leaves, and many-rayed umbels of small white or pinkish flowers. The fruit is thickly covered with incurved, rigid bristles. Hedges; abundant.—Fl. July, August. Annual.

TORILIS ANTHRISCUS
(*Upright Hedge Parsley*)

2. *T. infesta* (Spreading Hedge Parsley).—*Leaves* twice pinnate; *leaflets* oblong, sharply cut; *umbels* stalked; *general bracts* 1 or 0;

partial several. Smaller than the last, 6-18 inches high, with more branched stems and more rigid leaves. The fruit is covered with spreading hooked bristles. Hedges; common.—Fl. July, August. Annual.

3. *T. nodosa* (Knotted Hedge Parsley).—*Stem* prostrate; *umbels* simple, lateral, nearly sessile. Well distinguished from all other British umbelliferous plants by its prostrate mode of growth, its very small, almost globular umbels of whitish flowers, and by the outer carpels in each umbel being covered with hooked prickles, while the inner are warty. Hedges and waste places; common.—Fl. May to July. Annual.

CANDIX PECTEN (*Shepherd's Needle, Venus' Comb*)

30. SCANDIX (*Shepherd's Needle*)

1. *S. pecten* (Shepherd's Needle, Venus' Comb).—A small plant 3-9 inches high, with finely cut, bright green *leaves* and few-rayed *umbels* of small white *flowers*, which are succeeded by long, beaked *seed-vessels*. Common in cultivated ground. —Fl. June to September. Annual.

31. ANTHRISCUS (*Beaked Parsley*)

1. *A. vulgaris* (Common Beaked Parsley).—*Stem* smooth; *leaves* twice pinnate, with blunt segments; *umbels* lateral on rather short stalks; *fruit* bristly. Remarkable for its smooth, polished stem and delicate green leaves, which are slightly hairy beneath. The stem is 2-3 feet high, slightly swollen under each joint. The flowers are white, and grow in umbels opposite the leaves; partial bracts 5 or 6, with fringed edges. Waste ground, chiefly near towns.— Fl. May. Annual.

2. *A. sylvestris* (Wild Beaked Parsley). —*Stem* slightly downy below, smooth above; *leaves* thrice pinnate, the segments rough-edged; *umbels* terminal on long stalks, drooping when young; *fruit* smooth. One of our early spring flowers, distinguished when in bud by the drooping partial umbels, each of which has

ANTHRISCUS SYLVESTRIS (*Wild Beaked Parsley*)

PLATE XXXV.

Sea Holly   Hedge Parsley

Wild Carrot   Pig Nut

about 5 reflexed bracts, and afterwards by its smooth, shortly beaked fruit. Hedges; common.—Fl. April to June. Perennial.

A. cerefolium (Garden Chervil) is not a native plant, though sometimes found in the neighbourhood of houses. It may be distinguished from the preceding by having only 3 partial *bracts*, lateral *umbels*, and smooth *fruit*.

32. CHÆROPHYLLUM (*Chervil*)

1. *C. temulentum* (Rough Chervil).—The only British species; very common in woods and hedges. The *stem* is slender, 2–3 feet high, rough with short hairs, spotted with purple, and swollen beneath the joints; the *leaves* are twice pinnate, deeply lobed and cut, hairy, often making the plant conspicuous in autumn by their rich purple hue; the *flowers* are white, and grow in terminal umbels, which droop when in bud; *general bracts* either absent or very few; *partial bracts* several, fringed and deflexed.— Fl. June, July. Perennial.

CHÆROPHYLLUM TEMU-LENTUM (*Rough Chervil*)

33. MYRRHIS (*Cicely*)

1. *M. odorata* (Sweet Cicely).—Remarkable for its sweet and highly aromatic flavour. The *stem* is 2–3 feet high, furrowed and hollow; the *leaves* large, thrice pinnate, cut, and slightly downy. The *flowers* are white, and grow in terminal downy umbels; *bracts* partial only, whitish, and finely fringed. The *fruit* is remarkably large, dark brown, with very sharp ribs, and possesses the flavour of the rest of the plant in a high degree. Mountainous pastures in the north.—Fl. May, June. Perennial.

The foregoing descriptions contain only those umbelliferous plants which are most commonly to be met with. There are besides these a few others, which are either of unusual occurrence or have escaped from cultivation; these are :—

Physospernum Cornubiense (Cornish Bladder-seed).—An erect, smooth plant about 2 feet high, with thrice ternate *leaves* and white *flowers*, which are fur-

PHYSOSPERNUM CORNU-BIENSE (*Cornish Bladder-seed*)

K

nished with both *general* and *partial bracts*. The fruit when ripe is remarkably inflated and nearly globose, whence its name. It is found only near Bodmin, Cornwall, and Tavistock, Devon.

Trinia glaberrima (Honewort) grows on limestone rocks in Somersetshire and at Barry Head, Devon. It may be distinguished from all other British umbelliferous plants by bearing its *stamens* and *pistils* in separate flowers and on different plants.

Seseli Libanotis (Mountain Meadow Saxifrage) is of rare occurrence ; in Cambridgeshire and Sussex. It may be distinguished by its hemispherical *umbels* and hairy *fruit*, crowned by the reflexed *styles*.

Peucedanum officinale (Sea Hog's Fennel).—A rare plant, remarkable for its large *umbels* of yellow *flowers*. It occurs in salt marshes on the eastern coast of England.

P. palustre (Marsh Hog's Fennel).—Also a rare species, growing in marshes in Yorkshire and Lancashire, etc. The *stem* grows 4–5 feet high, and abounds in a milky juice, which dries to a brown resin.

Coriandrum sativum (Common Coriander).—Occasionally found in the neighbourhood of towns, but cannot be deemed a native plant. It is well marked by its globose, pleasantly aromatic *fruit*.

NATURAL ORDER XXXVII

ARALIACEÆ.—THE IVY TRIBE

Calyx attached to the ovary, 4–5-cleft ; *petals* 4, 5, or 10, occasionally wanting ; *stamens* equalling the petals in number or twice as many, inserted on the ovary ; *ovary* with more than 3 cells ; *styles* as many as the cells ; *fruit* fleshy or dry, of several 1-seeded cells. Trees, shrubs, or herbaceous plants, not confined to any particular climate, closely resembling the Umbelliferous Tribe in the structure of their flowers, but not partaking of their dangerous properties. Only two species are natives of Britain ; but one of these, Ivy, is so universally diffused as to be familiar to every one ; the other, Moschatell, is a humble plant, with solitary heads of green flowers and delicate leaves strongly scented with musk. Moschatell has lately been classed by some botanists among *Caprifoliaceæ*, but the genus having certain affinities to that and to *Araliaceæ*, it has been retained in its present place for the convenience of amateurs who have become used to the arrangement of the earlier editions of this book.

Ginseng, the favourite medicine of the Chinese, is the root of *Panax Ginseng*, a plant belonging to this tribe. A remarkable

PLATE XXXVI.

Moschatel   Honeysuckle

plant belonging to this Order is *Gunnera scabra*, found by Darwin growing on the sandstone cliffs of Chiloe. Both this and *Gunnera Manicata* bear a number of leaves resembling Rhubarb on a gigantic scale, single leaves often measuring 8 feet across. The plants form handsome garden specimens if grown by the waterside.

1. HEDERA (Ivy).—*Calyx* of 5 teeth, inserted in the ovary; *petals* 5–10; *stamens* 5–10; *styles* 5–10, often combined into 1; *berry* 5-celled and 5-seeded, crowned by the calyx. (Name, the Latin of the plant.)

2. ADOXA (Moschatell).—*Calyx* 3-cleft, inserted above the base of the ovary; *corolla* 4 or 5-cleft, inserted on the ovary; *stamens* 8 or 10, in pairs; *anthers* 1-celled; *berry* 4 or 5-celled. (Name in Greek signifying *inconspicuous*, from its humble growth.)

1. HEDERA (*Ivy*)

1. *H. Helix* (Common Ivy).—The only British species. An ever-green, woody climber or trailer. The main *stem* often attains 8 or 10 inches in diameter, and the plant will climb by means of small adventitious roots to a great height over rocks, trees, or buildings. The *leaves* are leathery and shining, the lower ones usually more or less deeply lobed, the upper ones more rounded. The *flowers* are greenish yellow, and are borne in globular *umbels* on *bushy* branches springing from the climbing stem. The *berries* are black. Common all over Britain.—Fl. October, November. Shrub.

HEDERA HELIX (*Common Ivy*)

2. ADOXA (*Moschatel*)

1. *A. moschatellina* (Common Moschatel).—The only species. A small herbaceous plant 4-6 inches high. Each plant bears several delicate *root-leaves* and two smaller leaves half-way up the stem. The *flowers* grow in terminal heads of 5 each, the *upper flower* with 4 petals and 8 stamens, the four *side flowers* having 5 petals and 10 stamens each. The latter are remarkable for being inserted in pairs, and for bearing 1-celled *anthers;* or the filaments may be considered to be forked, each fork bearing the lobe of an anther. The whole plant diffuses a musk-like scent, which, however, is not perceptible if the plant be bruised. Damp woods and hedge banks; not uncommon, though local.—Fl. April, May. Perennial.

Natural Order XXXVIII

CORNEÆ.—The Cornel Tribe

Sepals 4, attached to the ovary ; *petals* 4, oblong, broad at the base, inserted into the top of the calyx ; *stamens* 4, inserted with the petals ; *ovary* 2-celled ; *style* thread-like ; *stigma* simple ; *fruit* a berry-like drupe, with a 2-celled nut ; *seeds* solitary. Mostly trees or shrubs, with opposite leaves and flowers growing in heads or umbels. A small Order, containing few plants of interest, which inhabit the temperate regions of Europe, Asia, and America. In the United States several species are found, the bark of which is a powerful tonic, and has been used in place of quinine. *Benthamia fragifera*, a handsome shrub from the mountains of Nepal, was introduced into England in 1825. In Cornwall, where it was first raised from seed, it flowers and bears fruit freely, and forms a pleasing addition to the shrubbery. Two species of *cornus* are indigenous to Britain. The *cornus* of the ancients was the present Cornelian Cherry (*Cornus mascula*), whose little clusters of yellow starry flowers are among the earliest heralds of spring. Its fruit is like a small plum, with a very austere flesh, but after keeping, it becomes pleasantly acid. The Turks still use it in the manufacture of sherbet. A similar species is commonly cultivated in Japan for the sake of its fruit, which is a constant ingredient in the acid drinks of that country. The shrub now common in this country under the name of Spotted Laurel (*Aucuba Japonica*) belongs to this Order.

1. CORNUS (Cornel).—Characters described above. (Name from the shrub so called by the Latins, from the horn-like nature of the wood.)

1. CORNUS (*Cornel*)

1. *C. sanguinea* (Wild Cornel, Dog-wood).—A bushy shrub 5–6 feet high, with opposite, egg - shaped, pointed *leaves* and terminal *cymes* of creamy white *flowers ;* the *berries* are small and dark purple. The Spindle Tree (*Euonymus Europæa*) and the Guelder Rose (*Viburnum Lantana*) have wood of a similar nature, and the three were formerly much used for skewers, and are frequently confused under the common name Dog-wood. In autumn the leaves assume very

CORNUS SANGUINEA
(*Wild Cornel, Dog-wood*)

beautiful red and purple tints. Hedges
and thickets, especially on a chalk or limestone soil.—Fl. June. Shrub.

2. *C. succica* (Dwarf Cornel). — Very
different in habit from the last ; *root*
woody, creeping, and sending up annual
flowering stems, which are about six inches
high and bear each a terminal *umbel* of
minute dark purple *flowers* with yellow
stamens. At the base of each umbel are
four egg-shaped yellow *bracts* tinged with
purple. The *fruit*, a red berry, is said by
the Highlanders to create appetite, and
hence is called *Lus-a-chraois*, plant of
gluttony. Alpine pastures in Scotland and
the north of England ; rare.—Fl. July,
August. Perennial.

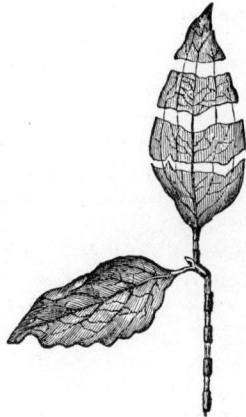

Young shoot of the Wild
Cornel

Sub-Class III

COROLLIFLORÆ

Petals united, bearing the *stamens*.

Natural Order XXXIX

LORANTHACEÆ.—Mistletoe Tribe

Stamens and *pistils* usually on different plants ; *calyx* attached
to the ovary, with 2 bracts at the base, sometimes almost wanting ;
petals 4–8, united at the base, expanding in a *valve*-like manner ;
stamens equalling the petals in number and opposite to them ; *ovary*
1-celled, 1-seeded ; *style* 1 or 0 ; *stigma* simple ; *fruit* succulent,
1-celled, 1-seeded ; *seed* germinating only when attached to some
growing plant of a different species. Shrubby plants of singular
structure and habit, growing only (with rare exceptions) on the
branches of other trees, and therefore true parasites. The leaves
are usually in pairs and fleshy, the flowers inconspicuous ; but this
is not always the case, for one species, *Nuytsia floribunda*, which
grows in the neighbourhood of King George's Sound, bears an
abundance of bright orange-coloured flowers, producing an appearance which the colonists compare to a tree on fire, and hence they
call it the *Fire-tree*. This species is not a parasite, but the greater
part of the tribe refuse to grow except on living vegetables. The
seed of most species is coated with a viscid substance, by which it
adheres to the bark, and which in a few days becomes a transparent
glue. Soon a thread-like radicle is sent forth, which, from whatever

part of the seed it proceeds, curves towards the supporting tree, and becomes flattened at the extremity like the proboscis of a fly. Finally it pierces the bark and roots itself in the growing wood, having the power of selecting and appropriating to its own use such juices as are fitted for its sustenance. Great virtues were attributed to the Mistletoe by the Druids, but at present its medicinal properties are in no repute, though at Christmas time the plant is gathered and sold in enormous quantities, and is at that season the symbol of a strange spirit of superstitious frivolity too well known to need description. Much of the Mistletoe sold in England at Christmas comes from the Continent.

The Mistletoe may readily be propagated by attaching the fresh seeds to the smooth bark of an Apple or other tree. This should not be done at Christmas, for though seeds are easily obtainable at that season they usually do not ripen until later. It should also be remembered that birds are likely to eat the planted berries unless they are protected by some means ; and also that though Mistletoe is a picturesque object in an orchard, much of it is apt to be detrimental to the health of the trees.

1. VISCUM (Mistletoe).—*Stamens* and *pistils* on separate plants. *Barren flower, calyx* 0 ; *petals* 4, fleshy, united at the base, each bearing an anther. *Fertile flower, calyx* a mere rim ; *petals* 4, very small; *stigma* sessile ; *berry* 1-seeded, crowned by the calyx. (Name, the Latin name of the plant, from the stickiness of the berries.)

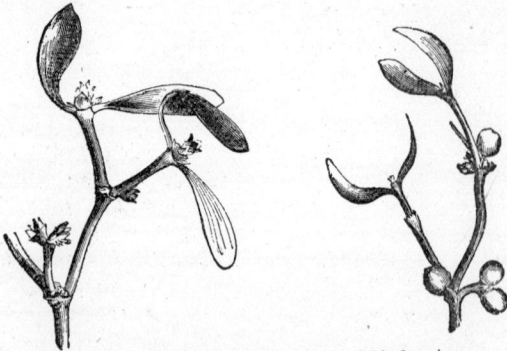

VISCUM ALBUM (*Common Mistletoe*)

1. VISCUM (*Mistletoe*)

1. *V. album* (Common Mistletoe).—The only British species. Growing on a great variety of trees, especially the Apple, exceedingly rare on the Oak. The *stem* is green and smooth, separating easily when dead into bone-like joints ; the *leaves* are thick and leathery, of a yellow hue, the whole plant being most conspicuous in winter, when its white berries ripen.—Fl. March to May. Perennial.

Natural Order XL

CAPRIFOLIACEÆ.—The Woodbine Tribe

Calyx attached to the ovary, usually with bracts at the base ; *corolla* regular or irregular, 4 to 5-cleft ; *stamens* equal in number to the lobes of the corolla and alternate with them ; *ovary* 3 to 5-celled ; *stigmas* 1–3 ; *fruit* usually fleshy, crowned by the calyx. This tribe comprises shrubs and herbaceous plants of very different habits, and is interesting from containing the fragrant Honeysuckle or Woodbine, and the elegant little plant which Linnæus fixed on to commemorate his name. They are principally confined to the northern hemisphere, and several are natives of Britain. The Common Elder was formerly held in high repute for its medicinal properties; and preparations of the leaves, flowers, and fruit are still used as medicine in rural districts, whilst a pleasant wine is often made from the fruit.

1. Sambucus (Elder).—*Calyx* 5-cleft ; *corolla* wheel-shaped, 5-lobed ; *stamens* 5 ; *stigmas* 3, sessile ; *berry* 3 to 5-seeded. (Name from the Greek, *sambúké*, a musical wind-instrument, in making which the wood is said to have been used.)

2. Viburnum (Guelder Rose).—*Calyx* 5-cleft ; *corolla* funnel-shaped, 5-lobed ; *stamens* 5 ; *stigmas* 3, sessile ; *berry* 1-seeded. (Name, the Latin of the plant.)

3. Lonicera (Honeysuckle).—*Calyx* small, 5-toothed ; *corolla* tubular, irregularly 5-cleft ; *stamens* 5 ; *style* thread-like ; *stigma* knobbed ; *berry* 1 to 3-celled, with several seeds. (Named in honour of *Adam Lonicer*, a German botanist.)

4. Linnæa.—*Calyx* 5-cleft ; *corolla* bell-shaped, 5-cleft, regular ; *stamens* 4, 2 longer ; *fruit* dry, 3-celled, 1 cell only containing a single seed.

1. Sambucus (*Elder*)

1. *S. niger* (Common Elder).—A small tree, remarkable for the large quantity of pith contained in its young branches and for the elasticity of its wood. The *leaves* are pinnate, of a strong, unpleasant odour ; the *flowers*, which are borne in cymes with 5 principal branches, are creamy white and of a sickly smell ; the *fruit* globose, shining, dark pur-

Sambucus Niger (*Common Elder*)

ple, or rarely white. Evelyn, speaking in its praise, says : " If the medicinal properties of the leaves, bark, berries, etc., were thoroughly known, I cannot tell what our countryman could ail for which he could not find a remedy from every hedge, either for sickness or wound." Hedges, etc.; common.—Fl. June. Tree. There are several garden varieties with variegated, golden, and finely cut foliage.

2. *S. ebulus* (Dwarf Elder, Danewort).—A herbaceous species 2–4 feet high, with *leaves* divided into 7–11 narrow segments, and 2 stipule-like, ovate, serrate *leaves* at the base of each leaf-stalk on the main stem. *Corymb* somewhat irregular, with 3 main branches ; *flowers* white, pink-tipped, and sweet-scented ; *fruit* black. Found in waste, bushy places in many parts of Britain, and said to have been introduced by the Danes.—Fl. July, August. Perennial.

2. VIBURNUM (*Guelder Rose*)

1. *V. lantana* (Wayfaring Tree, Mealy Guelder Rose).—A large shrub, with white, nearly flexible branches, and large elliptical *leaves*, heart-shaped at the base, serrated, and very downy beneath. The *flowers*, which are white and all perfect, grow in terminal cymes ; the *berries* are scarlet, turning black when fully ripe. It is most frequently met with in chalky or limestone soil.—Fl. May, June. Shrub.

VIBURNUM LANTANA (*Wayfaring Tree, Mealy Guelder Rose*)

2. *V. opulus* (Guelder Rose, Water Elder).—A small tree or shrub, with smooth leaves, lobed and cut, which assume a rich purple hue before falling, when they are very ornamental ; *leaf-stalks* with glands at the upper extremity. The *flowers*, which grow in flat-topped cymes, are white, the outer ones barren, and with broad corollas. The *berries* are bright coral-red, and are said to be sometimes fermented and eaten, a statement which will seem scarcely credible to any one who has chanced to smell them. The *bark* is very acrid. In the

VIBURNUM OPULUS
(*Guelder Rose, Water Elder*)

wild plant the cyme is flat, the outer flowers being large and showy, but destitute of stamens and pistils ; in the garden variety, called the Snowball Tree, the cyme is composed entirely of barren flowers, collected into a globular form. Moist woods and hedges ; not uncommon.—Fl. June, July. Small tree or shrub.

3. LONICERA (*Honeysuckle*)

1. *L. Periclymenum* (Honeysuckle, Woodbine).—*Leaves* ovate or oblong, sometimes lobed, and all distinct (not united at the base) ; *flowers* in terminal heads, gaping, red without, yellow within, fragrant; *berries* crimson. A common and favourite twining shrub, the first to expand its leaves in spring, or rather winter, and almost the last to blossom in autumn. Though highly ornamental to our woods, it is decidedly injurious to young trees, clasping them so tightly as to mark the rind with a spiral line, and finally becoming embedded in the wood. Handsome twisted walking-sticks are thus formed, but the growth of the tree is greatly checked.—Fl. July and again in October. Shrub.

Two other species of Woodbine are also occasionally found, but are not considered natives of Britain.

L. perfoliatum (Pale Perfoliate Honeysuckle), which is distinguished by having the uppermost pair of *leaves connate*, or united by their bases ; and *L. Xylosteum* (Upright Fly Honeysuckle), an erect shrub, with downy leaves, and pale yellow, scentless *flowers*, which grow in pairs.

4. LINNÆA

1. *L. borealis* (Linnæa).—The only species ; plant almost glabrous ; the *stem* trails along the ground, and bears at intervals pairs of opposite, broadly ovate, slightly crenate *leaves*. The flowering stalks are erect, and bear each two pendulous bell-shaped *flowers*, which are fragrant, and of a delicate pink colour. Deservedly regarded with peculiar interest as being the " little northern plant, long overlooked, depressed, abject, flowering early," which Linnæus himself selected as therefore most appropriate to transmit his name to posterity. It grows in woods, especially Fir, in Scotland

LINNÆA BOREALIS (*Linnæa*)

and in one English station, namely, a plantation of Scotch Firs in the parish of Hartburn, Northumberland.—Fl. June, July. Perennial.

Natural Order XLI

RUBIACEÆ.—The Madder Tribe

Calyx 4 to 6-lobed, or wanting; *corolla* 4 to 6-lobed, wheel-shaped or tubular, regular; *stamens* equal in number to the lobes of the corolla and alternate with them; *ovary* 2-celled; *style* 2-cleft; *stigmas* 2; *pericarp* 2-celled, 2-seeded. This Order, taken in its widest extension, is one of the largest with which we are acquainted, containing more than 2800 species, of which some are of the highest utility to man, both as food and medicine. Among the former, *Coffea Arabica* and *C. liberica* hold the first place. The seeds of these trees furnish the coffee of commerce. Several species of *Cinchona*, a South American family, furnish Peruvian Bark and Quinine; and drugs of similar properties are obtained from other plants of the same tribe.

Ipecacuanha is prepared from the root of a small plant, *Cephaelis Ipecacuanha*, which grows in the damp, shady forests of Brazil. The wood of another plant of this tribe, *Evosmia corymbosa*, is so poisonous that Indians have been poisoned by eating meat roasted on spits made of it. Not a few, moreover, are noted for the fragrance and beauty of their flowers. All the above-mentioned are natives of hot climates; the British species are very different, both in habit and properties. They are herbaceous plants, with slender, angular stems, leaves which with intermediate stipules of equal size form star-like whorls, and small flowers; possessing no remarkable properties, except that of containing a colouring matter in their roots, which is used as a dye. This group has been separated by botanists, and made to constitute a distinct order, under the name of STELLATÆ, a name particularly appropriate to them, from the star-like arrangement of their leaves and leaf-like stipules. The most important of all of these is *Rubia tinctoria*, the roots of which afford Madder, a valuable dye, and possess the singular property of imparting a red colour to the bones of animals which feed on them. Another species of Rubia, *R. cordifolia*, a native of India, affords the valuable red dye, Manjit, of that country. No British species are of any great value, though it is said that the seeds of *Galium*, when roasted, are a good substitute for coffee, and the flowers of *Galium vernum* (Lady's Bedstraw) have been used as rennet to curdle milk. The most attractive British species is Woodruff, well known for the fragrance of its leaves when dry.

1. RUBIA (Madder).—*Corolla* wheel-shaped or bell-shaped; *stamens* 4; *fruit* a 2-lobed berry. (Name from the Latin, *ruber*, red, from the dye of that colour afforded by some species.)

2. GALIUM (Bedstraw).—*Corolla* wheel-shaped; *stamens* 4; *fruit* dry, 2-lobed, 2-seeded, not crowned by the calyx. (Name

PLATE XXXVII.

Crosswort

Lady's Bedstraw

Water Bedstraw

from the Greek, *gala*, milk, for curdling which some species are used.)

3. ASPERULA (Woodruff).—*Corolla* funnel-shaped ; *stamens* 4 ; *fruit* dry, 2-lobed, 2-seeded, not crowned by the calyx. (Name from the Latin, *asper*, rough, from the roughness of the leaves of some species.)

4. SHERARDIA (Field Madder).—*Corolla* funnel-shaped ; *stamens* 4 ; *fruit* dry, 2-lobed, 2-seeded, crowned by the calyx. (Named in honour of *James Sherard*, an eminent English botanist.)

1. RUBIA (*Madder*)

1. *R. peregrina* (Wild Madder).—The only British species. A long straggling plant, many feet in length, with recurved *prickles* on the edges of its 4-angled *stems*, and on the edges of its rough *leaves*, which grow in whorls of 4–6, are glossy above, and recurved at the margin. The *flowers* are greenish yellow, with 5-cleft corollas, and grow in panicles ; the *berries* remain attached to the plant until late in winter ; they are black, 2-lobed, and about as big as currants. Rocky, bushy places in the south and west of England ; uncommon.—Fl. June to August. Perennial.

RUBIA PEREGRINA
(*Wild Madder*)

2. GALIUM (*Bedstraw*)

1. *G. cruciata* (Crosswort, Maywort).—*Stems* scarcely branched, prostrate or ascending ; *leaves* in whorls of 4, ovate, downy on both sides ; *flowers* yellow, fragrant, growing in cymes of 6–8 in the axils of the leaves, the *upper* ones having pistils only, the *lower* stamens only ; *fruit* smooth. Bushy hedges ; common.—Fl. May, June. Perennial.

2. *G. verum* (Yellow Bedstraw, Lady's Bedstraw).—*Leaves* about 8 in a whorl, very narrow (almost thread-like), grooved, and often downy below ; *flowers* small, yellow, in a conspicuous panicle. The Highlanders use the roots in conjunction with alum to dye red, and the rest of the plant as rennet to curdle milk. Dry banks ; common.—Fl. July, August. Perennial.

3. *G. palustre* (Water Bedstraw).—*Leaves* 4–6 in a whorl, oblong, blunt, tapering at the base ; *stem* weak, straggling, more or less rough ; *flowers* small, white, in loose spreading panicles. Variable in size and roughness, likely to be confounded with the following, from which it differs in its superior size and blunt leaves, which are frequently unequal in length, especially in the upper whorls. Watery places ; common.—Fl. July, August. Perennial.

4. *G. uliginosum* (Rough Marsh Bedstraw).—Smaller than the last ; *leaves* 6–8 in a whorl, narrow, tapering at both ends, bristle-pointed, their edges as well as the angles of the stem rough with recurved prickles. The slender, brittle *stems* rarely exceed a foot in length. Cymes of a few white *flowers*.

5. *G. saxitile* (Heath Bedstraw).—A small species, with numerous dense panicles of white *flowers* ; *leaves* about 6 in a whorl, inversely egg-shaped, pointed, the edges sometimes fringed with a few prickles, which point forwards ; *stem* much branched, smooth, prostrate below. Heathy places ; abundant.—Fl. June to August. Perennial.

6. *G. Mollugo* (Hedge Bedstraw).—*Stem* straggling, square, sometimes swollen at the nodes ; *leaves* usually 8 in a whorl, oblong, tapering at each end, with a bristly point, roughish at the edge with weak prickles, which point forwards; *flowers* white, in a loose spreading panicle. Common in England, found in the south of Scotland, rare in Ireland.—Fl. July, August. Perennial.

7. *G. Anglicum* (Wall Bedstraw).—Somewhat resembles the last ; *stems* about 6 inches in length, their edges rough with backward pointing bristles ; *leaves* narrow, about 6 in a whorl, and edged with forward pointing bristles ; *flowers* very small, whitish, the lobes of the corolla blunt. Old walls, etc., on the south coast of England ; rare.—Fl. June, July. Annual.

8. *G. boreale* (Cross-leaved or Northern Bedstraw).—*Leaves* 4 in a whorl, 3-nerved, smooth ; *stem* erect, 6–18 inches in length ; *flowers* white, in terminal panicles ; *fruit* rough, with hooked prickles. Well distinguished by its cruciform, smooth leaves and prickly fruit. Damp, rocky places in the north. —Fl. July, August. Perennial.

GALIUM APARINE
(*Goose Grass*)

9. *P. aparine* (Goose Grass, Cleavers).— *Leaves* 6–8 in a whorl, very rough, with recurved prickles ; *flowers* 2–3 together, greenish-white, axillary ; *fruit* rough, with hooked prickles. Well distinguished by its rough stems and leaves, which cling to the fingers when touched. The globular seed-vessels are also very tenacious, and disperse themselves by clinging to the coat of any animal which touches them ; hence they derive their popular name of cleavers. The whole plant is greedily devoured by geese. The seeds, it is said, have been used as a substitute for coffee. Hedges ; exceedingly common, and an objectionable weed in gardens.—Fl. June to August. Annual.

10. *G. tricorne* (Corn Bedstraw).—Not unlike the last, but smaller ; the *stems* are about
a foot long and rough, as well as the leaves,
with reflexed prickles ; the *flowers* grow in
ones, twos, or threes, and the *fruit* is reflexed
and granulated, not prickly. A cornfield
weed ; not uncommon in England.—Fl. June
to October. Annual.

3. ASPERULA (*Woodruff*)

1. *A. odorata* (Sweet Woodruff).—*Rootstocks* creeping ; *stems* 6-12 inches high, erect ;
leaves usually 8 in a whorl, slightly rough at
their margins, with forward pointing prickles ;
flowers in stalked, terminal panicles ; *fruit*
rough with prickles. A deservedly popular
plant, on account of its fresh green foliage and
pretty snow-white flowers, and also for its
agreeable perfume when dry, which resembles
new-mown hay.

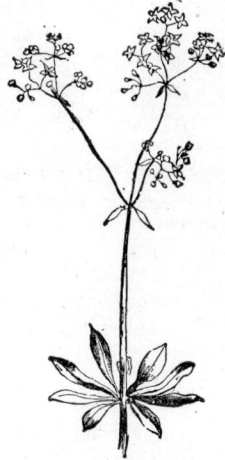

ASPERULA ODORATA
(*Sweet Woodruff*)

2. *A. Cynanchica* (Squinancy- wort). — *Leaves* 4 in a whorl,
linear, uppermost very unequal. A small plant
with very narrow leaves, and tufts of lilac or
whitish flowers. It derives its English name from
having been formerly used as a remedy for the
squinancy, or quinsy. Dry pastures, especially on
calcarious soil ; local.—Fl. June, July. Perennial.

4. SHERARDIA (*Field Madder*)

1. *S. arvensis* (Field Madder).—A small plant,
with branched, spreading *stems*, narrow, pointed
leaves, in whorls of about 6 each, and minute lilac
flowers, which form a small umbel in the terminal
whorl of leaves. Abundant in cultivated land.—
Fl. June to August. Annual.

SHERARDIA
ARVENSIS
(*Field Madder*)

NATURAL ORDER XLII

VALERIANACEÆ.—THE VALERIAN TRIBE

Calyx superior, finally becoming a border, or pappus, to the fruit ;
in the British genera the *corolla* is irregular, 5-lobed, pouched or
spurred at the base ; *stamens* 1–5, inserted into the tube of the
corolla ; *ovary* with 1–3 cells ; *fruit* dry, crowned with the calyx,

not bursting, 1-seeded, 2 of the cells being empty. Herbaceous
plants, with opposite leaves, no stipules, often strong-scented or
aromatic, inhabiting temperate countries, especially the north of
India, Europe, and South America. Many of the plants of this
Order possess properties worthy of notice ; but by far the most remarkable is *Nardostachys jatamansi*, the Spikenard of Scripture, and
the *Nardus* of the ancient classical authors. It grows on the hills
of Butan, in India, where it is called *Dshatamansi*. The root-leaves,
shooting up from the ground and surrounding the young stem, are
torn up along with part of the root, and having been dried in the
sun, or by artificial heat, are sold as a drug. Two merchants of
Butan, of whom Sir W. Jones caused inquiries to be made, related
that the plant shoots up straight from the earth, and that it is then,
as to colour, like a green ear of wheat ; that its fragrance is pleasant
even while it is green, but that its odorous quality is much strength-
ened by merely drying the plant ; that it grows in Butan on the
hills, and even on plains in many places ; and that in that country
it is gathered and prepared for medicinal purposes. In ancient
times this drug was conveyed by way of Arabia to Southern Asia,
and thus it reached the Hebrews. Judas valued the box of oint-
ment with which Mary anointed our Lord's feet at two hundred
Denarii (£6. 9s. 2d.). By the Romans it was considered so precious
that the poet Horace promises to Virgil a whole *cadus*, or about
three dozen modern bottles of wine, for a small onyx-box full of
spikenard. It was a Roman custom in festive banquets, not only
to crown the guests with flowers, but also to anoint them with
spikenard. Eastern nations procure from the mountains of Austria
the *Valeriana Celtica* and *V. Saliunca* to perfume their baths. Their
roots are grubbed up with danger and difficulty by the peasants of
Styria and Carinthia from rocks on the borders of eternal snow ;
they are then tied in bundles and sold at a very low price to merchants, who send them by way of Trieste to Turkey and Egypt,
where they are retailed at a great profit, and passed onwards to the
nations of India and Ethiopia. The seeds of *Centranthus ruber*
(Red Valerian) were used in former times in the process of embalm-
ing the dead ; and some thus employed in the twelfth century, on
being removed from the cere-cloth in the present century and
planted, have vegetated. The roots of our common Valerian
(*V. officinalis*) are still used in medicine ; their effect on cats is very
remarkable, producing a kind of intoxication. The young leaves of
Fedia olitoria (Lamb's Lettuce) are eaten as salad, and those of
Centranthus ruber (Red Valerian) are in Sicily eaten in the
same way.

1. CENTRANTHUS (Spur Valerian).—*Corolla* 5-cleft, spurred at the
base ; *stamen* 1 ; *fruit* crowned with a feathery pappus. (Name in
Greek denoting *spur-flower*.)

PLATE XXXVIII.

Red Spur Valerian   Small Valerian

2. VALERIANA (Valerian).—*Corolla* 5-cleft, bulged at the base ; *stamens* 3 ; *fruit* crowned with a feathery pappus. (Name from the Latin, *valeo*, to be powerful, on account of its medicinal properties.)

3. FEDIA (Corn Salad).—*Corolla* 5-cleft, bulged at the base ; *stamens* 3 ; *fruit* crowned with the calyx. (Name of uncertain origin.)

1. CENTRANTHUS (*Spur Valerian*)

1. *C. ruber* (Red Spur Valerian).—*Corolla* spurred at the base ; *stamen* 1 ; *leaves* egg-shaped, pointed, entire or slightly toothed. The *stems* are 1-2 feet high ; the *leaves* large, smooth, and glaucous ; the *flowers*, which grow in terminal bunches, vary from crimson to pink and white. Not a native plant, but not uncommon in limestone quarries and chalk-pits, on railway banks and old walls. An exceedingly handsome garden plant.—Fl. June to September. Perennial.

2. VALERIANA (*Valerian*)

1. *V. dioica* (Small Marsh Valerian).—Growing about a foot high, quite erect and unbranched, with runners ; *stamens* and *pistils* on different plants ; *corolla* bulged at the base ; *stamens* 3 ; *root-leaves* egg-shaped, stalked ; *stem-leaves* pinnatifid, with a large terminal lobe ; *flowers* pink, in a terminal corymb. The flowers which bear stamens are the largest. Not uncommon on marshy ground.— Fl. May. Perennial.

2. *V. officinalis* (Great Wild Valerian).—Much taller and stouter than the last, often attaining 3 or 4 feet, but resembling it in habit, as well as in the colour and smell of the flowers. *Corolla* bulged at the base ; *stamens* 3 ; *leaves* all pinnate, their sections lanceolate, toothed, slightly hairy on the under side. This is the species of which the roots are used in medicine, and of which cats are so fond, as also, it is said, are rats.—Fl. June, July. Perennial.

Besides the above the two following also occur : *V sambucifolia*, a variety of *V. officinalis*, distinguished by the fewer and broader segments of its leaves ; and *V. pyrenaica*, a Pyrenean species, which has become established in shrubberies, etc., in several places. It much resembles *V.officinalis*, but is taller, coarser, with large-stalked, heart-shaped leaves.

3. FEDIA (*Corn Salad*)

1. *F. olitoria* (Common Corn Salad, Lamb's Lettuce).—A small plant 4–8 inches high, with tender bright green *leaves ; stems* repeatedly 2-forked, and terminal leafy heads of very minute *flowers*, which resemble white glass ; *leaves* long and narrow, wider towards the end, a little toothed near the base ; *capsule* inflated, crowned by the 3 calyx teeth.   It is sometimes cultivated as a salad.   Cultivated ground, such as cornfields, etc. ;   common.—Fl. May, June. Annual.

FEDIA OLITORIA
(*Common Corn Salad,*
Lamb's Lettuce)

2. *F. dentata* (Toothed Corn Salad).—*Leaves* long and narrow, much toothed towards the base ; *flowers* in corymbs, with a solitary sessile one in the forks of the stem ; *capsule* not inflated, crowned by the 4-toothed calyx. Taller than the last and more rigid *habit.*   Cornfields, etc. ;   not uncommon.—Fl. June, July.   Annual.

Two or three other species of *Fedia* occur, but as they are neither frequent nor of special interest, and are chiefly distinguished by minute differences in the fruit, they are omitted from the present volume.

NATURAL ORDER XLIII
DISPACEÆ.—THE TEAZEL TRIBE

Calyx attached to the ovary, surrounded by several more or less rigid, calyx-like bracts ; *corolla* tubular, with 4–5 unequal lobes ; *stamens* 4, the *anthers* not united ; *style* 1 ; *stigma* not cleft ; *fruit* dry, 1-seeded, crowned by the pappus-like calyx ; *flowers* crowded together in heads like the Compositæ, but differing in the rigid bractioles which surround each ;   the leaves are usually opposite and without stipules.   A small Order of herbaceous plants inhabiting temperate regions, and possessing no remarkable properties.   *Dispacus Fullonum* is the Clothiers' Teazle, a plant with large heads of flowers, which are embedded in stiff, hooked bracts.   These heads are set in frames and used in the dressing of broadcloth, the hooks catching up and removing all loose particles of wool, but giving way when held fast by the substance of the cloth.   This is almost the only process in the manufacture of cloth which it has been found impossible to execute by machinery, for although various substitutes have been proposed, none has proved on trial exactly to answer the purpose intended.

1. DIPSACUS (Teazle).—*Stems* erect, angular, opposite; *leaves* usually joined round the stem; *flower-heads* usually elongated with an involucre of stiff, spreading bracts, and the *bracts* between the flouts prominent, rigid awns. (Name from the Greek, *dipsao*, I thirst, the leaves being united at their base, so as to form round the stem a hollow in which water collects. This little moat round the stem is a provision of Nature, to prevent insects *crawling* up to the flowers to rob them of the honey which attracts *flying* insects who, in a round of visits, unconsciously distribute the pollen from flower to flower and effect cross fertilization.)

2. SCABIOSA (Scabious).—Plants not prickly; *flower-heads* hemispherical or flattened, with an involucre of bracts beneath; *corolla* 4 or 5-lobed; *ovary* with a cup-shaped border, with 4–10 bristles. (Name from the Latin, *scabies*, the leprosy, for which disease some of the species were supposed to be a remedy.)

1. DIPSACUS (*Teazle*)

1. *D. sylvestris* (Wild Teazle).—*Leaves* opposite, united at the base and forming a cup; *bristles* of the receptacle not hooked. A stout herbaceous plant 3–6 feet high, with an erect prickly stem, large bright green leaves, which are prickly underneath and united at the base, and often contain water. The flowers grow in large conical, bristly heads, the terminal bristles being generally the longest. The flowers themselves are light purple, and expand in irregular patches on the head. Waste places; common.—Fl. July. Biennial.

2. *D. Fullonum* (Fuller's Teazle).— Differs from the above in having the *bristles* of the *receptacle* hooked; it is probably a variety of *D. sylvestris*, and is not considered a British plant, though occasionally found wild in the neighbourhood of the cloth districts.

DIPSACUS SYLVESTRIS
(*Wild Teazle*)

3. *D. pilosus* (Small Teazle).—*Leaves* stalked, with a small leaflet at the base on each side. Smaller than *D. sylvestris* in all its parts, and having more the habit of a Scabious than of a Teazel. The flowers are white and grow in small, nearly globose bristly heads; the whole plant is rough with bristles. Moist, shady places; not common.—Fl. August, September. Biennial.

L

2. SCABIOSA (*Scabious*)

1. *S. succisa* (Premorse or Devil's-bit Scabious).—*Corolla* 4-cleft, nearly regular; *heads* nearly globose. A slender, little-branched plant, with a hairy stem, few oblong, mostly entire leaves, and terminal heads of purplish blue flowers. The root is solid and abrupt, as if bitten off (premorse), which gave rise to the fable alluded to by John Parkinson in his " Theatrum Botanicum " (1640). He says " that the Devile, envying the good that this herbe might do to mankinde, bit away parte of the roote, and thereof came the name Succisa, Devil's-bit." Heaths and pastures ; common.—Fl. July to October. Perennial.

2. *S. Columbaria* (Small Scabious).—*Corolla* 5-cleft, the outer flowers longest ; *heads* nearly globose ; *root-leaves* oblong, variously cut ; *upper* pinnatifid. Well distinguished from the last by its radiate flowers and cut leaves. The foliage is of a much lighter hue, and the flowers lilac rather than purple. Pastures on chalky soil ; not uncommon.—Fl. July, August. Perennial.

3. *S. arvensis* (Field Scabious).—A tall bristly plant 2–3 feet high, not much branched, bearing several large, handsome, convex heads of lilac *flowers*, the inner flowers with 4-lobed, nearly regular corollas ; the outer are larger and usually labiate. The *root-leaves* are simple, the *upper leaves* pinnatifid. Cornfields and waysides; common.— Fl. July, August. Perennial.

NATURAL ORDER XLIV

COMPOSITÆ.—COMPOUND FLOWERS

This extensive and well-marked Order derives its name from having its flowers *compounded*, as it were, of numerous smaller ones, called *florets*, which are enclosed within a calyx-like assemblage of *bracts*, termed an *involucre*. These bracts, usually called *scales*, often overlap one another like the tiles of a house (Latin, *imbrex*, a tile) ; hence they are said to be *imbricated*. The flowers vary greatly in shape, but the following description will be found to include all the British species. *Calyx* rising from the top of the ovary and becoming a *pappus*, that is, either a chaffy margin of the fruit, or a tuft or ring of bristles, hairs, or feathery down ; *corolla* of 1 petal, either tubular or strap-shaped ; *stamens* 5, united by their anthers (*syngenesious*) ; *ovary* inferior, 1 to each style, 1-celled ; *style* simple, with a simple or 2-cleft *stigma*, sheathed by the tube of anthers ; *fruit* a solitary erect seed, crowned by the pappus, which is sometimes merely a chaffy margin, but more frequently an assemblage of simple, or serrated, or feathery hairs, sometimes elevated on a stalk. For convenience of reference this Order is divided into several Groups.

PLATE XXXIX.

Sheep's Scabious

Field Scabious

Small Scabious

I. CHICORACEÆ (Chicory Group).—In this all the florets are strap-shaped and perfect; that is, each contains 5 stamens and a pistil. The prevailing colour of British species is yellow, as the Dandelion; but Salsafy (*Tragopogon porrifolius*) and Alpine Sow-thistle (*Sonchus Alpinus*) have purple flowers; Chicory, blue.

In II, CYNAROCEPHALÆ (Thistle Group), the florets form a *convex* head, and are all tubular and perfect except in *Centaurea*, where the outer florets, which are larger than the inner, are destitute both of stamens and pistils; the stigma is jointed on the style. The flowers are purple, with a tendency to vary into white; but in Carline Thistle (*Carlina*) they are brownish yellow; in Cornflower (*Centaurea Cyanus*) bright blue.

In III, TUBIFLORÆ (Tansy Group), all the florets are tubular and perfect, and form a flat head; the style passes into the stigma without a joint; the flowers are mostly yellow; but Hemp-agrimony (*Eupatorium cannabinum*) has lilac flowers; Butter-bur (*Petasites vulgaris*) pale flesh-coloured; and in most species of *Artemisia, Gnaphalium*, and *Filago* the colour is determined rather by the involucre than the florets.

In IV, RADIATÆ (Daisy Group), the florets are of two kinds; those of the centre, or disk, being tubular and perfect, those of the margin, or ray, strap-shaped and having pistils only. The prevailing colour of the disk is yellow, Yarrow (*Achillea*) being the only exception, in which all the florets are white; the ray is either of the same colour, as in Coltsfoot (*Tussilago*), Golden-rod (*Solidago*), Rag-wort and Flea-wort (*Senecio*), Leopard's-bane (*Doronicum*), Elecampane (*Inula*), Flea-bane (*Pulicaria*), Corn-marigold (*Chrysanthemum segetum*), and Ox-eye Chamomile (*Anthemis tinctoria*); white, as in Daisy (*Bellis*), Fever-few and May-weed (*Matricaria*), Ox-eye (*Chrysanthemum Leucanthemum*), and several species of Chamomile (*Anthemis*); or purple, as in Star-wort (*Aster*), and *Erigeron*. In Groundsel (*Senecio vulgaris*) the ray is never per-fected. The limits of the Order COMPOSITÆ are exactly the same as those of the Linnæan Class SYNGENESIA; but the number of plants belonging to it exceeds the amount of all the plants known to Linnæus, so extensive have been the researches in Botany since his time. The number of genera alone amounts to some 800, of species nearly 10,000, or about one-tenth of all the known flowering plants; whilst the total number of species known to Linnæus was but 8500. The properties of the Order vary considerably in various parts of the world, but not according to any fixed rule. The Chicory Group are, however, most abundant in cold regions, the Daisy Group in hot climates. Again, it may be remarked that in cold and tem-perate regions the Compositæ are mostly herbaceous; but as we approach the equator they become shrubs, or even trees. The variety of properties which they possess is not proportionate to the immense number of species.   Bitterness, in a greater or less degree, is a characteristic of nearly all, to which is sometimes added astringency ; and many possess tonic or narcotic properties.   Chicory, or Succory, is cultivated as a salad, but more frequently for the sake of its roots, which are roasted and mixed with coffee.   The flavour is agreeable, but it is to be feared that less palatable and perhaps less wholesome roots, procurable at a less cost, are often substituted for it.   From the leaves a blue dye may be obtained.   Endive is another species of Chichory (*Chichorium endivia*), the bleached leaves of which afford a common winter salad.   The common Dandelion (a corruption of the French *Dent-de-lion*, Lion's tooth) supplies an extract which is said to have valuable medicinal properties ;   its roots are also used to adulterate coffee.   Lettuces afford a wholesome salad as well as an extract, the properties of which resemble those of opium.   The roots of *Scorzonera* and *Tragopogon porrifolius* (Cardoons) are esculent, but little grown. These all belong to the Chicory Group.

Among the Thistle Group we have the Artichoke (*Cynara Scolymus*), the young involucres and receptacles of which are edible ; the Bur-dock (*Arctium*), the root of which is said to be useful in rheumatism ; and the Carline Thistle, which was anciently used in magical incantations. In the third Group, Wormwood (*Artemisia*) is remarkable for its intense bitterness.   One species (*A. Abrotanum*) is the Southernwood of gardens, a fragrant shrub, used on the Continent in making beer ; *A. Dracunculus*, the Tarragon of gardeners, is used for giving a disagreeable flavour to vinegar.   Some species of *Eupatorium* have the reputed power of healing the bites of numerous animals ; and *E. glutinosum* is said to be the plant which, under the name of Matico, is extensively used as a styptic.   It is a shrubby plant inhabiting the Andes, and derived its name from a soldier named " Matico " (Little Matthew), who, having been wounded in battle, accidentally applied the leaves of this plant to his wound, which had the immediate effect of stopping the bleeding.

To the RADIATÆ belong the gorgeous Dahlia, so called from Dr. Dahl, who introduced it ; and the " wee " Daisy, or Day's-eye, which opens only in sunny weather, and peeps up through the grass as if it were an eye indeed.   The genus Helianthus contains the Sunflower (*H. annuus*) and Jerusalem Artichoke (*H. tuberosus*), " Jerusalem " being a corruption of the Italian word *girasole*, of the same meaning as Sunflower, the name Artichoke being given to mark the similarity of flavour in its roots with that of the true Artichoke mentioned above.   It rarely flowers in England, but produces abundance of tubers, which hold a high rank among esculent vegetables.   It is valuable not only for its productiveness, but for the freedom with which it grows in any soil.   Its roots are made into a dish which, by an absurd piece of pedantry, is called " Palestine soup." Chamomile and Fever-few possess valuable medicinal properties, especially the former. Coltsfoot and Elecampane are useful in pectoral complaints ; the flowers of Marigold are used to adulterate saffron ; the Ox-eye daisy is said to be destructive to fleas ; the yellow Ox-eye affords a yellow dye, and the petals of the Dahlia a beautiful carmine.

I. CHICORACEÆ.—*Chicory Group*
All the florets strap-shaped, having stamens and pistils

II. CYNAROCEPHALÆ.—*Thistle Group*
All the florets tubular, 5-cleft, having stamens and pistils (except in Centaurea, in which the outer florets are larger, and destitute of stamens and pistils), *and forming a convex head ; style jointed below the stigma*

III. TUBIFLORÆ.—*Tansy Group*
All the florets tubular, 5-cleft, having stamens and pistils, and forming a flat head ; style not jointed below the stigma

IV. RADIATÆ.—*Daisy Group*
Central florets tubular, 5-cleft, having stamens and pistils ; outer florets strap-shaped, forming a ray, and furnished with pistils only (*Senecio vulgaris*, Common Groundsel, has no rays)

I. CHICORACEÆ.—*Chicory Group*

1. TRAGOPOGON (Goat's beard).—*Involucre* simple, of 8–10 long scales, united below ; *receptacle* dotted ; *fruit* with longitudinal ridges, tapering into a long beak ; *pappus* feathery, with the down interwoven. (Name from the Greek, *tragos*, a goat, and *pogon*, a beard.)

2. HELMINTHIA (Ox-tongue).—*Involucre* of about 8 equal scales, surrounded by 3–5 leaf-like, loose bracts ; *receptacle* dotted ; *fruit* rough, with transverse wrinkles, rounded at the end and beaked ; *pappus* feathery. (Name from the Greek, *helmins, helminthos*, a worm, from the form of the fruit.)

3. PICRIS.—*Involucre* of 1 row of equal upright scales, with several small spreading ones at the base ; *receptacle* lightly dotted ; *fruit* rough, with transverse ridges, not beaked ; *pappus* of 2 rows, the inner only feathery. (Name from the Greek, *picros*, bitter.)

4. APARGIA (Hawk-bit).—*Involucre* unequally imbricated, with the outer scales smaller, black, and hairy, in several rows ; *receptacle* slightly dotted ; *fruit* tapering to a point ; *pappus* of 1 row, feathery. (Name of uncertain origin.)

5. THRINCIA.—*Involucre* of 1 row, with a few scales at the base ; *receptacle* lightly dotted ; *fruit* of the outer florets scarcely beaked ; *pappus* a chaffy, fringed crown ; *fruit* of the inner florets beaked ; *pappus* feathery.   (Name from the Greek, *thrincos,* a battlement, from the form of the seed-crown of the marginal florets.)

6. HYPOCHÆRIS (Cat's-ear).—*Involucre* oblong, imbricated ; *receptacle* chaffy ; *fruit* rough, often beaked ; *pappus* feathery, often with a row of short bristles outside.   (Name in Greek denoting its fitness for hogs.)

7. LACTUCA (Lettuce).—*Involucre* oblong, imbricated, its scales membranous at the margin, containing but few flowers ; *receptacle* naked ; *fruit* flattened, beaked ; *pappus* hairy.   (Name from *lac,* milk, which the juice resembles in colour.)

8. SONCHUS (Sow-thistle).—*Involucre* imbricated, with 2 or 3 rows of unequal scales, swollen at the base ; *receptacle* naked ; *fruit* flattened, transversely wrinkled, not beaked ; *pappus* hairy. (Name in Greek bearing allusion to the soft nature of the stems.)

9. CREPIS (Hawk's-beard).—*Involucre* double, inner of 1 row, outer of short, loose scales ; *receptacle* naked ; *fruit* not flattened, furrowed, tapering upwards ; *pappus* a tuft of soft white down. (Name in Greek signifying a *slipper,* but why given to this plant is not known.)

10. HIERACIUM (Hawk-weed).—*Involucre* imbricated, with numerous oblong scales ; *receptacle* dotted ; *fruit* angular, furrowed, abrupt, with a toothed margin at the top ; *pappus* bristly, sessile, not white.   (Name from the Greek, *hierax,* a hawk, because that bird was supposed to use the plant to strengthen its sight.)

11. LEONTODON (Dandelion).—*Involucre* imbricated with numerous scales, the outermost of which are loose, and often reflexed ; *receptacle* dotted ; *fruit* slightly flattened, rough, bearing a long and very slender beak; *pappus* hairy.   (Name from the Greek, *leon,* a lion, and *odons, odontos,* a tooth, from the tooth-like lobes of the leaves.)

12. LAPSANA (Nipple-wort).—*Involucre* a single row of erect scales, with 4–5 small ones at the base, containing but few flowers ; *receptacle* naked ; *fruit* flattened, furrowed ; *pappus* o.   (Name of classical origin.)

13. CHICORIUM (Chicory).—*Involucre* in 2 rows, inner of 8 scales, which bend back after flowering; outer of 5 smaller, loose scales ; *receptacle* naked, or slightly hairy ; *fruit* thick above, tapering downwards ; *pappus* a double row of small chaffy scales. (Name of Arabic origin.)

II. CYNAROCEPHALÆ.—*Thistle Group*

14. ARCTIUM (Bur-dock).—*Involucre* globose, scales ending in hooked points; *receptacle* chaffy; *fruit* oblong, 4-sided; *pappus* short. (Name from the Greek, *arctos*, a bear, from the roughness of the heads of flowers.)

15. SERRATULA (Saw-wort).—*Stamens* and *pistils* on different plants; *involucre* imbricated, scales not prickly; *receptacle* chaffy or bristly; *fruit* flattened, not beaked; *pappus* hairy. (Name from the Latin, *serrula*, a little saw, the leaves being finely serrated.)

16. SAUSSUREA. — *Involucre* imbricated, scales not prickly; *anthers* bristly at the base; *receptacle* chaffy; *pappus* double, outer bristly, inner longer, feathery. (Named in honour of the two *Saussures*, eminent botanists.)

17. CARDUUS (Thistle).—*Involucre* swollen below, imbricated with thorn-like scales; *receptacle* bristly; *pappus* hairy, united by a ring at the base, and soon falling off. (The Latin name of the plant.)

18. CNICUS (Plume-thistle).—Resembling *Carduus*, except that the *pappus* is feathery. (Name from the Greek, *cnizo*, to prick.)

19. ONOPORDIUM (Cotton-thistle). — *Receptacle* honeycombed; *fruit* 4-angled; *pappus* hairy, rough; in other respects resembling *Carduus*. (Name of Greek origin.)

20. CARLINA (Carline-thistle).—Resembling *Cnicus*, except that the inner scales of the *involucre* are chaffy and coloured, and spread like a ray. (Name, the same as *Carolina*, from a tradition that the root of one species, *C. acaulis*, was shown by an angel to *Charlemagne* as a remedy for the plague which prevailed in his army.)

21. CENTAUREA (Knap-weed, Bluebottle, etc).—*Involucre* imbricated; *receptacle* bristly; *pappus* hairy, or o; *outer florets* large, irregular, destitute of stamens and pistils. (Name from the *Centaur Chiron*, who is fabled to have healed wounds with it.)

III. TUBIFLORÆ.—*Tansy Group*

22. BIDENS (Bur-marigold).—*Fruit* crowned with 2 or 3 erect, rigid bristles, which are rough, with minute teeth pointing downwards. (Name from the Latin, *bis*, double, and *dens*, a tooth, from the structure of the fruit.)

23. EUPATORIUM (Hemp-agrimony).—*Heads* few-flowered; *involucre* imbricated, oblong; *receptacle* naked; *styles* much longer than the florets. (Name from *Mithridates Eupator*, who is said to have brought the plant into use.)

24. CHRYSOCOMA (Goldylocks).—*Involucre* a single row of loosely spreading scales ; *receptacle* honeycombed ; *fruit* flattened, silky ; *pappus* hairy, rough. (Name from the Greek, *chrysos*, gold, and *come*, hair.)

25. DIOTIS (Cotton-weed).—*Pappus* o ; *corolla* with two ears at the base, which remain and crown the fruit. (Name from the Greek, *dis*, double, and *ous*, *otos*, an ear, from the structure of the fruit.)

26. TANACETUM (Tansy).—*Involucre* cup-shaped, imbricated ; *receptacle* naked ; *fruit* crowned with a chaffy border. (Name altered from the Greek, *athanaton*, everlasting).

27. ARTEMISIA (Wormwood).—*Pappus* o ; *involucre* roundish, imbricated, containing but few flowers. (Named after *Artemis*, the Diana of the Greeks.)

28. ANTENNARIA (Everlasting).—*Stamens* and *pistils* on separate plants ; *pappus* hairy, that of the barren flowers thickened or feathery upwards ; *involucre* coloured, rigid. (Name from the *antennæ* of an insect, which the pappus of the barren flower resembles.)

29. GNAPHALIUM (Cudweed).—*Involucre* roundish, dry, imbricated, often coloured ; *receptacle* naked ; *pappus* hairy. (Name from the Greek, *gnaphalion*, soft down, with which the leaves are covered.)

30. FILAGO.—*Involucre* tapering upwards, imbricated, of a few long, pointed scales ; *receptacle* chaffy in the circumference ; *pappus* hairy ; *florets* few, the outer ones bearing pistils only. (Name from the Latin, *filum*, a thread, the whole plant being clothed with white, thread-like hairs or down.)

31. PETASITES (Butter-bur).—*Involucre* a single row of narrow scales ; *receptacle* naked ; *stamens* and *pistils*, for the most part, on different plants. (Name from the Greek, *petasos*, a covering for the head, from the large size of the leaves.)

IV. RADIATÆ.—*Daisy Group*

32. TUSSILAGO (Colt's-foot).—*Involucre* a single row of narrow scales ; *receptacle* naked ; *florets* of the ray narrow, in several rows ; of the disk few, all yellow. (Name from the Latin, *tussis*, a cough, from the use to which it is applied.)

33. ERIGERON (Flea-bane).—*Involucre* imbricated with narrow scales ; *receptacle* naked ; *florets* of the ray in many rows, very narrow, different in colour from those of the disk. (Name in Greek, signifying *growing old at an early season*, from the early appearance of the grey seed-down.)

34. ASTER (Star-wort).—*Involucre* imbricated, a few scales on the flower-stalk ; *receptacle* naked, honeycombed ; *florets* of the ray in 1 row, purple ; of the disk, yellow ; *pappus* hairy, in many rows. (Name from the Greek, *aster,* a star.)

35. SOLIDAGO (Golden-rod).—*Involucre* and *receptacle* as in Aster ; *florets* all yellow ; *pappus* hairy, in 1 row.   (Name from the Latin, *solidare,* to unite, on account of its supposed qualities of healing wounds.)

36. SENECIO (Rag-wort, Groundsel, and Flea-bane).—*Involucre* imbricated, oblong or conical, a few smaller scales at the base ; *receptacle* naked ; *florets* all yellow, the outer in *S. vulgaris* wanting. (Name from the Latin, *senex,* an old man, from the grey seed-down.)

37. DORONICUM (Leopard's-bane).—*Involucre* cup-shaped, scales equal, in 2 rows ; *florets* all yellow ; *pappus* hairy, wanting in the florets of the ray.   (Name of uncertain etymology.)

38. INULA (Elecampane).—*Involucre* imbricated, in many rows ; *receptacle* naked ; *florets* all yellow ; *anthers* with two bristles at the base ; *pappus* hairy, in 1 row.   (Name probably a corruption of *Helenula,* Little Helen.)

39. PULICARIA (Flea-bane).—*Involucre* loosely imbricated, in few rows ; *pappus* in 2 rows, outer one short, cup-shaped, toothed ; inner hairy, in other respects like *Inula.*   (Name from the Latin, *pulex,* a flea, which is supposed to be driven away by its powerful smell.)

40. BELLIS (Daisy).—*Involucre* of 2 rows of equal blunt scales ; *receptacle* conical ; outer *florets* white, inner yellow ; *pappus* o. (Name from the Latin, *bellus,* pretty.)

41. CHRYSANTHEMUM (Ox-eye).—*Involucre* nearly flat, the scales membranaceous at the margin ; *receptacle* naked ; *pappus* o. (Name from the Greek, *chrysos,* gold, and *anthos,* a flower.)

42. MATRICARIA (Wild Chamomile).—*Involucre* cup-shaped, or nearly flat ; the scales imbricated ; *receptacle* conical, naked ; *florets* of the ray white, of the disk yellow ; *pappus* o.   (Name from some supposed medicinal virtues.)

43. ANTHEMIS (Chamomile).—*Involucre* cup-shaped, or nearly flat, the scales membranaceous at the margin ; *receptacle* convex, chaffy ; *pappus* o, or a narrow, chaffy border.   (Name from the Greek, *anthos,* a flower, from the value of its blossoms as a medicine.)

44. ACHILLEA (Yarrow).—*Involucre* egg-shaped or oblong, imbricated ; *receptacle* flat, chaffy ; *florets* all of one colour, those of the ray 5-10, broad ; *pappus* o.   (Named after Achilles.)

I. CHICORACEÆ.—*Chicory Group*

1. TRAGOPOGON (*Goat's-beard*)

1. *T. pratensis* (Yellow Goat's-beard).—*Involucre* about as long as, or longer than the corolla; *leaves* broad at the base, very long, tapering, channelled, undivided; *flower-stalks* slightly thickened above. An erect glaucous plant about 2 feet high, with long grass-like leaves and large bright yellow flowers, which always close early in the day, and have hence gained for the plant the name of John-go-to-bed-at-noon. The pappus is very beautiful, the feathery down being raised on a long stalk, and interlaced so as to form a kind of shallow cup. Meadows; not uncommon.—Fl. June, July. Biennial.

2. *T. porrifolius* (Salsafy).—Though not a British species, is occasionally found in moist meadows. In habit it resembles the last, but has purple flowers. It was formerly much cultivated for the sake of its fleshy tap roots, which were boiled or stewed and eaten. Though still advertised in seedsmen's catalogues, its place is now largely supplied by *Scorzonera Hispanica*.

HELMINTHIA ECHIOIDES
(*Bristly Ox-tongue*)

2. HELMINTHIA (*Ox-tongue*)

1. *H. echioides* (Bristly Ox-tongue).—A stout and much-branched herb 2–3 feet high, well distinguished by its numerous *prickles*, each of which springs from a raised white spot, and by the large heart-shaped *bracts* at the base of the yellow *flowers*. Waste places; not uncommon.—Fl. June, July. Perennial.

3. PICRIS (*Picris*)

1. *P. hieracioides* (Hawk-weed Picris). —A rather slender plant 2–3 feet high, branched principally above; the *stems* are rough, with hooked bristles; the *leaves* narrow, rough, and toothed; the *flowers* are numerous, yellow, with *bracts* on the peduncles. Waste places; common.—Fl. July to September. Biennial.

PICRIS HIERACIOIDES
(*Hawk-weed Picris*)

PLATE XL.

Hemp Agrimony

4. APARGIA (*Hawk-bit*)

1. *A. hispida* (Rough Hawk-bit).—*Leaves* all from the root, pinnatifid, with the lobes pointing backwards, rough, with forked hairs; *stalk* single-flowered; *flowers* yellow, drooping when in bud. Meadows and waste places; frequent.—Fl. June to September. Perennial.

2. *A. autumnalis* (Autumnal Hawk-bit).—A tall plant 2–3 feet high, with a downy *involucre; leaves* all from the root, narrow, slightly hairy on the ribs beneath; *stalk* many flowered, swollen beneath the flowers; *flowers* large, deep yellow, erect when in bud. Meadows and cornfields; frequent.—Fl. August. Perennial.

APARGIA AUTUMNALIS
(*Autumnal Hawk-bit*)

THRINCIA HIRTA
(*Hairy Thrincia*)

5. THRINCIA

1. *T. hirta* (Hairy Thrincia, Hairy Hawk-bit).—A small plant 4–6 inches high, with spreading, more or less lobed, *leaves*, which are rough, with forked or simple hairs, and leafless, somewhat hairy *stalks* often of a purplish hue, each of which bears a yellow *flower;* flower-buds drooping. Heaths and downs; common.— Fl. July to September. Perennial.

6. Hypochæris (*Cat's-ear*)

1. *H. radicata* (Long-rooted Cat's-ear).—*Leaves* all from the root, pinnatifid, with the lobes pointing backwards, bristly; *stalks* branched, smooth, with a few scales below the flowers. Well distinguished by its long, branched flower-stalks, which are quite smooth throughout, and slightly swollen beneath the large yellow flowers, where there are also a few small scales. Hedges and waste places; common.—Fl. July, August. Perennial.

2. *H. glabra* (Smooth Cat's-ear).—Much resembling the above, but smaller, 3–10 inches high; *leaves* smooth, oblong; *flower-heads* small, yellow; *florets* scarcely longer than the *involucre*. Gravelly places; not common.—Fl. June to August. Annual.

Hypochæris Radicata
(*Long-rooted Cat's-ear*)

3. *H. maculata* (Spotted Cat's-ear).—*Leaves* obovate, not lobed, spreading, rough, spotted above; *stems* about a foot high, bearing usually 1 (rarely more) large deep yellow *flower*. Limestone and magnesian hills; rare.—Fl. July, August. Perennial.

7. Lactuca (*Lettuce*)

1. *L. muralis* (Ivy-leaved Lettuce).—*Florets* 5; *leaves* pinnatifid, variously cut, with the terminal lobe largest. A slender plant, leafy below, 1–2 feet high, with small yellow heads, each of which contains 5 similar florets, and thus resembles a simple flower of 5 petals. The panicle has a singularly angular growth; the fruit is black. Woods and old walls; not uncommon.—Fl. July to September. Biennial.

2. *L. scoriola* (Prickly Lettuce).—Erect, stiff, 2–4 feet high; *leaves* usually perpendicular, the lower leaves toothed or deeply pinnatifid; upper leaves narrow, entire, clasping the stem, leaves with bristles on the under side of midrib; *florets* 6–12, pale yellow. Waste places; rare.—Fl. July, August. Biennial.

Lactuca Muralis
(*Ivy-leaved Lettuce*)

PLATE XLI.

Sea Aster
Flea-bane

Flea-bane Erigeron
Golden-rod

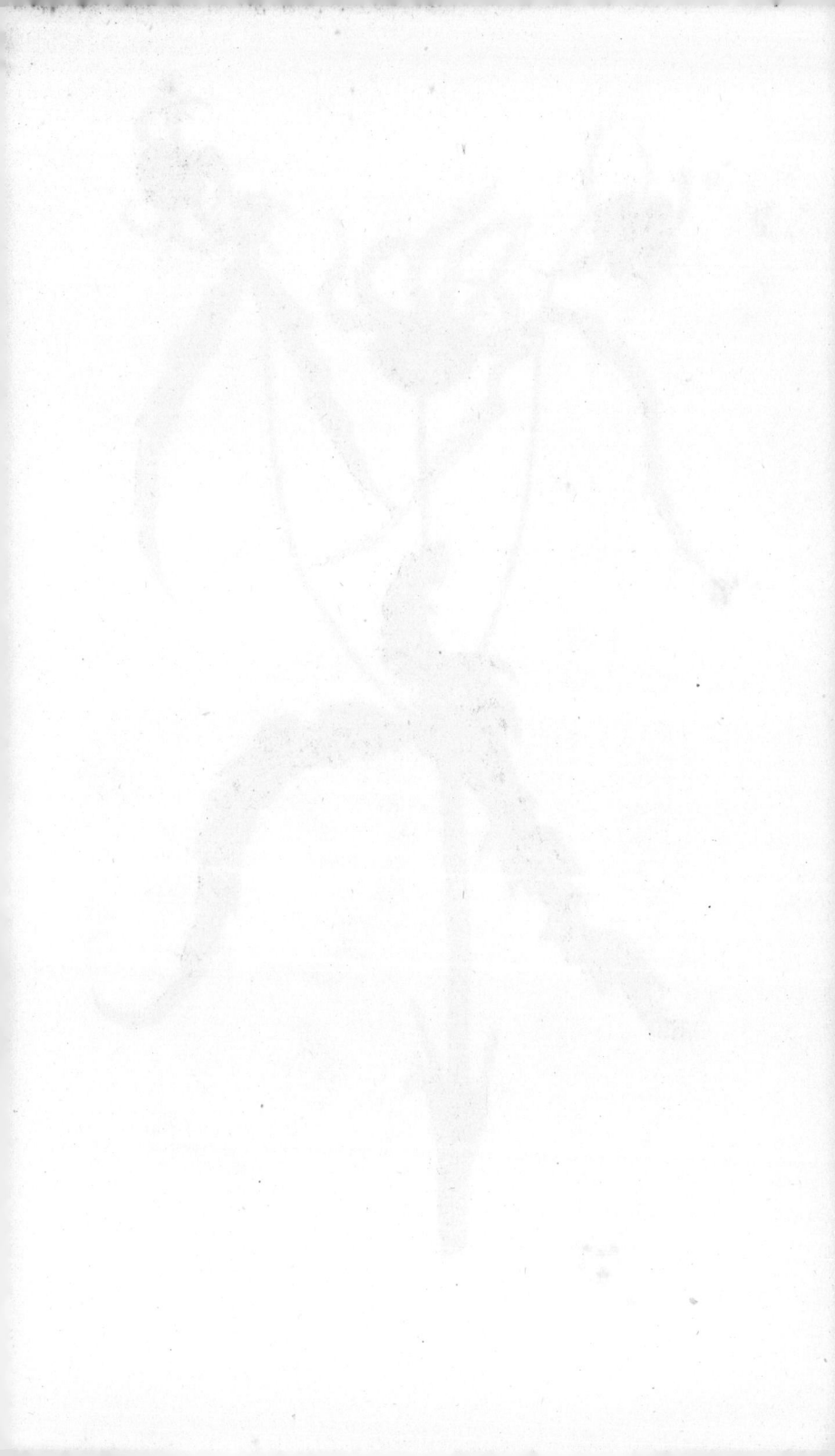

PLATE XLII.

Bur-Marigold

3. *L. saligna* (Willow Lettuce).—More slender than the last, *leaves* narrower, and perpendicular against the stem ; variable and likely to be confounded with *L. scoriola*. Rare ; confined in Britain to chalky situations, in the south-east, near the coast.—Fl. July, August. Biennial.

4. *L. Alpina* (Alpine Lettuce, or Blue Sow-thistle).—A handsome erect, unbranched plant 2–3 feet high, with a *panicle* of large blue *flower-heads*. It grows on the Clova Mountains, but is rare. Perennial. Known also as *Sonchus Alpinus*. The Garden Lettuce (*L. sativa*) belongs to this genus, but is not a native plant.

8. SONCHUS (*Sow-thistle*)

1. *S. oleraceus* (Common Sow-thistle, Milk-thistle). — Erect, branched, 1–4 feet high ; *stems* hollow ; *leaves* oblong, more or less pinnatifid or entire, toothed, often prickly, the upper ones often clasping the stem with spreading, arrow-shaped auricles ; *heads* somewhat umbellate ; *involucres* smooth. Waste places, and as a garden weed ; common. This plant makes light and salutary meals for rabbits.—Fl. June to September. Annual.

SONCHUS OLERACEUS
(*Common Sow-thistle, Milk-thistle*)

2. *S. arvensis* (Corn Sow-thistle).— *Stem* simple, 2–4 feet high, tubular, angular ; *leaves* oblong, pinnatifid or wavy, toothed and spinous. The lower ones stalked and heart-shaped at the base ; upper clasping the stem with auricles ; loose corymbs of large yellow *flower-heads ; involucre* and *flower-stalks* with dark glandular hairs. In similar situations with the last, from which it may be readily distinguished by its simple stem and much larger flowers. —Fl. August, September. Perennial.

3. *S. palustris* (Marsh Sow-thistle).—Much resembling the last, but taller ; *stem* 6–8 feet high, unbranched ; *leaves* long, narrow, clasping the stem with pointed auricles ; *flower-heads* large, pale yellow ; *involucres* with glandular hairs. Marshes in the south-east of England ; very rare.

A variety of *S. oleraceus*, frequently found growing with it, is *S. asper* (Rough Sow-thistle).—The *leaves* are more spinously toothed, with rounded auricles, and darker in colour, whilst the longitudinal ribs of the achenes are not transversely wrinkled.

9. CREPIS (*Hawk's-beard*)

1. *C. taraxacifolia*.—Plant hairy, 1-2 feet high ; *stem* furrowed, reddish, branched above ; *leaves* pinnatifid, with a large terminal lobe, mostly radicle ; *flower-heads* yellow, the outer florets reddish beneath, erect in bud, borne in a flat corymb ; *fruits* with beaks of their own length. Calcareous soils ; rare.—Fl. June, July. Biennial.

2. *C. fœtida* (Fœtid Hawk's-beard).—Plant about a foot high, hairy ; *stem* branched ; *root-leaves* pinnatifid ; *stem-leaves* narrow ; *flower-heads* bright yellow, on long stalks, drooping when in bud ; *fruits* beaked, the centre ones much longer than the outer. Calcareous soils in south-eastern England ; rare.—Fl. June, July. Biennial.

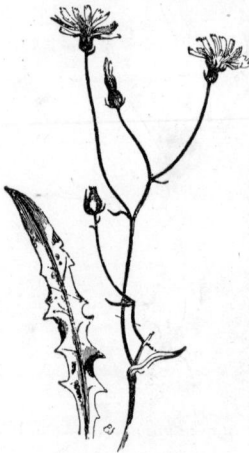

CREPIS VIRENS
(Smooth Hawk's-beard)

3. *C. virens* (Smooth Hawk's-beard).—*Leaves* smooth, pinnatifid, with the lobes pointing backwards, the upper ones narrow, arrow-shaped at the base, and clasping the stem ; the lower ones stalked ; varying in height from 6 inches to 2 feet, and producing abundance of small yellow *flowers*. Waste ground, and on roofs of cottages ; common. —Fl. July to September. Annual.

4. *C. biennis* (Rough Hawk's-beard).—A tall stout plant, resembling *C. taraxacifolia*, but the *stem* is not red ; 1-4 feet high, not much branched below ; *flower-heads* rather large, yellow, borne in a corymb ; *leaves* hairy ; *achenes* often of varying lengths on the same head. Chalky soils ; rare.— Fl. June, July. Biennial.

5. *C. hieracioides* (Blunt-leaved Hawk's-beard).—An erect slender plant, 1-2 feet high ; *radicle leaves* oblong, blunt, stalked ; *stem-leaves* narrow, clasping the stem ; *flower-heads* few ; *achenes* not beaked, many-ribbed. Found in a few localities in the north ; rare.—Fl. July, August. Perennial.

6. *C. paludosa* (Marsh Hawk's-beard).—*Stem* about 2 feet high, angular, unbranched ; *leaves* smooth, the lower ones pinnatifid, with the lobes pointing backwards, tapering into a stalk ; the upper ones narrow, heart-shaped at the base, and clasping the stem ; *flower-heads* few, corymbose, yellow, the buds yellow ; *involucre* with black hairs. Damp woods, chiefly in Scotland and Northern England.—Fl. July to September. Perennial.

PLATE XLIII.

Corn Feverfew

10. HIERACIUM (*Hawk-weed*)

1. *H. Pilosella* (Mouse-ear Hawk-weed).—*Stem* single-flowered, leafless, 2–10 inches high ; *leaves* radicle, small, oblong or lanceolate, entire, a few long hairs above, hoary beneath with stellate down ; *flower-heads* borne singly, bright lemon colour, often reddish on the under side. Well distinguished from all other British plants of the Order by its creeping scions, by its hairy undivided leaves, which are hoary underneath, and by its bright lemon-coloured flowers. Banks and dry pastures ; common.—Fl. May to July. Perennial.

2. *H. murorum* (Wall Hawk-weed).—A very variable plant, 1–2 feet high ; the *stem* bears usually one, sometimes more, *leaves ;* is branched above, and bears usually 3 or 4, sometimes more, yellow *flower-heads ;* the *root-leaves* are stalked, hairy, ovate or oblong, sometimes toothed, very variable. Walls and rocks ; common.—Fl. July, August. Perennial.

3. *H. sylvaticum* (Wood Hawk-weed).—*Stem* many flowered, with a few leaves ; *leaves* narrow, egg-shaped, toothed, with the teeth pointing upwards ; *involucre* hoary with down. A very variable plant, both in size and habit. The leaves are sometimes very slightly toothed, at other times deeply so, and often spotted with purple ; the flowers are large and yellow. There are many varieties intermediate between *H. sylvaticum* and *H. murorum*. Woods and banks ; common.—Fl. August, September. Perennial.

4. *H. Sabaudum* (Shrubby Hawk-weed).—*Stem* rigid, many-flowered, leafy ; lower *leaves* tapering into a short stalk ; upper sessile, rounded at the base. As variable a plant as the last. Woods and banks ; frequent.—Fl. August, September. Perennial.

5. *H. umbellatum* (Narrow-leaved Hawk-weed).—*Stem* rigid many flowered, leafy ; *leaves* narrow, slightly toothed ; *flowers* in a terminal corymb ; scales of the *involucre* reflexed at the point. A tall plant, 2–3 feet high, with a remarkably erect growth, unbranched, and terminating in an almost umbellate tuft of large, yellow flowers. Woods ; not unfrequent.—Fl. August, September. Perennial.

6. *H. aurantiacum* (Orange Hawk-weed).—This is a garden escape, and grows about a foot high, bearing dense corymbs of deep orange flower-heads, with a fragrance not unlike that of the garden Heliotrope.

This is an exceedingly difficult genus ; even the six species here given, though comparatively distinct, are most variable. Over a hundred have been classified as distinct species, but it is a moot point whether many of these should not be considered mere varieties. In any case it is not thought necessary to give even the names here.

11. LEONTODON (*Dandelion*)

1. *L. Taraxacum* (Common Dandelion).—Dandelion, (from the French *Dent-de-lion*, lion's tooth) is the popular name of many of the larger yellow flowers belonging to this Sub-order. The true Dandelion may, however, be readily known by the following characters. The *leaves* all spring from the root, and are deeply cut, with the sharp lobes pointing backwards ; the *flower-stalks* are hollow, smooth, and leafless, and bear a single flower ; the *outer* scales of the *involucre* are reflexed ; the *pappus* is stalked and white ; the *heads* when in fruit are of a globular form ; and the *receptacle*, after the fruit has been blown away, is convex and dotted. The dandelion has valuable medicinal properties, and is sometimes used as a salad.—Fl. nearly all the year round.   Perennial.

12. LAPSANA (*Nipple-wort*)

1. *L. communis* (Common Nipple-wort). —*Leaves* stalked, toothed, heart-shaped at the base ; *stem* branched ; *flowers* numerous. A leafy plant, 2–3 feet high, with numerous small yellow flowers ; the lower leaves often have several small lobes running along the opposite sides of the stalks. Hedges and waste ground ; common.—Fl. July, August. Annual.

13. CHICHORIUM (*Chicory*)

1. *C. Intybus* (Wild Chicory, or Succory).—Well distinguished by its tough, angled, hispid, alternately-branched *stems*, clasping *leaves*, and large blue sessile *flower-heads*, of which each floret is 5-toothed. Not uncommon on chalky

LAPSANA COMMUNIS
(*Common Nipple-wort*)

soils.—Fl. July to October. Perennial.

II. CYNAROCEPHALÆ.—*Thistle Group*

14. ARCTIUM (*Bur-dock*)

1. *A. Lappa* (Common Bur-dock).—A large stout herbaceous plant, 3–5 feet high, with very large handsome lower *leaves*, and a terminal panicle of large heads of purplish *florets*, enclosed in a globular *involucre* of hooked scales, which, becoming attached to the coats of passing animals, the seeds are conveyed to a distance. The scales are often interwoven with a white cottony down.   Some

PLATE XLIV.

Corn Marigold
Butter-bur

Corn Tansy
Colt's-foot

artists love to introduce this plant into the foregrounds of their pictures, thereby obtaining a somewhat obvious effect of picturesqueness. Waste places ; common.—Fl. July, August. Biennial.

Some other varieties have been described, of which the most distinct are *A. majus*, *A. minus*, and *A. tomentosum*. Their characteristics, however, are not very definite.

ARCTIUM LAPPA
(*Common Bur-dock*)

SERRATULA TINCTORIA
(*Common Saw-wort*)

15. SERRATULA (*Saw-wort*)

1. *S. tinctoria* (Common Saw-wort).—The only British species. A slender plant, 1–2 feet high, with a stiff, erect, angular *stem*, slightly branched above, deeply cut and serrated *leaves ;* and small terminal heads of purple *flowers* in a corymb ; the outer scales of the *involucre* are smooth and close pressed, the inner tinged with purple. Pastures ; frequent.—Fl. August. Perennial.

16. SAUSSUREA

1. *S. Alpina* (Alpine Saussurea).—The only British species. The stem is from 8–12 inches high ; the *leaves* cottony beneath ; *flower-heads* of light purple florets, in a dense terminal corymb, fragrant. Mountains in the north ; rare.—Fl. August. Perennial.

17. CARDUUS (*Thistle*)

1. *C. nutans* (Musk Thistle).—*Heads* solitary, drooping ; scales of the *involucre* tapering to a rigid point, cottony, the outer ones

bent back ; *stem* winged by the thorny leaves.   A very handsome plant, about 2 feet high, with a furrowed cottony stem, deeply lobed thorny leaves, which are downy on the veins beneath, and large deep purple flowers, to which the radiated involucre is a very ornamental appendage.   This is sometimes called the Scotch Thistle, but incorrectly.   The upper part of the flower-stalk is nearly bare of leaves, and the flower itself has a powerful odour. Waste places ;   common.—Fl. June to August.   Biennial.

2. *C. acanthoides* (Welted Thistle).—*Heads* clustered, round ; scales of the *involucre* lined, thorny, spreading, or erect ;   *stem* winged by the thorny leaves.   A branched, very thorny plant, 3–4 feet high, with small heads, of deep purple or sometimes white, *flowers*.   Waste places ;   common.—Fl. June, July.   Annual.

3. *C. tenuiflorus* (Slender-flowered Thistle).—*Heads* clustered, cylindrical ;   scales of the *involucre* thorny. erect ;   *stem* winged by the thorny leaves, which are cottony beneath.   Well distinguished by the small heads of pink *flowers*, and the very long erect *scales* of the involucre.   The stems are 2–4 feet high, and bear all the flowers at the summit.   Waste places, especially near the sea.— Fl. June to August.   Biennial.

4. *C. Marianus* (Milk Thistle) is a stouter plant than either of the preceding, and is distinguished at once by the white veins on its leaves, from which it derives its popular name.   It grows in waste places, is not indigenous, neither is it common.—Fl. June, July.   Biennial.

18. CNICUS (*Plume-thistle*)

1. *C. lanceolatus* (Spear Plume-thistle).—*Heads* mostly solitary, sometimes 2 or 3 together, stalked, egg-shaped ;   *scales* of the *involucre* thorny, spreading, woolly ;   *stem* winged by the thorny *leaves*, the lobes of which are 2-cleft.   This is more like the Cotton - thistle (*Onopordium*) than any other species of this genus.   It grows 3–5 feet high ;   the *leaves* are downy beneath, and the heads of flowers, though not so large as those of the *Cotton-thistle*, have the same dull purple hue.   Waste places and hedges ;   common.—Fl. July to September.   Biennial.

2. *C. palustris* (Marsh Plume-thistle).— *Heads* clustered, egg-shaped ;   *scales* of the involucre closely pressed, pointed ; *stem* winged by the thorny leaves.   The tallest of the British Thistles, 4–10 feet high, consisting of a single, stout, hollow *stem*, which is branched near the summit,

CNICUS PALUSTRIS
(*Marsh Plum-thistle*)

PLATE XLV.

Common Ragwort   Marsh Ragwort

PLATE XLVI.

Musk Thistle

and bears numerous clusters of rather small, deep purple (sometimes white) *flowers*. The *leaves* are thickly armed with short thorns, which are often of a brownish hue. Moist meadows and borders of fields ; very common.—Fl. July, August. Biennial

3. *C. arvensis* (Creeping Plume-thistle). — *Heads of flowers* numerous, stalked ; the *scales* of the *involucre* closely pressed, pointed, but scarcely thorny ; *stem* not winged ; *root* creeping. A handsome weed, about 2 feet high ; the flowers, which grow in a corymbose manner, are of a light purple colour, and smell like those of the *Musk Thistle*. The staminate and pistillate flower-heads grow on separate plants, the former being roundish, and the latter egg-shaped. Borders of fields ; very common.—Fl. July. Perennial.

4. *C. pratensis* (Meadow Plume-thistle).—*Heads* of flowers mostly solitary ; *stem-leaves* few, soft, wavy. A small plant, 12–18 inches high, with a cottony *stem*, bearing a few *leaves*, and rarely more than one small purple *flower*. Moist meadows ; not general.— Fl. July. Perennial.

5. *C. acaulis* (Dwarf Plume-thistle).—*Heads* of flowers solitary, and stemless or nearly so. A low plant, consisting of a few thorny *leaves*, and a single, almost stemless, purple *flower*, by which cha-racter it is readily distinguished from all the rest of the Thistle Tribe. Dry gravelly or chalky pastures ; not general, but in some places very abundant, and a pernicious weed.—Fl. July, August. Perennial.

Less common species of *Cnicus* are *C. eriphorus* (Woolly-headed Plume-Thistle), distinguished by the thick white wool which clothes the *scales* of the very large *flowers ; C. tuberosus* (Tuberous Plume-Thistle), which grows only in Wiltshire, an erect single-stemmed plant, with a single large, purple *flower ; C. heterophyllus* (Melan-choly Plume-Thistle), a mountain plant, with an erect, cottony *stem*, and a single, hand-some, purple *flower*.

19. ONOPORDIUM (*Cotton-thistle*)

1. *O. Acanthium* (Scotch Thistle).—The *involucre* is globose, with the *scales* spreading in all directions ; the *stem* is winged, with rough cottony *leaves*, and attains a height of 4–6 feet ; the *flowers* are large, of a dull purple hue, and mostly solitary, or but slightly clus-tered at the ends of the branches. This species is the true Scotch Thistle, the national emblem. Waste ground and roadsides chiefly in the south.—Fl. July, August. Biennial.

ONOPORDIUM ACANTHIUM
(*Scotch Thistle*)

20. CARLINA (*Carline-thistle*)

1. *C. vulgaris* (Common Carline-thistle). — The only British species, readily distinguished from every other British Thistle by the long inner *scales* of the *involucre*, which are straw-coloured and glossy, and spread in a radiate manner so as to resemble petals. In dry weather they lie flat, but when the atmosphere is moist, they rise and form, as it were, a pent-house over the florets. Their texture is like that of the garden Everlasting Flowers, hence they scarcely alter their appearance when dead, and as the whole plant is remarkably durable, they often retain their form and position till the succeeding spring. On the Continent the large white flower of one species, *C. acaulis*, is often nailed upon cottage doors by way of a hygrometer, as it closes before rain. Dry heaths.—Fl. June to September. Biennial.

21. CENTAUREA (*Knapweed, Blue-bottle*)

1. *C. nigra* (Black Knap-weed).—The outer *scales* of the *involucre* egg-shaped, fringed with spreading *bristles ;* lower *leaves* toothed, often with a few small lobes at the base, upper narrow, tapering ; *flowers* with or without a ray ; *pappus* very short, tufted. A tough-stemmed plant, 1–2 feet high, with heads of dull purple *flowers*, which are remarkable for the brown, or almost black, hue of the scales of the involucre. This plant is popularly known by the name of *Hard-head*. Meadows ; common.—Fl. June to August. Perennial.

2. *C. scabiosa* (Greater Centaurea, Greater Knap-weed). Outer *scales* of the *involucre* egg-shaped, somewhat downy, fringed ; *leaves* pinnatifid, roughish, segments tapering to a point. Meadows and cornfields; common. Larger and stouter than the last, from which it is distinguished by the brighter hue of its handsome radiate *flowers*, and the light-coloured *fringe* on the scales of the involucre.—Fl. July, August. Perennial.

3. *C. cyanus* (Corn Blue-bottle).— *Outer scales* of the involucre deeply toothed ; *leaves* very narrow, slightly toothed, cottony. One of the prettiest of flowers, and well meriting the distinctive name, often given to it, of *Corn-flower*. The flowers are bright blue, with dark anthers. The juice of the flowers, expressed and mixed with cold alum-water, may be used in water-colour drawing. Rose-coloured, white, and dark purple varieties are commonly

C. CYANUS AND C. CALCITRAPA
(*Corn Blue-bottle and Common Star-Thistle*)

PLATE XLVII.

Spear Thistle

to be met with in gardens, and are occasionally to be found as escapes.—Fl. July, August ; and, in turnip fields, again in October and November. Annual or Biennial.

4. *C. aspera* (Jersey Centaurea).—*Stems* much branched and prostrate ; *leaves* narrow ; *flower-heads* solitary ; the florets purple, and each of the outer bracts of the involucre with 3–5 *prickles.* Channel Islands.—Biennial.

5. *C. calcitrapa* (Common Star-Thistle).—*Scales* of the *involucre* ending each in a long stiff thorn. Well marked by its purplish *flowers*, which are armed below with spreading thorns, and resemble in figure the cruel iron instrument, named a *caltrops*, which was used in war to lame horses, being thrown on the ground when it was expected that cavalry would pass. The instrument is so constructed that, in whatever position it lies, one point sticks upwards. Gravelly and sandy places in the south of England ; rare.—Fl. July, August. Annual.

6. *C. solstitialis* (Yellow Star-Thistle).—*Stems* 1–2 feet high, winged ; *leaves* hoary ; *flower-heads* solitary, terminal, furnished with spines ; *florets* yellow. Occasionally in cornfields, etc.— Fl. July, September. Annual.

III. Tubifloræ.—*Tansy Group*

22. Bidens (*Bur-Marigold*)

1. *B. cernua* (Nodding Bur-Marigold).—*Heads* of *flowers* drooping ; *leaves* serrated, undivided ; *bristles* of the fruit 3–4. A somewhat succulent plant, 1–2 feet high, with narrow, serrated, smooth *leaves*, and button-like, drooping heads of brownish yellow *flowers*, at the base of which are several leafy *bracts.* The *fruit* is oblong, and terminates in several stiff bristles, each of which is thickly set with minute points, which are turned back like the barbs of an arrow, so as to take a firm hold on the coat of any animal which comes in contact with them. Watery places ; frequent.—Fl. July to September. Annual.

2. *B. tripartita* (Trifid Bur - Marigold).— *Heads* of *flowers* nearly erect ; *leaves* 3-parted. Distinguished from the last by its somewhat smaller heads of *flowers*, which frequently have ray florets (*B. cernua* being usually without), 3-parted *leaves*, and by having 3–5 *bristles* on the fruit. Watery places ; common.—Fl. July to September. Annual.

Bidens Tripartita
(*Trifid Bur-marigold*)

23. EUPATORIUM (*Hemp-agrimony*)

1. *E. cannabinum* (Common Hemp-agrimony).—The only British species. A tall downy plant, 3–6 feet high, with a reddish *stem ; leaves* palmately divided into 3–5 lanceolate serrate leaflets, and terminal corymbs of small crowded heads of dull lilac *flowers,* which are remarkable for their very long, deeply cloven *styles.* Moist shady places ; common.—Fl. July, August. Perennial.

24. CHRYSOCOMA (*Goldylocks*)

1. *C. Linosyris* (Flax-leaved Goldylocks).—A herbaceous plant, 12–18 inches high, with erect, simple *stems,* which are thickly set with smooth, linear *leaves,* and bear a few heads of yellow *flowers* at the extremity. Limestone cliffs ; very rare.—Fl. August, September. Perennial.

25. DIOTIS (*Cotton-weed*)

1. *D. maritima* (Seaside Cotton-weed).—The only species. The *roots* run deeply into the sand ; the *stems,* which are about a foot high, are thickly set with oblong, blunt *leaves,* which, as well as the rest of the plant, are covered with thick white cotton, and almost hide the small terminal heads of yellow *flowers.* Sandy sea-shores ; rare.—Fl. August, September. Perennial.

26. TANACETUM (*Tansy*)

1. *T. vulgare* (Common Tansy).—*Stems* 2–3 feet high, angular. Well distinguished by its deeply twice-pinnate, cut *leaves* and terminal corymbs of bright yellow, button-like *flowers.* The whole plant is bitter and aromatic, and is not only used in medicine, but forms the principal ingredient in the nauseous dish called *Tansy pudding.* Hedges and waste ground; common.—Fl. August. Perennial.

27. ARTEMISIA (*Wormwood, Mugwort*)

1. *A. absinthium* (Common Wormwood).—*Leaves* with bluntish segments, twice pinnatifid, silky on both sides ; *heads* hemispherical, drooping. A bushy plant, with silky stems and leaves, and panicles of numerous small heads of dull yellow flowers. The whole plant is bitter and aromatic, and is much used in rural districts, where it abounds, as a tonic. Waste ground ; common.—Fl. July to September. Perennial.

ARTEMISIA ABSINTHIUM
(*Common Wormwood*)

PLATE XLVIII.

Creeping Thistle

PLATE XLIX.

Common Carline   Meadow Thistle

2. *A. vulgaris* (Mug-wort).—*Leaves* pinnatifid, with acute segments ; white with down beneath ; *heads* oblong, reddish. Taller and more slender than the last ; well distinguished by the leaves being green above and white below, and by the absence of aromatic odour. Hedges and waste places ; common. A tea made from this plant is used in country districts as a remedy for rheumatism. —Fl. July to September. Perennial.

3. *A. maritima* (Sea Wormwood).—*Leaves* twice pinnatifid, downy on both sides; *heads* in racemes, oblong. Somewhat resembling *A. absinthium*, but smaller, and well distinguished by the above characters. The clusters of reddish flower-heads are sometimes drooping, sometimes erect. Salt marshes ; frequent.— Fl. July to September. Perennial.

4. *A. campestris* (Field Wormwood).—A rare species, growing on sandy heaths in Norfolk and Suffolk. In this species the segments of the *leaves* are narrow, terminating in points ; and the *stems*, until flowering, are prostrate.

28. ANTENNARIA (*Everlasting*)

1. *A. dioica* (Mountain Cudweed).—The only British species. A pretty little plant, 3-6 inches high, with oblong *leaves*, which are broadest towards the end, green above, cottony below ; the *heads of flowers* grow 4-6 together, and are rendered conspicuous by the white or rose-coloured *involucre*, which is of the texture commonly termed *everlasting*. Mountain heaths ; frequent.—Fl. July, August. Perennial.

ANTENNARIA DIOICA
(*Mountain Cudweed*)

2. *A. margaritacea* (the White Everlasting of gardens) is 2-5 feet high, with cottony narrow *leaves*, and flat corymbs of small yellowish *flower-heads* with white *involucres*. It is not indigenous, but is found naturalized in South Wales, the Channel Isles, and Scotland.—Fl. July, August. Perennial.

29. GNAPHALIUM (*Cudweed*)

1. *G. uliginosum* (Marsh Cudweed). — *Stems* much branched, woolly ; *leaves* very narrow, downy, over-topping the clustered terminal heads. A small plant, 3-6 inches high, rendered conspicuous by its tufted white stems and leaves, and by the glossy, yellowish brown scales of its small clustered flowers. Wet sandy places, especially where water has stood during winter ; common. —Fl. August, September. Annual.

2. *G. sylvaticum* (Wood Cudweed).—A cottony plant, with a simple *stem*, 6–12 inches high; narrow *leaves ;* and bearing its heads of yellow *florets* in a leafy spike. Woods and gravelly pastures; common.—Fl. July to September. Perennial.

3. *G. supinum* (Dwarf Cudweed).—2–3 inches high, with tufted *leaves*, and flowering *stems* almost bare of leaves. Confined to the summits of Highland mountains.—Fl. July, August. Perennial.

4. *G. Luteo album* (Jersey Cudweed).—About 6 or 8 inches high, cottony; *leaves* narrow; *flower-heads* in dense corymbs, with the involucral *bracts* yellowish, and reddish *florets*. Channel Isles and some of the eastern counties of England.—Fl. July, August. Annual.

Gnaphalium leontopodium is the famous " Edelweiss " of the Swiss Alps.

30. FILAGO

1. *F. Germanica* (Common Filago). — *Stem* cottony, erect, terminating in a globular assemblage of *heads*, from the base of which rise two or more *flower-stalks*, which are proliferous in like manner. A singular little plant, 6–8 inches high, well distinguished by the above character. From this curious mode of growth the plant was called by the old botanists *Herba impia*. (the undutiful herb), as if the young shoots were guilty of disrespect by overtopping the parent. Dry gravelly places; common.—Fl. June, July. Annual.

FILAGO GERMANICA   2. *F. minima* (Least Filago).—*Stem* erect, re-
   (*Common Filago*)   peatedly forked; *leaves* very narrow, cottony,
                        pressed to the stem; *heads* conical, in lateral
and terminal clusters, shorter than the leaves. Yet smaller than the last, growing 4–6 inches high, with cottony stem and leaves, and brownish yellow leaves. Dry gravelly places; common.— Fl. July, August. Annual.

3. *F. Gallica* (Narrow-leaved Filago).—Like the last, but more branched; *leaves* narrow, long, and pointed; those surrounding the small flower-heads longer than the involucres. Local, chiefly Channel Isles and South-eastern England.—Fl. July to September.

Two other forms are described : *F. apicaluta*, taller than *F. Germanica*, with blunt *leaves*, purple *bracts*, and smelling of Tansy ; and F. *spathulata*, short; with spathulate *leaves* and yellow-tipped *bracts*. Both are annuals, growing in sandy places in the south-east of England.

PLATE L.

Greater Centaurea   Knapweed

31. Petasites (*Butter-bur*)

1. *P. vulgaris* (Common Butter-bur).—The only British species. The largest, and where it abounds, the most pernicious of all the weeds which this country produces. The *flowers*, which are of a dull lilac colour, and are borne in a raceme on a thick *stem* 6–12 inches high, appear early in the spring, and are succeeded by downy, kidney-shaped *leaves*, 1–5 feet in diameter, which, by shading the ground, check the growth of all other plants. " The early blossoming of this rank weed induces the Swedish farmers to plant it near their bee-hives. Thus we see in our gardens the bee assembled on its affinities. *P. alba* and *P. fragrans*, at a season when scarcely any other flowers are expanded" (Hooker and Arnott). These two last species are common in shrubberies, almost hiding the ground with their broad leaves, thriving beneath the shade of trees and shrubs, but overpowering all herbaceous plants, and eventually, it is said, even the shrubs themselves. Damp meadows, etc.; common.—Fl. April, May. Perennial.

IV. Radiatæ.—*Daisy Group*

32. Tussilago (*Colt's-foot*)

1. *T. Farfara* (Colt's-foot).—The only species. The *flower-stalks*, which spring directly from the roots, are covered with scale-like *bracts*, and bear each a single yellow *flower-head*, with numerous yellow rays; the *leaves*, which do not appear until the flowers have withered, are roundish, heart-shaped, and angular, with dark teeth, and are covered with cottony down beneath, cobwebby above. The *heads of flowers* droop before expansion, and the *stalks* after flowering lengthen considerably. The goldfinch frequently lines its nest with the pappus of this plant. The cotton of the leaves was formerly used as tinder, and the leaves themselves are rolled into cigars and smoked as a remedy for asthma. A pernicious weed, abounding in clayey fields.—Fl. March, April. Perennial.

33. Erigeron (*Flea-bane*)

1. *E. acris* (Blue Flea-bane).—*Branches* erect, rough, alternate, bearing single heads; *leaves* narrow, entire, blunt. A much branched plant, 6–18 inches high, with small heads of inconspicuous *flowers*, of which the inner florets are yellowish, the outer dull blue. The pappus is very long and tawny. Dry places and walls; not common.—Fl. August. Biennial.

2. *E. Alpinus* (Alpine Flea-bane).—*Leaves* mostly radicle, hairy, lanceolate; *stems* 2–8 inches high, hairy, each bearing a solitary *flower-head* about half an inch in diameter, the ray florets of which

are light purple. Found only on some of the mountains of the
eastern Highlands ; rare.—Fl. July, August. Perennial.

3. *E. Canadensis* (Canadian Flea-bane).—An erect plant, somewhat resembling Groundsel ; 1–2 feet high, with a few spreading
hairs ; lanceolate *leaves* ; and dingy yellow *flowers* with whitish
ray florets, borne in a narrow panicle. Grows as a weed in waste
places ; local.—Fl. August, September. Annual.

34. ASTER (*Star-wort*)

1. *A. Tripolium* (Sea Star-wort).—A stout succulent plant,
2–3 feet high, with long, smooth, fleshy *leaves*, and corymbs of large
handsome *flowers*, the inner *florets* of which are yellow, the outer
purple. In salt marshes the whole plant is often covered with
mud, which gives it an unsightly appearance, but when growing
on sea-cliffs it is a highly ornamental plant. Salt marshes ; frequent.—Fl. August, September. Perennial.

35. SOLIDAGO (*Golden-rod*)

1. *S. Virgaurea* (Golden-rod).—The only British species. An
erect, scarcely branched plant, 2–3 feet high, with roughish, angular
stems, simple, serrated *leaves*, which gradually become narrower
the higher they are on the stem ; and conspicuous, terminal clusters
of small bright yellow *flowers*. Dry woods ; common.—Fl. July
to September. Perennial.

On mountainous heaths a variety (*Cambrica*) occurs, with very
short *stems*, and large *leaves* and *flowers*.

SENECIO VULGARIS
(*Common Groundsel*)

36. SENECIO (*Groundsel, Rag-wort*)

1. *S. vulgaris* (Common Groundsel). — *Flowers* without rays, in
crowded clusters ; *leaves* half embracing the *stem*, deeply lobed and
toothed. A common weed in cultivated ground ; a favourite food of
many small birds.—Fl. all the year
round. Annual.

2. *S. sylvaticus* (Mountain Groundsel).—Distinguished from the last
by its larger size—1–2 feet high ;
and its conical, rather than cylindrical, heads of dull yellow *flowers*,
with a few rays which are rolled
back and inconspicuous, or often
wanting ; the *leaves* are pinnatifid,
with narrow lobes, toothed ; the

PLATE LI.

Star-thistle   Mouse-ear Hawkweed

PLATE LII.

Yellow Goat's-beard

stems are branched. Gravelly places; common.—Fl. July to September. Annual.

3. *S. viscosus* (Viscid Groundsel).—Near *S. sylvaticus* in habit, but clothed with viscid *down ;* the *flower-heads* are less numerous, with the outer *bracts* of the *involucre* about half as long as the inner. Similar situations, but more local than *S. sylvaticus.*—Fl. July to September. Annual.

4. *S. Jacobœa* (Common Rag-wort).—*Stem* erect, 2–3 feet high ; *flower-heads* large, bright yellow, with spreading rays, corymbose ; *leaves* pinnatifid, with smaller lobes at the base. Meadows and wet places ; common.—Fl. July to September. Perennial.

5. *S. aquaticus* (Marsh Rag-wort).—Much resembling the last, but more spreading ; the *flower-heads* larger, in a looser corymb ; *lower leaves* undivided, toothed ; *upper* with a few oblong lobes near the base. Wet places ; common.—Fl. July to September. Perennial.

6. *S. tenuifolius* (Hoary Rag-wort).—*Flowers* with spreading rays ; *leaves* pinnatifid, with very narrow segments, downy beneath. Much like *S. Jacobœa*, but distinguished by its sending up numerous cottony *stems* from the same root, and by its regularly divided *leaves*, the segments of which are slightly rolled back at the edges. Dry banks in a limestone or chalky soil ; not common.—Fl. July, August. Perennial.

7. *S. palustris* (Marsh Flea-wort).—Shaggy ; a stout plant, 2–3 feet high, with a hollow, much branched *stem ;* and numerous lanceolate, sessile *leaves*, which are wavy at the edges and toothed, *flowers* yellow, in a corymb. Found only in the Fen districts of Eastern England ; rare.—Fl. June, July. Perennial.

8. *S. campestris* (Field Flea-wort).—A small plant, 6–8 inches high, shaggy ; *stem* unbranched ; *root-leaves* oblong, nearly entire ; *stem-leaves* narrow, tapering ; *flower-heads* of a few yellow flowers in a terminal corymb, which is almost an umbel. Chalky downs ; rare.—Fl. May, June. Perennial.

9. *S. squalidus* (Inelegant Rag-wort).—Grows about a foot high, with large bright yellow *flowers ;* the *leaves* are glabrous, somewhat thick, and are deeply pinnatifid. The naming is inapt, for it is quite the prettiest British species. Old walls about Oxford, and Bideford, Devon. Not indigenous.—Fl. June to October. Annual or biennial.

10. *S. paludosus* (Great Fen Rag-wort).—A large aquatic plant, 2–6 feet high ; *stem* hollow, unbranched ; *leaves* lanceolate, toothed, cottony beneath ; *flower-heads* large, many-rayed, in a loose corymb Confined to the Fen districts of Eastern England ; rare.—Fl. May to July. Perennial.

11. *S. saracenicus* (Broad-leaved Rag-wort).—Somewhat resembling the last, but not so tall ; glabrous ; *leaves* lanceolate, toothed ; *flower-heads* smaller, more numerous, and borne in a more compact corymb than in the last, and they also have fewer rays. Not indigenous ; local.—Fl. July, August. Perennial.

37. DORONICUM (*Leopard's-bane*)

1. *D. Pardalianches* (Great Leopard's-bane).—*Stem* 2-3 feet high, erect, solitary, hollow, hairy ; *leaves* soft ; *lower leaves* heart-shaped, toothed, on long stalks, *upper* with two ears at the base embracing the stem ; *heads of flowers* yellow, the earlier ones over-topped by the later. Damp hilly woods ; rare, not a native.—Fl. May to July. Perennial.

2. *D. plantagineum* (Plantain-leaved Leopard's-bane).—Differs from the last in having egg-shaped *leaves* and solitary *heads of flowers*. It is rare, and is not indigenous.

38. INULA (*Elecampane, Ploughman's Spikenard*)

1. *I. Helenium* (Elecampane).— *Leaves* oblong or egg-shaped, wrinkled, downy beneath, toothed, upper ones embracing the stem ; *scales* of the *involucre* egg-shaped, downy. A stout plant, 3-5 feet high, with very large leaves and a few terminal very large heads of bright yellow flowers. The root contains a white starchy powder, named Inuline, a volatile oil, a soft acrid resin, and a bitter extract ; it is used in diseases of the chest and lungs, and furnishes the Vin d'Aulnée of the French. Moist pastures ; not common.—Fl. July, August. Perennial.

INULA HELENIUM (*Elecampane*)

2. *I. Conyza* (Ploughman's Spikenard). — *Leaves* narrow, egg-shaped, downy, toothed ; *heads of flowers* panicled ; *scales* of the *involucre* rolled back. Distinguished by its dull, green foliage, numerous heads of dingy yellow flowers, the rays of which are inconspicuous, and by the leaf-like scales of the involucre, which are rolled back. Hedges, principally on a limestone or chalky soil ; uncommon.—Fl. July to September. Perennial.

PLATE LIII.

Dandelion   Wall Lettuce

3. *I. Crithmoides* (Golden Samphire).—*Leaves* very narrow, fleshy, smooth, blunt, or 3-pointed. Well distinguished from every other British plant by its fleshy leaves and large yellow flowers, which grow singly at the extremity of the branches. Salt marshes and sea cliffs, rare.—Fl. July, August. Perennial.

4. *I. salicina.*—Erect, about 18 inches high, almost glabrous; *leaves* lanceolate, toothed, clasping the stem; *flower-heads* large, usually solitary. Found only by Lough Derg, Galway.

39. PULICARIA (*Flea-bane*).

1. *P. dysenterica* (Common Flea-bane).—*Stem* woolly; *leaves* oblong, heart- or arrow-shaped at the base, embracing the stem; *scales* of the *involucre* bristle-shaped. From -2 feet high, growing in masses, and well marked by its soft hairy foliage and large flat heads of bright yellow flowers, those of the ray being very numerous, narrow, and longer than the disk. Watery places; common, rare in Scotland. —Fl. August. Perennial.

PULICARIA
DYSENTERICA
(*Common Flea-bane*)

2. *P. vulgaris* (Small Flea-bane).—*Stem* hairy; *leaves* narrow, tapering, hairy. Resembling the last, but not above half the size, nor by any means so hoary. Sandy heaths, where water has stood; not common. Not found in Scotland or Ireland.— Fl. September. Annual.

40. BELLIS (*Daisy*)

1. *B. perennis* (Common Daisy).—The only British species, too well known and admired to need any description or comment. — Fl. nearly all the year round. Perennial.

BELLIS PERENNIS
(*Common Daisy*)

41. CHRYSANTHEMUM (*Ox-eye*)

1. *C. Leucanthemum* (White Ox-eye).— *Florets* of the ray white; *lower leaves* stalked, *upper* sessile, pinnatifid at the base. Almost as well known as the common daisy. A great favourite with children, who string the flowers on a stout grass-straw, or bit of wire, and make a very

CHRYSANTHEMUM LEUCAN-
THEMUM (*White Ox-eye*) and
CHRYSANTHEMUM SEGETUM
(*Yellow Ox-eye*)

fair imitation of the feather formerly worn by soldiers. It is said to be destructive to fleas. Meadows; abundant.—Fl. June, July. Perennial.

2. *C. segetum* (Yellow Ox-eye, Corn Marigold).—*Florets* of the ray yellow; *leaves* clasping the stem, oblong, acute, toothed, glabrous, glaucous. The whole plant is remarkably smooth and glaucous; the *flowers* are large, of a brilliant yellow, and contrast beautifully with Poppies and Bluebottles. Cornfields; abundant, but local.—Fl. June, July; and, in summer, ploughed fields; again in October and November. Annual.

42. MATRICARIA (*Wild Chamomile, Feverfew*)

1. *M. Parthenium* (Common Feverfew).—1–2 feet high. *Leaves* stalked, pinnate; *leaflets* pinnatifid and deeply cut; *stem* erect; *flowers* corymbose. Well marked by its repeatedly cut, curled, delicate green leaves and its numerous small heads of flowers, of which the ray florets are white. The leaves are conspicuous in mid winter, and the whole plant has a powerful and not unpleasant odour, which is said to be particularly offensive to bees. The English name is a corruption of *Febrifuge*, from its tonic properties. Hedges and waste ground; common.—Fl. July, August. Perennial.

2. *M. inodora* (Corn Feverfew, Scentless May-weed).—*Leaves* sessile, repeatedly cut into numerous hair-like segments; *stem* branched, spreading, 12–18 inches high; *flowers* solitary. Of a very different habit from the last, but resembling it in the colour of the flowers, which are, however, much larger, and remarkable for their very convex disk. Cornfields; common.—Fl. July to October. Annual.

A seaside form, perennial, with fleshy leaves, is by some considered a species, under the name *M. maritima* (Sea Feverfew).

3. *M. Chamomilla* (Wild Chamomile).—*Flower-heads* about ½ inch across; *disk* yellow; *ray florets* white. Often confused with *M. inodora* and *Anthemis Cotula*, but may be distinguished by the scales of the involucre being not chaffy at the margin, and by the receptacle of the florets being hollow. Not uncommon in cornfields.—Fl. June to August. Annual.

PLATE LIV.

Chicory   Corn Sow Thistle

43. ANTHEMIS (*Chamomile*)

1. *A. nobilis* (Common Chamomile).—
Stems prostrate; *leaves* repeatedly cut into
hair-like segments, slightly downy. Well
distinguished by its solitary heads of flowers,
which droop before expansion, and by its
pleasant aromatic smell, which resembles
that of fresh apples, whence it derived its
name of Chamomile, signifying in Greek
ground-apple. The whole plant is very
bitter, and is valuable in medicine for its
tonic properties. Heaths; abundant. —
Fl. August. Perennial.

2. *A. Cotula* (Stinking Chamomile).—*Stem*
erect, branched; *leaves* repeatedly cut into
hair-like segments, smooth and with glandular
dots. Distinguished from the last by its
strong disagreeable odour and upright stems.
The heads of flowers are solitary, coloured
as in the last, but larger. The juice is very
acrid, and is said to blister the hands of
those who gather it.—Waste places; common.—Fl. July, August. Annual.

ANTHEMIS NOBILIS
(*Common Chamomile*)

Less common species of Chamomile are :—

A. maritima, or more correctly *A. Anglica* (Sea Chamomile),
which has repeatedly-cut fleshy *leaves*, which are somewhat hairy.
On the sea-coast; very rare.

A. arvensis (Corn Chamomile), the deeply-cut *leaves* of which are
white with down.

These two have *white flowers* with a *yellow disk*.

And *A. tinctoria* (Ox-eye Chamomile), which has downy, much
divided leaves, and large bright yellow *flowers*, resembling those of
Chrysanthemum segetum.

44. ACHILLEA (*Yarrow*)

1. *A. millefolium* (Common Yellow Milfoil). — *Leaves* twice
pinnatifid, woolly, or slightly hairy; *leaflets* cut into hair-like
segments; *flowers* in dense terminal corymbs. A common roadside plant, with very tough, angular stems, about a foot high, and
corymbs of small, white, pink, or purplish flowers, which to an
unpractised eye might be supposed to belong to an umbelliferous
plant. It has a strong and slightly aromatic odour, and is said to
have the property of healing wounds. Waste ground; frequent.—
Fl. June to September. Perennial.

2. A. Ptarmica (Sneeze-wort).—*Leaves* un-divided, very narrow, and tapering to a sharp point, serrated. Somewhat taller and slenderer than the last, from which it may be at once distinguished by its undivided leaves and larger heads of *flowers*, of which both the *disc* and *ray* are white. The pounded leaves have been used as snuff, hence its name. Meadows and waste ground; not uncommon.—Fl. July, August. Perennial.

NATURAL ORDER XLV

CAMPANULACEÆ.—THE BELL-FLOWER TRIBE

ACHILLEA PTARMICA
(*Sneeze-wort*)

Calyx growing from the ovary, 5-lobed, re-maining till the fruit ripens; *corolla* rising from the mouth of the calyx, 5-lobed, regular or irregular, withering on the fruit; *stamens* equalling in number the lobes of the corolla, and alternate with them; *anthers* distinct, except in *Jasione* and *Phyteuma*, when they are united; *ovary* inferior, of two, or more, many-seeded cells; *style* 1, covered with hairs; *stigma* simple or lobed; *fruit* dry, crowned by the withered calyx and corolla, splitting, or opening by valves at the side or top; *seeds* numerous, fixed to a central column. Herbaceous or slightly shrubby plants, with a milky, bitter juice, mostly alternate leaves without stipules, and showy blue or white flowers, inhabiting principally the temperate regions of the northern hemisphere. Many species are highly ornamental, but very few are valuable either as food or medicine. The roots of *Campanula Rapunculus*, under the name of Rampion or Ramps, were formerly cultivated in this country for the table, but are now scarcely known. *Lobelia inflata* (Indian Tobacco) of North America is used in small doses for Asthma, but in over doses is dangerously emetic and narcotic. *L. cardinalis* (Scarlet Cardinal), one of our most brilliantly coloured garden flowers, is also very acrid; and the rare British species, *L. urens* (Acrid Lobelia), derives its name from the blistering pro-perties of its juice. Some species contain a considerable quantity of caoutchouc.

1. CAMPANULA (Bell-flower).—*Corolla* bell-shaped (rarely wheel-shaped), with 5 broad and shallow lobes; *filaments* broad at the base; *stigma* 2 to 5 cleft; *capsule* 2 to 5-celled, opening the pores at the side, rarely near the top. (Name from the Latin, *campana*, a bell.)

2. PHYTEUMA (Rampion).—*Corolla* wheel-shaped, with 5 deep lobes; *filaments* broad at the base; *stigma* 2 to 3-cleft; *capsule*

PLATE LV.

Clustered Campanula
Nettle-leaved Campanula

Water Lobelia
Rampion

2 to 3-celled, bursting at the side. (Name from the Greek, *phyton*, a plant.)

3. JASIONE (Sheep's Scabious).—*Corolla* wheel-shaped, with 5 long narrow segments ; *anthers* united at the base ; *stigma* 2-cleft ; *capsule* 2-celled, opening at the top ; *flowers* in heads. (Name of uncertain origin.)

4. LOBELIA.—*Corolla* 2-lipped, the upper part split to the base of the tube. (Name from *Matthias Lobel*, a Flemish botanist.)

1. CAMPANULA (*Bell-flower*)

1. *C. rotundifolia* (Hair-bell).—Smooth ; *root-leaves* roundish kidney-shaped, notched, stalked, very soon withering ; *stem-leaves* very narrow, tapering ; *flowers* light blue or rarely white. The name Hair-bell is frequently, though not correctly, given to the Wild Hyacinth or Blue-Bell (*Scilla festalis*), a plant with a thick juicy flower-stalk ; but when applied to this *Campanula* is most appropriate, its stalks being exceedingly slender and wiry. The specific name, *rotundifolia* (round-leaved), is far from being descriptive of the leaves which accompany the flower, as they are long and narrow, but is peculiarly applicable to the root-leaves, as they appear in winter or early spring, at which season Linnæus is said to have first observed them on the steps of the university at Upsala. Heaths and dry meadows ; abundant.—Fl. July to September. Perennial.

2. *C. trachelium* (Nettled-leaved Bell-flower). — *Lower leaves* stalked, heart-shaped ; *upper* nearly sessile, tapering to a point, all strongly serrated and bristly ; *flowers* in axillary clusters of 2–3. A remarkably rough plant, 2–3 feet high, with leaves very like those of the nettle, and large, deep blue, bell-shaped flowers, the stalks of which are recurved when in fruit. Woods and hedges ; not unfrequent.—Fl. July, August. Perennial.

3. *C. glomerata* (Clustered Bell-flower).—*Stem* simple, roughish ; *leaves* oblong, tapering, crenate, rough—the *lower* stalked and heart-shaped at the base, the *upper* sessile, embracing the stem ; *flowers* sessile, in heads. A stiff, erect plant, 3–18 inches high, with terminal and (in large specimens) axillary heads of deep blue, funnel-shaped, erect flowers, which have a few clasping, taper-pointed bracts at the base. Dry pastures ; not unfrequent.— Fl. July, August. Perennial.

4. *C. hederacea* (Ivy-leaved Bell-flower).—*Stem* straggling, thread-like ; *leaves* stalked, roundish heart-shaped, angular and toothed ; *flowers* solitary, on long stalks. An exquisite little plant, generally growing with Bog Pimpernel and the Cornish Money-wort, plants certainly of a different habit, but scarcely less elegant than itself.

N

CAMPANULA HEDERACEA
(*Ivy-leaved Bell-flower*)

The leaves are of a remarkably fine
texture, and delicate green hue; the
flowers of a pale blue, sometimes
slightly drooping, and supported on
long stalks scarcely thicker than a
hair. Its usual height is 4-6 inches,
but when it grows among grass or
rushes, it climbs by their help to a
height of 12 inches or more. Wet
heaths, and by the side of streams in
the south and west; very abundant
in Cornwall.—Fl. July to September.
Perennial.

5. *C. latifolia* (Giant Bell-flower).—
A stout species, 3-4 feet high; *leaves*
ovate lanceolate, toothed, the lower
ones stalked; *flowers* large, blue or white, hairy within. Woody
glens; not uncommon in Scotland and Northern England, becoming
more rare towards the south.

6. *C. Rapunculoides* (Creeping Bell-flower).—*Stems* about 1-2
feet high; *lower-leaves* heart-shaped, stalked; *upper* ones ovate
lanceolate; *flowers* pale blue, axillary, drooping all on one side.
Very rare.—Fl. July, August. Perennial.

7. *C. Rapunculus* (Rampion Bell-flower, Ramps).—A tall species,
2-3 feet high, with clustered panicles of rather small, erect, pale
blue *flowers*, the calyx of which is divided into 5 awl-shaped segments. Not common; local. Formerly cultivated in gardens
for the sake of its tuberous roots.—Fl. July, August. Biennial.

8. *C. hybrida* (Corn Campanula).—A small plant, 4–12 inches
high, with a rough wiry *stem*, oblong, rough, wavy *leaves*, and a
few small terminal purple *flowers*, the calyx of which is much
longer than the corolla; *corolla* wheel-shaped; *capsule* triangular,
elongated. Cornfields; not common. By some botanists this is
called *Specularia hybrida*.—Fl. June to September. Annual.

2. PHYTEUMA (*Rampion*)

1. *P. orbiculare* (Round-headed Rampion).—*Flowers* in a round
terminal head; *lower leaves* notched, heart-shaped, stalked; *upper*
narrow, sessile. A singular plant, consisting of a solitary erect
leafy stalk, 6–18 inches high, surmounted by a round head of blue
flowers. The head when in fruit becomes oval. Chalky downs in
the south; rare.—Fl. July. Perennial.

2. *P. spicatum* (Spiked Rampion).—Much taller than the last,
and bears its *flowers*, which are cream-coloured, in a terminal

PLATE LVI.

Great Campanula   Spreading Campanula

oblong head, which lengthens with maturity.   Found only in Sussex
—Fl. May to July.   Perennial.

3. JASIONE (*Sheep's Scabious*)

1. *J. montana* (Sheep's Scabious, Sheep's-bit).—
The only British species. Growing about a foot
high, and having a strong resemblance to a Scabious,
or one of the Compositæ, from the former of which,
however, it may be distinguished by its united
anthers ; from the latter by its having a 2-celled
capsule. The *leaves* are oblong, blunt, and hairy ;
the *flowers*, which are blue, grow in terminal heads,
with a leafy *involucre* at the base. The whole plant
when bruised has a strong and disagreeable smell.
Dry heathy places ; common.—Fl. July, August.
Biennial.

4. LOBELIA (*Lobelia*)

1. *L. Dortmanna* (Water Lobelia).—An aquatic
plant, often forming a matted bed at the bottom of
the water, and sending above the surface slender,
almost leafless *stems*, having a terminal raceme of
distant, light blue, drooping *flowers*. Not uncommon
in lakes in Scotland and Western England.—
Fl. July, August. Perennial.

JASIONE
MONTANA
(*Sheep's
Scabious,
Sheep's-bit*)

2. *L. urens* (Acrid Lobelia).—Erect, 12–18 inches high, with a
roughish, leafy *stem*, which contains a milky, acrid juice, and bears
a bracteate raceme of erect purple *flowers*. Very rare ; Axminster,
Devon.—Fl. August, September. Perennial.

NATURAL ORDER XLVI

VACCINIACEÆ.—THE CRANBERRY TRIBE

Calyx growing from the ovary, of 4–6 lobes, which are sometimes
so shallow as to be scarcely perceptible ; *corolla* of one petal, with
as many lobes as the calyx ; *stamens* not united, twice as many as
the lobes of the corolla, inserted into the disk of the ovary ; *anthers*
opening by 2 pores, and often furnished with 2 bristles ; *ovary*
with a flat disk, 4 to 10-celled ; *cells* 1 or many-seeded ; *style*
and *stigma* simple ; *fruit* a berry crowned by the remains of the
calyx, juicy, containing many small seeds. Small shrubby plants,
with undivided, alternate leaves, inhabiting temperate regions,
especially mountainous and marshy districts. By some botanists
they are placed in the same order as the Heaths, from which they
differ chiefly in having the ovary beneath the calyx. The leaves

and bark are astringent, the berries slightly acrid and agreeable to the taste. Under the name of Cranberries the fruit of *Schollera Occycoccus* and *S. macrocarpus* are imported from Russia and North America respectively, and are used for making tarts. Many species are cultivated in gardens, more, however, for their pretty flowers than for the sake of their fruit.

1. VACCINIUM (Whortleberry, Cranberry, etc.).—*Calyx* 4 to 5-lobed, sometimes with the lobes so shallow as to be scarcely perceptible ; *corolla* bell-shaped, or wheel-shaped, 4 to 5-cleft ; *stamens* 8–10 ; *berry* globose, 4 to 5-celled, many-seeded. (Name of doubtful etymology.)

1. VACCINIUM (*Whortleberry, Cranberry, etc.*)

Leaves not evergreen ; anthers with two bristles at the back

VACCINIUM MYRTILLUS
(*Whortleberry, Whinberry*)

1. *V. myrtillus* (Whortleberry, Bilberry, Whinberry).—A small branched shrub, with acutely-angled *stems*, 6-18 inches high ; *leaves* egg-shaped, serrated ; *flowers* solitary, drooping, nearly globular, flesh-coloured, wax-like ; *berries* black, covered with grey bloom. They are agreeable to the taste, and are often made into tarts ; but when thus used are rather mawkish unless mixed with some more acid fruit. They are popularly known by the name of *whorts*. Heathy and mountainous places ; abundant.—Fl. May. Shrub.

2. *V. uliginosum* (Bog Whortleberry, or Great Bilberry).—*Stem* not angular ; *leaves* inversely egg-shaped, entire, glaucous, and veined beneath. Distinguished from the last by its more woody, rounded stem, and by its strongly veined, glaucous leaves, which are broader towards the extremity. The flowers are smaller and grow nearer together. Mountainous bogs in Scotland and the north of England.—Fl. May.—Shrub.

Leaves evergreen ; anthers without bristles

3. *V. vitis idæa* (Red Whortleberry, Cowberry).—A low, straggling shrub, with inversely egg-shaped *leaves* resembling those of the box ; dotted beneath, and the margins rolled back ; the *flowers* are pink with 4 deep lobes, and are borne in terminal drooping clusters ; the *berries* red. Mountainous heaths in the north.— Fl. May, June. Shrub.

PLATE LVII.

Harebell   Harebell (variety)

4. *V. oxycoccos* (Marsh Whortleberry, Cranberry).— *Stem* very slender, prostrate, rooting ; *leaves* egg-shaped, glaucous beneath, the margins rolled back ; *corolla* wheel-shaped, with 4 deep, reflexed segments. A very low plant, with straggling, wiry stems, and solitary terminal, bright red flowers, the segments of which are bent back in a very singular manner. (" The fruit is highly agreeable, making the best of tarts ; at Langtown, on the borders of Cumberland, it forms no inconsiderable article of trade."—Sir W. J. Hooker.)—Fl. June. Shrub.

Natural Order XLVII
ERICACEÆ.—The Heath Tribe

Calyx 4 to 5-cleft, nearly equal, inferior, remaining till the fruit ripens ; *corolla* of one petal 4 to 5-cleft, often withering and remaining attached to the plant ; *stamens* equal in number to the segments of the corolla, or twice as many, inserted with the corolla, or only slightly attached to its base ; *anthers* hard and dry, the cells separating at one extremity, where they are furnished with bristles or some other appendage, opening by pores ; *ovary* not adhering to the calyx, surrounded at the base by a *disk* or by *scales*, many-seeded ; *style* 1, straight ; *stigma* 1 ; *fruit* a berry or dry capsule, many-seeded. Shrubs or small bushy trees with evergreen, often rigid, opposite or whorled leaves. This well-known and highly prized Order contains a large number of beautiful plants, many of which are remarkable for their social nature ; extensive tracts of country being often found entirely covered with a few species, so as to give name (heaths) to the kinds of places on which they grow. They are very abundant in South Africa, whence they are often called by gardeners " Cape plants." They are common also in Europe, in North and South America, both within and without the tropics, and in the mountainous parts of Asia. The extensive genus Erica (Heath) contains no plant possessing useful properties, save *Erica arborea*, from which briar-root pipes are made ; briar is a corruption of its French name *bruyère*. *Calluna vulgaris* (Ling, or Heather) is astringent, and is sometimes used for dyeing ; its tough branches are a common material for brooms ; its flowers are a favourite resort of bees, and its seeds and young tender shoots enter largely into the food of moor-fowl. Of the plants belonging to this Order which produce juicy berries, the fruit is in some instances edible. *Arbutus Unedo* bears an abundance of handsome berries, which, when thoroughly ripe, are not unpalatable, and which, from the resemblance they outwardly bear to strawberries, give the plant its English name, Strawberry-tree. Some species, especially *Kalmia* and *Rhododen dron*, possess dangerous narcotic properties, which extend to the flesh of animals that have fed on them. It is stated that the honey which poisoned Xenophon's Grecian troops during the famous Retreat of the Ten Thousand, had been collected by bees from the flowers of some plant of this Order, probably *Azalea pontica*, which possesses this property, and is still found on the shores of the Euxine, or Black Sea. The berries of some species are, nevertheless, used in medicine with good effect.

1. ERICA (Heath).—*Calyx* deeply 4-cleft ; *corolla* bell-shaped or egg-shaped, 4-cleft ; *stamens* 8 ; *capsule* 4-celled. (Name from the Greek, *erico*, to break, from some fancied medicinal properties.)

2. CALLUNA (Ling, Heather).—*Calyx* of 4 coloured sepals, which are longer than the corolla, having at the base outside 4 green *bracts ; corolla* bell-shaped ; *stamens* 8 ; *capsule* 4-celled. (Name from the Greek, *calluno*, to cleanse, from the frequent use to which its twigs are applied of being made into brooms.)

3. MENZIESIA.—*Calyx* deeply 4 to 5-cleft ; *corolla* inflated ; *stamens* 8–10 ; *capsule* 4 to 5-celled. (Named in honour of *Archibald Menzies*, an eminent Scotch botanist.)

4. AZALEA.—*Calyx* deeply 5-cleft ; *corolla* bell-shaped, 5-cleft ; *stamens* 5 ; *anthers* bursting lengthways ; *capsule* 2 to 3-celled, and valved. (Name from the Greek, *azaleos*, parched, from the nature of the places in which it grows.)

5. ANDROMEDA.—*Calyx* deeply 5-cleft ; *corolla* egg-shaped, with a 5-cleft reflexed border ; *stamens* 10 ; *anthers* with two bristles at the back ; *capsule* dry, 5-celled, and 5-valved. (Named in allusion to the fable of *Andromeda*, who was chained to a rock, and exposed to the attack of a sea-monster. So does this tribe of beautiful plants grow in dreary northern wastes, feigned to be the abode of preternatural monsters."—Sir W. J. Hooker.)

6. ARBUTUS (Strawberry-tree).—*Calyx* deeply 5-cleft ; *corolla* egg-shaped, with a 5-cleft reflexed border ; *stamens* 10 ; *fruit* fleshy, rough, 5-celled ; *cells* many-seeded. (Name, the Latin name of the plant.)

7. ARCTOSTAPHYLOS (Bear-berry).—*Calyx* deeply 5-cleft ; *corolla* egg-shaped, with a 5-cleft reflexed border ; *stamens* 10 ; *fruit* fleshy, smooth, 5-celled ; *cells* 1-seeded. (Name in Greek denoting *Bear's grape*.)

1. ERICA (*Heath*)

1. *E. tetralix* (Cross-leaved Heath).—Well distinguished from all other English species by its *leaves* being placed crosswise in whorles of four, and by its terminal heads of drooping, rose-coloured *flowers*, which are all turned to one side, and are of a larger size than the other common species *E. cinerea*. The part of the flower nearest the stem is of a lighter colour than that which is exposed, where it

PLATE LVIII.

Lesser Periwinkle
Bell Heather

Common Ling
Cross-leaved Heath

deepens to a delicate blush ; the whole flower appearing as if it had been modelled in wax. It is sometimes found of a pure white. Peaty moors, abundant.—Fl. July, August, with occasional blooms throughout the autumn. Shrub.

2. *E. cinerea* (Fine-leaved Heath, Bell Heather).—*Leaves* in threes, narrow, smooth ; *flowers* egg-shaped, in irregular, whorled, leafy clusters. This and No. 1 are the only *Heaths* which can be called common. It is a bushy plant, with tough, wiry stems, exceedingly narrow leaves, and numerous oblong purple flowers, which form broken, leafy clusters, not confined to one side of the stem. The flowers are sometimes white. Heaths, abundant.—Fl. July, August. Shrub.

3. *E. vagans* (Cornish Heath). — *Stems* much branched, and, in the upper parts, very leafy, 2–4 feet high ; *leaves* 3–5 in a whorl, crowded, very narrow, smooth ; *flowers* bell-shaped, shorter than the stamens, forming a leafy, irregular, taper-ing cluster, light purple, rose-coloured, or white. In the purple variety the anthers are dark purple ; in the white, bright red ; and in all cases they form a ring outside the corolla until they have shed their pollen, when they droop to the sides. Abundant on various heaths in Cornwall ; and on the Goonhilley Downs, in Cornwall, all three varieties of this Heath grow together in the greatest profusion, covering many thousands of acres, and almost excluding the two species so common elsewhere.—Fl. July to Sep-tember. Shrub.

ERICA VAGANS
(Cornish Heath)

4. *E. Mediterranea* (Mediterranean Heath).—Dis-tinguished by its coloured *calyx* and flesh-pink *corolla ;* the *leaves* are four in a whorl ; *anthers* only slightly protruding from mouth of corolla. Cultivated in Great Britain, and found wild in Connemara.—Fl. April, May. Shrub.

5. *E. ciliaris* (Ciliated Heath).—By far the most beautiful of all the British species ; the *leaves* are four in a whorl ; and the *flowers,* which are bright purple and half an inch long, grow in terminal, interrupted, spike-like clusters. Sandy heaths ; of local occurrence in Dorset and Cornwall, though where found often very abundant.— Fl. June to September.

A variety of *E. Tetralix,* known as *E. Mackaiana,* is found in Connemara. It differs in being more bushy, with broader *leaves* and more numerous heads of smaller *flowers.*

2. Calluna (*Ling, Heather*)

1. *C. vulgaris* (Ling, or Heather).—The only species. A strag-gling, branched shrub 1–3 feet high. The *leaves* are very small, more or less downy (sometimes even hoary), and arranged in four rows on opposite sides of the stem. The *corolla* is very small and bell-shaped, and is concealed by the rose-coloured *calyx*, at the base of which are four small green *bracts*, which have the appearance of a second calyx. The *flowers* remain attached to the plant long after the seed is ripe ; indeed, it is not at all unusual to find plants in full bloom with the withered flowers of the preceding year still adhering to the lower part of the stem. A beautiful variety has been found in Cornwall, with double flowers ; and white specimens, which are not unfrequent, are supposed to bring the finder good luck. Heaths and moors ; abundant.—Fl. July, August. Shrub.

3. Menziesia

1. *M. cærulea* (Scotch Menziesia).—*Leaves* numerous, linear, minutely toothed ; *flower-stalks* covered with glandular hairs ; *flowers* in terminal tufts ; *corolla* 5-cleft ; *stamens* 10. A small, shrubby plant, naked below, very leafy and hairy above, with large, pale purplish blue flowers. Very rare ; found on the " Sow of Athol," in Perthshire, but " nearly, if not quite, extirpated by an Edinburgh nurseryman " (Babington).—Fl. June, July. Shrub.

2. *M. polifolia* (Irish Menziesia, or St. Dabeoc's Heath).—*Leaves* egg-shaped, with the margins rolled back, white, and downy be-neath ; *corolla* 4-cleft ; *stamens* 8. A small shrub, with large purple, sometimes white, flowers, which grow in terminal, leafy, 1-sided clusters. Mountainous heaths in Ireland ; rare.—Fl. June, July. Shrub.

4. Azalea

1. *A. procumbens* (Trailing Azalea).—A low trailing shrub, of a very different habit from most of the garden plants cultivated under the name of Azaleas. The *stems* are prostrate and tangled ; the *leaves* small, smooth, and rigid, with the margins remarkably rolled back ; the *flowers* are flesh-coloured, and grow in short terminal clusters or tufts. Highland mountains.—Fl. May, June. Shrub.

5. Andromeda

1. *A. polifolia* (Marsh Andromeda).—The only British species, growing in peat bogs in the north. A small leafy, evergreen shrub, with slender *stems*, narrow, pointed *leaves*, and terminal tufts of flesh-coloured, drooping *flowers*.—Fl. June to August. Shrub.

6. ARBUTUS (*Strawberry-tree*)

1. *A. unedo* (Strawberry-tree).—*Leaves* elliptical, tapering, serrated, smooth ; *flowers* in drooping panicles ; *fruit* rough. A beautiful evergreen tree, with a rough, reddish *bark*, large deep green *leaves*, and numerous terminal clusters of greenish white *flowers*. The *berries*, which ripen in the following autumn, are nearly globular, orange-scarlet, and rough, with minute, hard grains. They are eatable, but so much less attractive to the taste than to the eye as to have originated the name "Unedo" ("One-I-eat"), as if no one would choose to try a second. The flowers are in full perfection at the time when the fruit, formed

ARBUTUS UNEDO
(*Strawberry-Tree*)

in the preceding year, is ripening ; and then, of course, the tree presents its most beautiful appearance. About the lakes of Killarney in a wild state, and very common in English gardens.— Fl. September, October. Tree.

7. ARCTOSTAPHYLOS (*Bear-berry*)

1. *A. uva-ursi* (Red Bear-berry).—*Stems* prostrate ; *leaves* inversely egg-shaped, entire, evergreen ; *flowers* in terminal clusters. A small shrub, distinguished by its long trailing stems, blunt leaves, which turn red in autumn, rose-coloured flowers, and small red berries, which are a favourite food of moor-fowl. The leaves are used in medicine as an astringent. Mountainous heaths in the north ; abundant.—Fl. May. Shrub.

2. *A. Alpina* (Black Bear-berry).—Resembles the last in its mode of growth, but the *leaves* are wrinkled and serrated, and not evergreen ; the *flowers* are white, with a purplish tinge ; the *berries* black. It is most common on mountains in the north of Scotland.

NATURAL ORDER XLVIII

MONOTROPACEÆ.—THE BIRD'S-NEST TRIBE

Sepals 4–5, not falling off ; *corolla* regular, deeply divided into as many lobes or petals as there are sepals ; *stamens* twice as many as the lobes of the corolla ; *anthers* opening by pores ; *ovary* 4 to 5-celled, sometimes imperfectly so ; *style* 1, often bent ; *stigma* generally lobed ; *fruit* a dry capsule ; *seeds* covered with a loose skin. A small, unimportant Order, containing but two British genera— *Pyrola*, a family of plants with somewhat shrubby, unbranched *stems*, simple, smooth, veiny evergreen *leaves*, and large, often fragrant, *flowers*, which grow either singly or in a stalked terminal cluster ; and *Monotropa*, a leafless parasitic plant, with the habit of an *Orobanche* (Broom-rape), growing on the roots of firs and other trees.

1. PYROLA (Winter-green).—*Sepals* 5 ; *corolla* of 5 deep lobes or petals ; *stamens* 10 ; *anthers* 2-celled ; *stigma* 5-lobed. (Name signifying *a little pear*, from a fancied resemblance between its leaves and those of that tree.)

2. MONOTROPA (Bird's-nest).—*Sepals* 4–5 ; *petals* 4–5, swollen at the base ; *stamens* 8–10 ; *anthers* 1-celled ; *stigma* flat, not lobed. (Name from the Greek, *monos*, one, and *trepo*, to turn, the flowers being turned all one way.)

1. PYROLA (*Winter-green*)

1. *P. uniflora* (Single-flowered Winter-green).—A remarkably pretty plant, bearing several roundish egg-shaped, smooth, and veiny *leaves*, and running up into a single *flower-stalk*, which bears one large elegant white drooping, highly fragrant *flower*. Mountainous woods in Scotland ; rare.—Fl. July. Perennial.

2. *P. rotundifolia* (Round-leaved winter-green).—*Flowers* numerous, white ; distinguished by its long *style* bent down, and at the extremity curved upwards. Damp woods, Kent, Norfolk, and Suffolk, or as far north as Inverness ; very rare. —Fl. July to September. Perennial.

3. *P. media* (Intermediate Winter-green). —Resembling both *P. rotundifolia* and *P. minor*, but the *style* is erect, nearly straight, and much longer than the stamens. Found chiefly in Northern Britain. —Fl. July, August. Perennial.

4. *P. minor* (Common Winter-green).— *Flowers* on short stalks, tinged with pink, enclosing the rather large *stigma*. Found chiefly in the north.—Fl. July, August. Perennial.

5. *P. secunda* (One-sided Winter-green). —*Flowers* numerous, greenish, all turned to one side ; *style* long and straight, protruding from the incurved petals. Found in Yorkshire and Scotland. — Fl. July. Perennial.

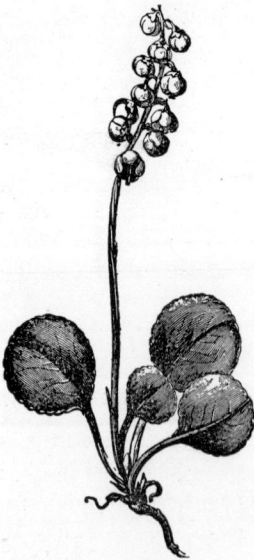

The Pyrolas are all of very local occurrence in Britain.

PYROLA MEDIA
(*Intermediate Winter-green*)

2. MONOTROPA (*Birds'-nest*)

1. *M. hypopitys* (Pine Bird's-nest, Fir-rape).—The only British species, occurring sparingly in dry woods of Fir and Beech, on the roots of which trees it is said by some to be parasitical. The whole plant consists of a single juicy *stalk*, without leaves, but clothed throughout with scaly *bracts*, and terminating in a drooping cluster of brownish yellow *flowers*, which eventually turn almost black. This must not be confounded with plants of the genus *Orobanche*, which all have a ringent corolla of 1 petal, and 4 stamens, two of which are shorter than the others. The flowers of *Monotropa* have 8 stamens, with the exception of the terminal one, which has 10. Local in England and Southern Scotland.—Fl. June to August. Perennial.

MONOTROPA
HYPOPITYS
(*Pine Bird's-nest, Fir-rape*)

NATURAL ORDER XLIX

ILICINEÆ.—THE HOLLY TRIBE

Sepals 4–6, imbricated when in bud; *corolla* 4 to 6-lobed, imbricated when in bud; *stamens* inserted into the corolla, equalling its lobes in number, and alternate with them; *filaments* erect; *anthers* 2-celled, opening lengthwise; *ovary* fleshy, abrupt, 2 to 6-celled; *stigma* nearly sessile, lobed; *fruit* a fleshy berry, not bursting, containing 2–6 bony seeds. Evergreen trees or shrubs, with tough leaves and small axillary, white or greenish flowers, occurring in various parts of the world, the only European species being the common Holly. Nearly all the plants of this tribe possess astringent and tonic properties. The leaves of Holly, for instance, are said to be equal to Peruvian bark in the cure of intermittent fever. The berries are, undoubtedly, poisonous. The bark furnishes bird-lime, and the wood, which is white and remarkably close-grained, is much used by cabinet-makers in inlaying; whilst its green twigs, as well as those of Hazel and Willow, are employed by water-finders, or water-diviners, in their remarkable and obscure art of "dowsing."

I. Paraguayensis furnishes *maté*, or Paraguay Tea, which is so extensively used in Brazil and other parts of South America.

1. ILEX (Holly).—*Calyx* 4 to 5-cleft; *corolla* wheel-shaped, 4 to 5-cleft; *stamens* 4–5; *stigmas* 4–5; *berry* round, containing 4–5 bony seeds. (Name applied by the Latins to some tree, though not our Holly.)

ILEX AQUIFOLIUM (*Holly*)

1. ILEX (*Holly*)

1. *I. aquifolium* (Holly).— The only British species. A shrub or small tree, with glossy evergreen, spinous leaves, the upper ones of which have often only one spine, and that at the extremity. The berries are red or yellow. The name *Aquifolium* means *needle-leaved*. Holly is probably a corruption of the word " holy," from the use to which its boughs are applied in ornamenting churches at Christmas. The berries are POISONOUS. Many varieties are grown in gardens, with variously shaped and variegated leaves.— Fl. May, June. Tree.

NATURAL ORDER L
OLEACEÆ.—THE OLIVE TRIBE

Calyx divided, not falling off ; *corolla* of 1 petal, 4 to 8-cleft, sometimes wanting ; *stamens* 2, alternate with the lobes of the corolla ; *ovary* 2-celled ; *cells* 2-seeded ; *style* 1 ; *fruit* a berry, drupe, or capsule, of 2 cells, each cell often perfecting only a single seed. Trees or shrubs, the branches of which often end in conspicuous buds ; the leaves are opposite, either simple or pinnate ; the flowers grow in clusters, or panicles. The plants of this Order inhabit the temperate regions of many parts of the world. By far the most important among them is the plant from which the Order takes its name, *Olea*, the Olive, among the earliest of plants cultivated by man. The bark of the Olive is bitter and astringent, the wood remarkably close-grained and durable. The fruit is a drupe, or hard bony seed, enclosed in a fleshy, closely-fitting case. From this outer coat, and not from the seed itself, oil is obtained by pressure. Several kinds of Ash (*Fraxinus* and *Ornus*) produce manna, and are valued for the strength and elasticity of their timber.

1. LIGUSTRUM (Privet).—*Corolla* funnel-shaped, 4-cleft ; *calyx* with 4 small teeth ; *fruit* a 2-celled berry. (Name from the Latin name of the plant, and that from *ligo*, to bind, from the use made of its twigs.)

2. FRAXINUS (Ash).—*Calyx* 4-cleft, or o ; *corolla* o ; *fruit* a winged 2-celled capsule. (Name, the Latin name of the tree, denoting the ease with which it may be split.)

1. LIGUSTRUM (*Privet*)

1. *L. vulgare* (Privet).—The only British species. A common hedge bush, with opposite, narrow-elliptical, evergreen *leaves*, dense panicles of white, sickly smelling *flowers*, and black, shining *berries*, about the size of currants. It is much used for hedges, especially in conjunction with White-thorn, over which it has the advantage of being a rapid grower. It is particularly useful as a hedge-plant in towns, not being liable to injury by smoke.—Fl. May, June. Shrub.

LIGUSTRUM VULGARE (*Privet*)　　　FRAXINUS EXCELSIOR (*Ash*)

2. FRAXINUS (*Ash*)

1. *F. excelsior* (Ash).—*Calyx* and *corolla* both wanting; *leaves* pinnate, with an odd leaflet. A noble tree, characterized by the light, ash-coloured, smooth bark of its younger branches, of which the lower ones droop and curve upwards again at the extremities; by its large, black, terminal buds, the twigs supporting which are flattened at the end, and by its gracefully feathered foliage. The tufts of seed-vessels, popularly called " keys," remain attached to the tree until the succeeding spring. A variety is occasionally found with undivided leaves, but it is not so handsome as the common form of the tree. Woods and hedges; common.—Fl. April, May, forming at first fruit-like, terminal heads, and finally loose panicles. Tree.

Natural Order LI

APOCYNACEÆ.—Periwinkle Tribe

Calyx deeply 5-cleft, not falling off ; *corolla* regular, 5-lobed, the lobes twisted when in bud, and when expanded having the sides of the margin unequally curved ; *stamens* 5, inserted in the tube of the corolla ; *anthers* distinctly 2-celled ; *pollen* large ; *ovary* 2-celled, or double ; *pistil* resembling the shaft of a pillar, with a double capital ; *fruit* various.   Trees, shrubs, or herbaceous plants, with showy flowers, remarkable for the twisted lobes of the corolla when in bud, and yet more so for the symmetrical pistil.   Many of them abound in a milky juice, and a large portion are poisonous. *Tanghinia venenifera* is one of the most deadly of known vegetable poisons, a single seed, though not larger than an almond, being sufficient to destroy twenty people.   (For an account of the horrible use to which it was formerly applied in Madagascar, see *Wonders of the Vegetable Kingdom*.)   The beautiful *Oleander* (Nerium Oleander), a common greenhouse shrub, is also a formidable poison, the powdered wood of which is used to destroy rats.   In 1809, when the French troops were lying before Madrid, some of the soldiers went out marauding, every one bringing back such provisions as could be found.   One soldier formed the unfortunate idea of cutting the branches of the *Oleander* for spits and skewers for the meat when roasting.   This tree, it may be observed, is very common in Spain where it attains considerable dimensions.   The wood having been stripped of its bark, and brought in contact with the meat, was productive of most direful consequences ; for of twelve soldiers who ate of the roast seven died, and the other five were dangerously ill. Some species, in which the characteristic properties are moderated, are, however, used as medicines.   Several species furnish caoutchouc, or India-rubber, of good quality.   The only genus represented among British plants is *Vinca*, which has astringent and acrid properties.

1. Vinca (Periwinkle).—*Corolla* salver-shaped, with 5 angles at the mouth of the tube, 5-lobed, the lobes oblique ; *fruit* consisting of 2 erect, horn-like capsules, which do not burst.   (Name from the Latin, *vincio*, to bind, from the cord-like stems.)

Vinca (*Periwinkle*)

1. *V. major* (Greater Periwinkle).—*Stem* nearly erect ; *leaves* egg-shaped, with the margins minutely fringed.   A handsome plant, with large deep green leaves, which are smooth, except at the margins, and large purplish blue flowers, the mouth of which is angular, and the tube closed with hairs and the curiously curved

anthers.   The pistil of this flower, as well as of the following species, is a singularly beautiful object.   A doubtful native, being found only in the neighbourhood of dwelling-houses.—Fl. May, June. Perennial.

2. *V. minor* (Lesser Periwinkle).—*Stem* trailing, sending up short, erect, leafy shoots, which bear the flowers ; margins of the *leaves* not fringed.   Woods, especially in the West of England, where it often entirely covers the ground with its evergreen leaves.   It is smaller than the last.   A white variety occurs in Devonshire, and in gardens it is often met with bearing variegated leaves and double purple, blue, or white flowers.—Fl. March to June.   Perennial.

NATURAL ORDER LII

GENTIANACEÆ.—THE GENTIAN TRIBE

Calyx usually 5, sometimes 4 to 8-cleft, not falling off ; *corolla* of 1 petal, its lobes equalling in number those of the calyx, not falling off, twisted when in bud, often fringed about the mouth of the tube ; *stamens* equalling in number the lobes of the corolla, and alternate with them ; *ovary* of 2 carpels, 1 or imperfectly 2-celled ; *style* 1 ; *stigmas* 2 ; *fruit* a many-seeded capsule.   Mostly herbaceous plants, with opposite, generally sessile leaves, and often large, brilliantly coloured flowers.   This is an extensive Order, containing between four and five hundred species, which are distributed throughout all climates, from regions of perpetual snow to the hottest regions of South America and India.   Though able to bear the most intense cold, they are very rare both in the Arctic and Antarctic regions.   Under the equator, the lowest elevation at which they have been found is 7850 feet.   On the Himalaya and Rocky Mountain ranges species have been found at a height of 16,000 feet ; another in Ceylon at 8000 feet ; in Southern Europe one species, *Gentiana prostrata*, flourishes at between 6000 and 9000 feet ; and in the Straits of Magellan and Behring's Straits just above the level of the sea.   In South America and New Zealand the prevailing colour of the flower is red ; in Europe, blue ; yellow and white being of rare occurrence.   All the known species are remarkable for the intensely bitter properties residing in every part of the herbage, hence they are valuable tonic medicines.   That most commonly used in Europe is *G. lutea* (Yellow Gentian) ; but there is little doubt that other species might be employed with equally good effect.

1. GENTIANA (Gentian).—*Calyx* 4 to 5-cleft ; *corolla* funnel- or salver-shaped ; *stamens* 5, rarely 4 ; *stigmas* 2. (Name from Gentius, an ancient King of Illyria, who discovered its medicinal value.)

2. ERYTHRÆA (Centaury).—*Calyx* 5-cleft ; *corolla* funnel-shaped, 5-cleft, not falling off ; *stamens* 5 ; *anthers* becoming spirally twisted.

3. CICENDIA (Gentianella).—*Calyx* 4-cleft, tubular ; *corolla* funnel-shaped, 4-cleft ; *stamens* 4 ; *anthers* not twisted ; *stigma* undivided. (Name, according to Hooker and Arnott, from the Greek, *cicinnus*, curled hair ; but, if so, particularly inappropriate to the only British species, which is singularly rigid.)

4. CHLORA (Yellow-wort).—*Calyx* deeply 8-cleft ; *corolla* with a very short tube, 8-cleft ; *stamens* 8 ; *stigma* 2 to 4-cleft. (Name from the Greek, *chloros*, yellow, from the colour of the flowers.)

5. MENYANTHES (Buck-bean).—*Calyx* deeply 5-cleft ; *corolla* funnel-shaped, with 5 lobes, fringed all over the inner surface ; *stamens* 5 ; *stigma* 2-lobed. (Name of doubtful origin.)

6. VILLARSIA.—*Calyx* deeply 5-cleft ; *corolla* wheel-shaped, with 5 lobes, which are fringed only at the base ; *stamens* 5 ; *stigma* with 2 toothed lobes. (Name in honour of *M. de Villars*, a French botanist.)

1. GENTIANA (*Gentian*)

1. *G. pneumonanthe* (Marsh Gentian).—*Stem* erect, 6–12 inches high, few-flowered ; *calyx* 5-cleft ; *corolla* between bell and funnel-shaped, 5-cleft, not fringed. Well distinguished by its large, bell-shaped, deep blue flowers, with 5 green stripes. There are rarely more than 1 or 2 flowers on the same stalk. Boggy heaths, principally in Northern England.—Fl. August, September. Annual.

2. *G. verna* (Spring Gentian).—A very rare species. *Stems* simple, and often extremely short, each bearing a solitary large intensely blue *flower* which is 5-cleft, and has between the lobes 5 smaller 2-cleft segments. Found only in one or two places in Northern England and in Ireland.—Fl. April to June. Perennial.

3. *G. nivalis* (Small Gentian).—Taller than the last and usually branched, each branch bearing a *flower* resembling *G. verna* in shape and colour, but smaller. Very rare ; only found on the summits of some of the Highland mountains.—Fl. August, September. Annual.

4. *G. amarella* (Autumnal Gentian).—*Stem* erect, branched, many-flowered ; *calyx* 5-cleft ; *corolla* salver-shaped, fringed in the throat. A remarkably erect plant, with a square, leafy, purplish stem, 6–12 inches high, and numerous, rather large purplish flowers, which only expand in bright sunshine. Dry chalky pastures, not common.—Fl. August, September. Annual.

5. *G. campestris* (Field Gentian).—*Stem* erect, branched, many-flowered ; *calyx* 4-cleft, the two outer lobes much larger ; *corolla* salver-shaped, 4-cleft, fringed in the throat. Resembling the last

PLATE LIX.

Field Gentian   Common Centaurea

Yellow-wort   Buck-bean

in habit, but at once distinguished by its 4-cleft flowers, which are of a dull purplish colour. Dry pastures, common.—Fl. August, September. Annual.

2. ERYTHRÆA (*Centaury*)

1. *E. centaurium* (Common Centaury).—A pretty herbaceous plant 2–18 inches high, with square, erect *stems*, which are much branched above, and terminate in variously divided flat tufts of small rose-coloured *flowers ;* the *leaves* are oblong, with strong parallel ribs, and remarkably smooth ; the flowers only expand in fine weather. This is the common form of the plant as it occurs in dry fields and waste places. In other situations it varies so greatly that some botanists enumerate several supposed species, which, however, run into one another so closely that they may be taken to be varieties. The following are the more distinct forms :—

E. pulchella (Dwarf Centaury).—A minute plant 2–8 inches high, with an exceedingly slender *stem* and a few stalked *flowers* (often only one) ; this is found on the sandy sea-shore, especially in the west of England.

E. littoralis (Dwarf Tufted Centaury).—A stunted plant, with broad *leaves*, and all the *flowers* crowded into a kind of head. This occurs on turfy sea-cliffs.

E. latifolia (Broad-leaved Centaury).—Has even broader *leaves* than the last, and bears its *flowers* in forked tufts, the main *stem* being divided into three branches. There are other minute differences, for which the student may consult more scientific works. The genus was formerly called *Chironia*, from the Centaur, *Chiron*, who was famous in Greek mythology for his skill in medicinal herbs. The English name, Centaury, has the same origin.— Fl. July, August. Annual.

3. CICENDIA (*Gentianella*)

1. *C. filiformis* (Slender Gentianella).—A minute slender plant, in habit resembling *Erythrœa pulchella*, and growing to about the same size, 2–4 inches ; the pairs of opposite *leaves* are very narrow and soon wither ; the *flowers* are yellow, and expand only in bright sunshine. It grows in sandy heaths where water has stood during the winter. South-west of England.—Fl. July. Annual.

2. *C. pusilla* (Least Gentianella).—A smaller plant than the last, found in the Channel Isles ; it is more branched than *C. filiformis ;* the *flowers* white, pink, or yellow, with the *calyx* deeply divided.—Fl. July. Annual.

CICENDIA
FILIFORMIS
(*Slender
Gentianella*

o

4. CHLORA (*Yellow-wort*)

1. *C. perfoliata* (Perfoliate Yellow-wort).—The only British species. An erect plant 2–12 inches high, remarkable for its glaucous hue and for its pairs of *leaves*, which are rather distant, being united at the base (connate), with the *stem* passing through them ; hence its name, *Perfoliate*. The *flowers*, which are large and handsome, are of a pale yellow, and expand only during sunshine. Chalk and limestone pastures ; not uncommon.—Fl. June to September. Annual.

5. MENYANTHES (*Buck-bean*)

1. *M. trifoliata* (Buck-bean, Marsh Trefoil).—The only species. The only British plant belonging to the Order which has divided leaves. The *stem* scarcely rises above the soil or water in which it grows, but is overtopped by the large ternate (composed of 3 leaflets) *leaves*, which in shape and colour resemble those of the Windsor Bean ; each leaf-stalk has a sheathing base, opposite to one of which rises a compound cluster of exceedingly beautiful flowers, which when in bud are of a bright rose colour, and when fully expanded have the inner surface of the corolla thickly covered with a white fringe. The root, which is intensely bitter, is said to be the most valuable of known tonics. Spongy bogs and stagnant water.—Fl. June, July. Perennial.

VILLARSIA NYMPHŒOIDES
(*Water Villarsia*)

6. VILLARSIA

1. *V. nymphœoides* (Water Villarsia). —The only British species. A rare floating aquatic, found in some of the still ditches communicating with the Thames, and in a few other places. As its specific name implies, it has the habit of a Water-lily. The leaves are nearly round ; the flowers large, yellow, and fringed.—Fl. July, August. Perennial.

Natural Order LIII

POLEMONIACEÆ.—Jacob's Ladder Tribe

Calyx deeply 5-cleft, not falling off ; *corolla* regular, 5-lobed ; *stamens* 5, from the middle of the tube of the corolla ; *ovary* 3-celled ; *style* single ; *stigma* 3-cleft ; *capsule* 3-celled, 3-valved. Herbaceous plants, often with showy flowers, which are remarkable for the blue colour of their pollen. They are most common in the temperate parts of America, but within the tropics are unknown. None of the species possess remarkable properties, but several are favourite garden flowers, as *Phlox*, *Gilia*, *Polemonium*, and *Cobœa*.

1. Polemonium (Jacob's Ladder).—*Corolla* wheel-shaped, with erect lobes; *stamens* bearded at the base ; *cells* of the capsule many-seeded. (Name, the Greek name of the plant.)

POLEMONIUM
CŒRULEUM
(*Blue Jacob's Ladder*)

1. Polemonium (*Greek Valerian*)

1. *P. cœruleum* (Greek Valerian, Blue Jacob's Ladder).—The only British species. A tall, erect plant 1–2 feet high, with an angular *stem ;* pinnate, smooth *leaves ;* and numerous terminal large blue or white *flowers.* Occasionally found in woods in the north, but very rare ; a common garden flower, not easily rooted out when it has once established itself.—Fl. June, July. Perennial.

Natural Order LIV

CONVOLVULACEÆ.—The Bindweed Tribe

Calyx in five divisions, imbricated, often very unequal, not falling off ; *corolla* of 1 petal, regular, plaited when in bud ; *stamens* 5, from the base of the corolla ; *ovary* 2 to 4-celled, few-seeded, surrounded below by a fleshy ring ; *style* 1 ; *stigmas* 2 ; *capsule* 1 to 4-celled. An extensive and highly valuable tribe of plants, most of which are herbaceous climbers, with large and very beautiful flowers. They are most abundant within the tropics, where they are among the most ornamental of climbing plants. As medicines, also, they occupy an important station. The roots of *Convolvulus Scammonia*, a Syrian species, furnishes scammony ; jalap is prepared from a resin which abounds in the roots of several kinds of *Exogonium*, a beautiful climber, with long crimson flowers ; and

C. Batatas is no less valuable in tropical countries, supplying the sweet potato, the roots of which abound in starch and sugar, and are a nourishing food. *Cuscuta* (Dodder) is a parasitic genus, with branched, climbing, cord-like stems, no leaves, and globular heads of small wax-like flowers. The seeds germinate in the ground, and the young plants climb the stems of the adjoining plants; and when they have taken root in them lose their connection with the ground. One British species is very abundant on the Furze; another on Flax, with the seeds of which it is supposed to be introduced; and a third grows on Thistles and Nettles.

1. CONVOLVULUS (Bindweed).—*Corolla* trumpet-shaped, with 5 plaits and 5 very small lobes; *calyx* without bracts; *style* 1; *stigmas* 2; *capsule* 2-celled, 2-valved. (Name from the Latin, *convolvo*, to entwine, from the twisting habit of many species.)

2. CALYSTEGIA (Bindweed).—*Corolla* as in Convolvulus; *calyx* enclosed within 2 bracts; *style* 1; *stigmas* 2; *capsule* 1-celled, 2-valved. (Name in Greek, denoting a beautiful covering.)

3. CUSCUTA (Dodder).—*Calyx* 4 to 5-cleft; *corolla* bell-shaped, 4 to 5-cleft, with 4-5 scales at the base within. (Name said to be derived from the Arabic, *Kechout.*)

1. CONVOLVULUS (*Bindweed*)

1. *C. arvensis* (Field Bindweed).—*Stem* climbing; *leaves* arrow-shaped, with acute lobes; *flowers* 1–3 together; *bracts* minute, distant from the flower. A common weed in light soil, either trailing along the ground among short grass, or climbing wherever it finds a support. The flowers are rose-coloured with dark plaits, handsome and fragrant, opening only in sunny weather.—Fl. June, July. Perennial.

2. CALYSTEGIA (*Bindweed*)

1. *C. sepium* (Great Bindweed).—*Stem* climbing; *leaves* arrow-shaped, with abrupt lobes; *flowers* solitary on square stalks; *bracts* large, heart-shaped, close to the flower. The flowers are among the largest which this country produces; while in bud they are entirely enclosed in the large bracts, and when expanded are pure white and very handsome. The fruit is not often perfected. In bushy places, common; and a most mischievous weed in gardens, not only exhausting the soil with its roots, but strangling with its twining stems the plants which grow near.—Fl. July to September. Perennial.

2. *C. Soldanella* (Sea Bindweed).—*Stem* not climbing; *leaves* fleshy, roundish, or kidney-shaped; *flowers* solitary, on 4-sided, winged stalks; *bracts* large, egg-shaped, close to the flower. A very

PLATE LX.

Great Bindweed   Sea Bindweed

PLATE LXI.

Lesser Bindweed   Lesser Dodder

beautiful species, growing only on the sandy sea-coast, and decorating the sloping sides of sandhills with its large, pale rose-coloured flowers striped with red. The stems are frequently almost entirely buried beneath the sand, and the flowers and leaves merely rise above the surface. The flowers, which are nearly as large as those of the preceding species, expand in the morning, and in bright weather close before night. By some botanists these two plants are placed in the genus *Convolvulus.*—Fl. June to August. Perennial.

3. CUSCUTA (*Dodder*)

1. *C. Epithymum* (Lesser Dodder).—*Stems* parasitical, thread-like, branched ; *flowers* in dense, sessile heads ; *tube* of the *corolla* longer than the calyx ; *style* longer than the corolla. Parasitic on Heath, Thyme, Milk Vetch, Potentilla, and other small plants ; but most abundant on Furze, which it often entirely conceals with tangled masses of red thread-like stems. The flowers are small, light flesh-coloured, and wax-like. Soon after flowering the stems turn dark brown, and in winter disappear.—Fl. August, September. Annual.

2. *C. Europæa* (Greater Dodder).—*Flower-heads* sessile ; *calyx* of blunt sepals ; *corolla* longer than the calyx, yellowish, enclosing the stamens and styles. Whole plant greenish yellow, or sometimes reddish. Parasitic on Thistles, Nettles, etc.—Fl. July to September. Annual.

3. *C. Epilinum* (Flax Dodder).—Resembles the last ; *flowers* somewhat larger and less numerous, and white. Parasitical on Flax, to crops of which it is sometimes very destructive.—Fl. July, August. Annual.

4. *C. Trifolii* (Clover Dodder).—A variety with reddish *stems* and white *flowers.* Parasitical on Clover, with the seeds of which it is supposed to have been introduced.—Fl. July, August. Annual.

NATURAL ORDER LV
BORAGINACEÆ.—THE BORAGE TRIBE

Calyx in 5, rarely 4, deep divisions, not falling off ; *corolla* of 1 petal, 5- or rarely 4-cleft, frequently having valves or teeth at the mouth of the corolla tube ; *stamens* 5, inserted into the corolla and alternate with its lobes ; *ovary* 4-parted, 4-seeded ; *style* 1, rising from the base of the divided ovary ; *fruit* consisting of 4, rarely 2, nut-like, distinct seeds, each enclosed in a pericarp. Herbs, or rarely shrubs, with alternate leaves, which are usually covered with hairs or bristles rising from a swollen base. This character was considered by Linnæus sufficiently constant to give to the Order

the name of *Asperifoliæ*, or Rough-leaved plants ; but the present
name of the Order is now preferred as being more comprehensive,
a few plants in it having perfectly smooth leaves. The Borage
Tribe are natives principally of the temperate regions of the
northern hemisphere, especially of the warmer parts, and are more
numerous in the Old than the New World. Most of them bear
their flowers in spikes or racemes, which are rolled up round the
terminal flowers as a centre, and expand a few at a time. The prevailing colour is blue or purple, but many, when first opening, are
of a reddish hue, which subsequently deepens, so that it is not unusual to see flowers of different tints on the same spike. They
possess no remarkable properties, but abound in a soft mucilaginous
juice, which gives a coolness to beverages in which they are steeped,
on which account Borage is a constant ingredient in the various
forms of drink known as " cup." The roots of Alkanet and some
others contain a red substance which is used as a dye. Comfrey
(*Symphytum officinale*) is sometimes grown as an esculent vegetable,
but is little valued except as food for horses. The plants of the
genus *Myosotis* are popularly known by the name " Forget-me-not."
The true Forget-me-not is *M. Palustris*. The fragrant *Heliotrope*,
or Cherry-pie, of our gardens belongs to a genus of this Order.

1. ECHIUM (Viper's Bugloss).—*Corolla* irregular, with an open
mouth ; *stamens* unequal in length. (Name from the Greek, *echio*,
a viper, against the bite of which it was formerly considered an
antidote.)

2. PULMONARIA (Lungwort).—*Calyx* tubular, 5-cleft ; *corolla*
funnel-shaped, its throat naked ; *stamens* enclosed within the corolla. (Name from the Latin, *Pulmo*, the lungs, which the spotted
leaves were supposed to resemble.)

3. LITHOSPERMUM (Gromwell).—*Calyx* deeply 5-cleft ; *corolla*
funnel-shaped, its throat naked, or with 5 minute scales ; *filaments*
short ; *seeds* stony. (Name from the Greek, *lithos*, a stone, and
sperma, seed, from the hardness of the seeds.)

4. MERTENSIA (Smooth Gromwell).—*Calyx* deeply 5-cleft ; *corolla*
funnel-shaped ; *filaments* long ; *seeds* somewhat fleshy. (Name in
honour of *M. Mertens*, a German botanist.)

5. SYMPHYTUM (Comfrey).—*Calyx* deeply 5-cleft ; *corolla* bell-
shaped, closed with 5 awl-shaped scales. (Name from the Greek,
symphyo, to unite, from its imagined healing qualities.)

6. BORAGO (Borage).—*Calyx* deeply 5-cleft ; *corolla* wheel-
shaped, its throat closed with 5 short, erect, notched scales ; *stamens*
forked. (Name, a corruption of *corago*, from *cor*, the heart, and *ago*,
to bring, from its use in stimulating drinks.)

7. LYCOPSIS (Bugloss).—*Calyx* deeply 5-cleft ; *corolla* funnel-

PLATE LXII

Hound's Tongue
Viper's Bugloss

Common Comfrey
Water Forget-me-not

shaped, with a bent tube, its throat closed by prominent blunt scales. (Name in Greek signifying a *wolf's face*, from some fancied resemblance between the flower and a wolf's head.)

8. ANCHUSA (Alkanet).—*Calyx* deeply 5-cleft ; *corolla* funnel- or salver-shaped, with a straight tube, its throat closed by prominent blunt scales. (Name from the Greek, *anchousa*, paint, from the use of its roots as a dye.)

9. MYOSOTIS (Scorpion Grass, Forget-me-not).—*Calyx* 5-cleft ; *corolla* salver-shaped, its lobes blunt, twisted when in bud, and its throat nearly closed by blunt scales. (Name in Greek signifying a *mouse's ear*, from the shape of the leaves.)

10. ASPERUGO (Madwort).—*Calyx* 5-cleft, with alternate smaller teeth ; *corolla* funnel-shaped, with rounded scales in the throat. (Name from the Latin, *asper*, rough, from the excessive roughness of the leaves.)

11. CYNOGLOSSUM (Hound's-tongue).—*Calyx* 5-cleft ; *corolla* funnel-shaped, with a short tube, its mouth closed by prominent blunt scales; *nuts* flattened, prickly. (Name in Greek, signifying a *dog's tongue*, from the shape and size of the leaves.)

1. ECHIUM (*Viper's Bugloss*)

1. *E. vulgare* (Common Viper's Bugloss).—A handsome plant 1–2 feet high, remarkable for its bristly or almost prickly *stems* and *leaves*, and numerous curved spikes of *flowers*, which on their first opening are bright reddish colour, turning with age to a brilliant blue ; the leaves are narrow, tapering, the root-leaves usually withering early. The roots are very long, and descend perpendicularly into the loose soil in which the plant usually grows. A variety with white flowers is occasionally found. The name Bugloss, which is of Greek origin, signifies an *ox's tongue*, from the roughness and shape of the leaves. Walls, old quarries, and gravel pits ; not uncommon in the south, but rarer in the north of England. —Fl. June to August. Biennial.

2. *E. plantagineum* (Purple Echium).—A more spreading plant than *E. vulgare*, with larger *flowers*, and the *root-leaves* not withering so early. Found in Jersey and Cornwall.—Fl. June to September. Biennial.

2. PULMONARIA (*Lungwort*)

1. *P. angustifolia* (Narrow-leaved Lungwort).—Plant about a foot high, with narrow *leaves*, sometimes faintly spotted ; *flowers* pink, changing to blue. It occurs in Hampshire, Dorsetshire, and the Isle of Wight.—Fl. February to June. Perennial.

2. *P. officinalis* (Common Lungwort).—*Leaves* broader than in the last, and curiously spotted with white ; *root-leaves* stalked ; *stem-leaves* sessile ; *flowers* purple. Woods and thickets, rare. Often an escape from gardens, but said to be only truly wild in Hampshire and Dorsetshire.—Fl. April, May. Perennial.

3. LITHOSPERMUM (*Gromwell*)

1. *L. officinale* (Common Gromwell, or Grey Millet). —Distinguished by its erect *stems*, 2–3 feet high, much branched towards the summit, which generally grow 5 or 6 from the same root ; oblong *leaves* tapering to a point, bristly above, hairy beneath ; by its small yellowish white *flowers ;* and, above all, by its hard, white, highly polished *seeds*. Dry, stony, and bushy places, not unfrequent.—Fl. June, July. Perennial.

PULMONARIA
OFFICINALIS
(*Common
Lungwort*)

2. *L. arvense* (Corn Gromwell).—*Stem* branched ; *leaves* narrow, tapering, hairy ; *nuts* wrinkled ; *stem* about a foot high, branched from the lower part, and having rather small white flowers, the calyx of which lengthens when in fruit, and contains 3 or 4 brown wrinkled seeds. Cornfields, common.—Fl. May to July. Annual.

3. *L. purpuro-cœruleum* (Purple Gromwell).—A rare species, distinguished by its prostrate barren *stems*, from which arise erect flowering *stems*, bearing rather large purple-blue *flowers*. Shady places on chalky or limestone soils, in Wales and the south of England.—Fl. May to July. Perennial.

4. MERTENSIA (*Smooth Gromwell*)

1. *M. maritima* (Seaside Smooth Gromwell).—The only species. A singular plant, the *leaves* of which are fleshy and covered with a glaucous bloom ; they are destitute of bristles, but are sprinkled with hard *dots*, which are very evident in dried specimens ; the *flowers* are purplish blue, and the plant when fresh is said to have the flavour of oysters. Sea-shores of North Wales, Scotland, and Ireland.—Fl. May, June. Perennial.

LITHOSPERMUM
OFFICINALE (*Common
Gromwell*)

5. SYMPHYTUM (*Comfrey*)

1. *S. officinale* (Common Comfrey).—A large and handsome plant, 2–3 feet high, with branched leafy *stems*, the stem winged in the upper part ; the *leaves* elliptical, pointed, tapering towards the base, and running down the stem ; the *flowers* white, pink, or purple, drooping in 2-forked clusters. Often introduced into gardens, from which it is very difficult to eradicate it when it has once established itself, owing to the brittleness of its fleshy roots, the least bit of which will grow. Watery places and banks of rivers, common.— Fl. May to August. Perennial.

2. *S. tuberosum* (Tuberous Comfrey).—A more slender plant than the preceding ; the *stem* is scarcely branched, and but slightly winged ; the *root* is tuberous. North of England, very rare, and slightly more frequent in Southern Scotland.—Fl. June, July. Perennial.

6. BORAGO (*Borage*)

1. *B. officinalis* (Common Borage). —The only British species. The *stems* are 1–2 feet high, and, as well as the leaves, are covered with thick whitish bristles ; the *flowers*, which are large, deep blue, and very handsome, grow in terminal drooping

BORAGO OFFICINALIS
(*Common Borage*)

clusters, and may readily be distinguished from any other plant in the Order by their prominent black anthers. The juice has the smell and flavour of cucumber, and is an ingredient in claret, cider, and other "cups." A variety sometimes occurs with white flowers. Not uncommonly naturalized in waste ground.—Fl. June to September. Biennial.

LYCOPSIS ARVENSIS
(*Small Bugloss*)

7. LYCOPSIS (*Bugloss*)

1. *L. arvensis* (Small Bugloss).—The only British species. A branched, prickly plant 6–18 inches high, with oblong wavy *leaves*, the lower ones stalked, the upper ones sessile or sometimes clasping the stem. The *flowers*, borne in forked clusters, are minute,

blue, and the tube of the *corolla* is bent, which distinguishes it from any other British plant of the Order.   Waste ground, common.—Fl. June to August.   Annual.

8. ANCHUSA (*Alkanet*)

ANCHUSA
SEMPERVIRENS
(*Evergreen Alkanet*)

1. *A. sempervirens* (Evergreen Alkanet.)— A stout bristly plant, with deep green, egg-shaped *leaves* and short spikes of rather large salver-shaped *flowers*, which are of an intense azure-blue.   It is not a native, but in Devon-shire it is not an uncommon hedge plant.— Fl. June to August.   Perennial.

2. *A. officinalis* (Common Alkanet).—*Flowers* purple, funnel-shaped, growing in one-sided spikes, the segments of the *calyx* being longer than the *corolla*.   It is frequent in gardens, from which it is a not uncommon escape, but it is extremely rare in a wild state.—Fl. June, July.   Biennial.

9. MYOSOTIS (*Mouse-ear, Scorpion-grass, Forget-me-not*)

1. *M. palustris* (Forget-me-not).—*Calyx* covered with straight, closely-pressed bristles, open when in fruit; *root* creeping.—Watery places, common.   Few flowers have been more written about than the Forget-me-not, yet there is great disagreement among writers as to the plant to which the name properly belongs.   Some appear to have had the *Alkanet* in view; others, the *Speedwell ;* and others, again, some of the smaller species of *Myosotis*, which last, though very like the true Forget-me-not, are inferior in size and brilliancy of colour.   The real Forget-me-not is an aquatic plant, with a long rooting stem, bright-green, roughish leaves, and terminal, leafless, one-sided clusters of bright blue flowers, with a yellow eye, and a small white ray at the base of each lobe of the corolla.   The species which is most like it is *M. repens* (Creeping Water Scorpion-grass), which, as its name implies, has also a creeping root; the hairs of the calyx are closely pressed, as in *M. palustris*, but the calyx is closed when in fruit, and the clusters of flowers usually have a few leaves on the stalk. *M. cæspitosa* (Tufted Water Scorpion-grass) resembles the above, but has a fibrous root, and the flowers of both the last are smaller than those of *M. palustris*.   All three grow in watery places, *M. palustris* being most common, and flowering from June to October; *M. repens* least so, and, as well as *M. cæspitosa*, not flowering so late in the year.   Five other and yet smaller species

are common, but these do not grow in watery places, and are of a different habit.

2. *M. arvensis* (Field Scorpion-grass).—*Calyx* covered with spreading, hooked bristles, closed when in fruit, divided deeply into five narrow segments ; *stalks* of the fruit spreading. The whole plant roughish with spreading bristles ; the stems are from 6–18 inches high or more ; the flowers blue, small, but very beautiful. In cultivated ground, hedges, etc. This is the commonest species of all.—Fl. June to August. Annual.

3. *M. collina* (Early Field Scorpion-grass).—*Calyx* covered with spreading, hooked bristles, open when in fruit ; *cluster* with a solitary flower in the axil of the uppermost leaf. The whole plant rarely exceeds 3 inches in length ; the stems usually spread near the ground, and terminate in clusters of very minute bright blue flowers (never pink or yellow). On its first appearance, in April, the flowers are buried among the leaves, but the stems finally lengthen into clusters, and as the season advances the whole plant dries up and disappears. Dry banks, not uncommon, but frequently overlooked in consequence of its minute size.—Fl. April, May. Annual.

MYOSOTIS
VERSICOLOR
(*Parti-coloured
Scorpion-grass*)

4. *M. versicolor* (Parti-coloured Scorpion-grass).—*Calyx* covered with spreading, hooked bristles, closed when in fruit ; *cluster* on a long, leafless stalk; *stalk* of the fruit erect. A very distinct species, 3–6 inches high ; the stem is leafy below, naked above, and ends in a cluster of flowers, which are singularly coiled up when in bud, and when they first expand are yellow, changing to blue as they fade. Fields and banks; common.—Fl. April to June. Annual.

5. *M. sylvatica* (Wood For-

MYOSOTIS
ALPESTRIS
(*Mountain
Forget-me-not*)

get-me-not).—Hairs of the calyx spreading and hooked; *calyx* deeply cleft into narrow segments ; *corolla* bright blue, and as large as the Water Forget-me-not. A rare species, growing in woods in Scotland and the north of England. An Alpine form known as *M. Alpestris*, of dwarf stature. and having larger flowers than the last, is found on the mountains of Yorkshire, Westmoreland, and Perthshire; it is extremely rare.—Fl. July, August. Perennial.

10. ASPERUGO (*Madwort*)

1. *A. procumbens* (German Madwort).—The only species, occurring very sparingly in Scotland and the north of England. The *stems* are prostrate, angular, and thickly set with rigid, curved bristles; the *flowers* are small, blue, 1–3 in the axils of the upper leaves.—Fl. June, July. Annual.

11. CYNOGLOSSUM (*Hound's-tongue*)

1. *C. officinale* (Common Hound's-tongue).—A stout, herbaceous plant 1–2 feet high, with large downy *leaves*, lurid purple *flowers*, and large flattened *seeds*, which are covered with barbed prickles, and stick to the wool of animals or the clothes of passengers as closely as burs. The whole plant has a strong disagreeable smell, like that of mice. Waste ground, not uncommon.—Fl. June to August. Biennial.

2. *C. montanum* (Green Hound's-tongue).—A more slender plant than the last, the *leaves* greener, with a few stiff scattered hairs; the *flowers* smaller than in *C. officinale*, reddish, changing to blue. Shady places; of local occurrence in the south and Midlands.— Fl. May, June. Biennial.

NATURAL ORDER LVI

SOLANACEÆ.—NIGHTSHADE TRIBE

Calyx deeply 5- rarely 4-cleft, inferior ; *corolla* 5- or rarely 4-cleft, regular, plaited when in bud ; *stamens* equalling in number the divisions of the corolla and alternate with them ; *anthers* bursting lengthwise, or opening by pores ; *ovary* 2-celled ; *style* 1 ; *stigma* simple ; *fruit* a 2 or partially 4-celled capsule or berry ; *seeds* numerous. A large and highly important order, containing about a thousand species of herbaceous plants or shrubs, which inhabit most parts of the world except the coldest, and are most abundant within the tropics. The prevailing property of plants belonging to the Nightshade Tribe is narcotic, and many are, in consequence, highly poisonous ; in others, certain parts of the plant have poisonous properties, the rest being harmless, and some even contain a large quantity of nutritious matter. The genus *Solanum* is a very extensive one, comprising as many as six hundred species. First among these in importance stands the Potato (*S. tuberosum*), a native of Chili, which was introduced into Spain about 1580, and

PLATE LXIII.

Thorn Apple

PLATE LXIV.

Henbane

into Ireland by the colonists sent out by Sir Walter Raleigh, who brought it from Virginia in 1586. It was first planted on Sir Walter Raleigh's estate at Youghall, near Cork, and was cultivated for food in that country long before its value was known in England. Its leaves and berries are narcotic, but its tubers contain no noxious matter, abounding in an almost tasteless starch, on which account it is less liable to cloy on the palate than any other vegetable food except bread. *S. melongena* (the Egg-plant), a common greenhouse plant, is remarkable for bearing a large berry of the size and colour of a pullet's egg. *S. dulcamara* (Nightshade, or Bittersweet), a common English plant, with purple and yellow flowers, has narcotic leaves and scarlet berries, which possess the same property. *S. nigra* a smaller species, a common weed in England and most other countries except the coldest, has white flowers and black berries. It is narcotic to a dangerous degree. *Atropa belladonna*, a stout herbaceous plant, with dingy, purple, bell-shaped flowers, is the Deadly Nightshade, so called from the poisonous nature of every part of the plant, especially the berries, which are large, black, and shining, and of a very attractive appearance. Its juice possesses the singular property of dilating the pupil of the eye, on which account it is extensively used by oculists when operations are to be performed, and by some ladies, who persuade themselves that it adds to their beauty, from which latter use it has received its specific name. The Mandrake (*Mandragora officinalis*) was anciently thought to possess miraculous properties. It was said to shriek when taken from the ground, and to cause the instant death of any one who heard its cries. The person who gathered it, therefore, always stopped his ears with cotton, or harnessed a dog to the root, who in his efforts to escape uprooted the plant and instantly fell dead. The forked root was then trimmed so as to resemble the human form, a berry being left to represent the head. The fruit is eatable. Tobacco is the foliage of several species of *Nicotiana*, a violent poison when received into the stomach, though commonly employed in other ways without apparent ill effects. *Hyoscyamus niger*, or Henbane, is a stout herbaceous plant, with sticky, fœtid leaves and cream-coloured flowers veined with purple; it is a powerful narcotic, and in skilful hands is scarcely less valuable than opium. *Datura Stramonium* (Thorn-apple) bears large white trumpet-shaped flowers and prickly seed-vessels; it is also a dangerous poison, though employed with good effect in several nervous and other disorders, especially asthma. *Physalis Alkekengi* is the Winter Cherry, remarkable for bearing an orange-coloured berry in the enlarged calyx of the same hue. An improved form, *P. Franchetti*, is largely grown for the sake of its sprays of large orange calyces, which resemble miniature Japanese lanthorns, and are extremely decorative. Another species of *Physalis*, known as the Cape Gooseberry, is extensively grown in South Africa for the sake of its fruit,

which is made into a most luscious jam. The genus *Capsicum* affords
Cayenne pepper, which is prepared by grinding the dried seed-
vessels with their contents ; and Tomatoes belong to the genus
Lycopersicum.

1. Solanum (Nightshade).—*Corolla* wheel-shaped, 5-cleft, the
segments spreading or reflexed ; *anthers* opening by 2 pores at the
summit ; *berry* roundish, with 2 or more cells. (Name of doubtful
origin.)

2. Atropa (Deadly Nightshade).—*Corolla* bell-shaped, with 5
equal lobes ; *stamens* distant ; *berry* of 2 cells. (Name from
Atropos, one of the Fates, who was supposed to cut the thread of
human destiny.)

3. Hyoscyamus (Henbane).—*Corolla* funnel-shaped, with 5 unequal lobes ; *capsule* 2-celled, closed by a lid. (Name in Greek,
signifying *Hog's-bean.*)

1. Solanum (*Nightshade*)

1. *S. dulcamara* (Woody Nightshade, Bittersweet). — *Stem*
shrubby, climbing; *leaves* heart-shaped, the upper ones eared at
the base; *flowers* drooping. This plant, which is frequently
though incorrectly called *Deadly Nightshade,* is well marked by its
straggling woody stem, which climbs among bushes to the length of
8 or 10 feet, and by its purple flowers, the yellow anthers of which
unite in the form of a cone. At the base of each lobe of the corolla
are two green spots. The flowers grow in drooping, loose tufts, and
are succeeded by shining scarlet berries, the length of which slightly
exceeds the breadth. Damp hedges and thickets ; common.—
Fl. June, July. Perennial.

2. *S. nigrum* (Black Nightshade).—*Stem* branching, herbaceous,
a foot or less high ; *leaves* egg-shaped, wavy at the edge, and
bluntly toothed ; *flowers* white, with yellow anthers, in drooping
umbels ; *berries* globular, black, or occasionally yellow or dull red.
Waste ground ; common.—Fl. July to September. Annual or
Biennial.

2. Atropa (*Deadly Nightshade*)

1. *A. belladonna* (Deadly Nightshade, Dwale).—A stout herbaceous plant 3–4 feet high, with large egg-shaped *leaves* and solitary,
drooping, bell-shaped *flowers,* which grow in the axils of the upper
leaves, and are of a lurid purple hue. The *berries* are black and as
large as cherries, which they somewhat resemble in appearance, but
may be readily distinguished by the calyx at the base. This noxious
plant, which is the most dangerous growing in Britain, on account
of its active poisonous properties and the attractive appearance of
its berries, is fortunately of rare occurrence, growing principally in

PLATE LXV.

Woody Nightshade   Black Nightshade

PLATE LXVI.

Deadly Nightshade

old quarries and among ruins. It is said that rabbits can eat the leaves of this plant with impunity to themselves, though they render their flesh dangerously poisonous for human food by the indulgence. It is said that in a case of poisoning from this plant the best " first aids " to administer are a powerful emetic, a dose of magnesia, and the prevention of dozing.—Fl. June to August. Perennial.

3. HYOSCYAMUS (*Henbane*)

1. *H. niger* (Common Henbane).—The only British species. An erect, branched, herbaceous plant 2–3 feet high, with large viscid, hairy *leaves*, and numerous funnel-shaped, cream-coloured *flowers* with purple veins and a dark eye. The flowers are arranged in rows along one side of the stem, and are succeeded by 2-celled capsules, which are enclosed by the calyx and covered by a lid which falls off when the seeds are ripe. The whole plant has a disagreeable smell, and is dangerously narcotic, especially at the time when the seeds are ripening. An extract is used in medicine, and is often of great service, producing the effect of opium without the unpleasant symptoms which frequently follow the administration of that drug. The capsules and seeds of Henbane, smoked like tobacco, are a rustic remedy for toothache ; but convulsions and temporary insanity are said to be sometimes the consequences of their use. Common in waste places, especially near the sea.— Fl. June, July. Annual or biennial.

Two other genuses are represented in Britain, though neither is indigenous if even truly naturalized. They are :—

Datura Stramonium (Thorn-apple).—A stout, rather handsome weed 1–2 feet high, with large *leaves* angularly lobed and large white *flowers*, standing erect on short stalks in the angles of the stems, followed by ovate, spinous *capsules*. The plant has an offensive smell when bruised. Waste ground ; rare.—Fl. June, July. Annual.

L. barbarum (the Duke of Argyll's Tea-tree).—A straggling shrub with smooth, rather fleshy *leaves*, purple *flowers*, and small scarlet *fruits.* Cottage gardens, hedges, and waste places, chiefly in the eastern counties near the sea.—Fl. June to August. Shrub.

NATURAL ORDER LVII

OROBANCHACEÆ.—BROOM-RAPE TRIBE

Calyx variously divided, not falling off ; *corolla* irregular, usually 2-lipped, imbricated in the bud ; *stamens* 4, 2 long and 2 short ; *anthers* often pointed or bearded at the base ; *ovary* in a fleshy disk, many-seeded ; *style* 1 ; *stigma* 2-lobed ; *capsule* 2-valved ; *seeds* small, numerous, attached to the valves of the capsule in 2–4 rows.

A tribe of herbaceous plants, distinguished by a stout succulent stem, which is of a peculiar dingy red hue, bearing no leaves, but more or less clothed with taper-pointed scales, which are most abundant about the swollen base of the stem. The flowers are large for the size of the plant, and in all British species are of nearly the same hue as the stem, and arranged in a spike not unlike a head of asparagus, with one or more scale-like bracts at the base of each flower. All the species are parasitical on the roots of other plants. The seeds, it is said, will lie buried for some years in the ground without vegetating, until they come in contact with the young roots of some plant adapted to their wants, when they immediately sprout and seize on the points of the roots, which swell and serve as a base to the parasite. There are but two British genera belonging to this Order, *Orobanche* and *Lathræa*, of which some attach themselves to particular species ; others infest particular tribes ; and others, again, have a wider range of subjects. Several of those belonging to the genus *Orobanche* are very difficult of discrimination ; botanists, indeed, are not agreed as to the number of species, some uniting under a common name specimens found growing on various plants, others considering a slight variation in structure, joined to a difference of situation, enough to constitute a specific distinction.

1. OROBANCHE (Broom-rape).—*Calyx* of 2 lateral sepals, which are usually 2-cleft, and often combined in front, with 1–3 bracts at the base ; *corolla* gaping, 4–5 cleft, not falling off. (Name from the Greek, *orobos*, a vetch, and *ancho*, to strangle, from the injurious effects produced in the plants to which they attach themselves.)

2. LATHRÆA (Tooth - wort).—*Calyx* bell - shaped, 4-cleft ; *corolla* gaping, 2-lipped, the upper lip arched, entire, not falling off. (Name in Greek signifying *concealed*, from the humble growth of the plants among dead leaves.)

1. OROBANCHE (*Broom-rape*)

Bracts one to each flower

1. *O. major* (Great Broom-rape).—*Corolla* tubular, the lower lip in 3 lobes, of which the middle one is blunt and longer than the others ; *stamens* smooth below, downy above ; *style* downy. A stout, leafless, club-like plant, much swollen at the base, of a reddish-brown hue, viscid, and clothed with tapering scales, which pass into bracts as they ascend the stem. The flowers are of a pinkish-brown hue, and are crowded into a dense spike. The juice is bitter

OROBANCHE MAJOR
(*Great Broom-rape*)

PLATE LXVII.

Dark Mullein

White Mullein   Toothwort   Blue Broom-rape

and astringent, and has been used medicinally. On the roots of Furze, Broom, and other plants of the Order *Leguminosæ*, frequent. —Fl. June, July. Perennial.

2. *O. minor* (Lesser Broom-rape).—*Stamens* hairy below, smooth above ; *style* nearly smooth. Under this description are included several species, or varieties, which are parasitical severally on Clover, Ivy, and Sea Carrot. They all resemble the last in habit, but are of smaller size.

To this group belong *O. caryophyllacea* (Clove-scented Broom-rape), a species with hairy *stamens* and a dark purple *stigma ;* growing in Kent, on the roots of *Galium Mollugo ;* *O. elatior*, a rare species, parasitical on *Centaurea scabiosa ;* and *O. rubra*, abundant on basaltic rock in Scotland and the north of Ireland, and on magnesian rock at the Lizard Point, Cornwall. This species appears to be parasitical on the roots of Wild Thyme.

Bracts three under each flower

3. *O. ramosa* (Branched Broom-rape).—Distinguished from the preceding by its lighter colour and branched *stem*. On the roots of Hemp, very rare.—Fl. August, September. Annual.

O. cærulea (Blue Broom-rape).—Distinguished by its 3 *bracts* and its bluish purple hue. A very rare species, found in Norfolk, Hertfordshire, and the Isle of Wight.

2. LATHRÆA (*Tooth-wort*)

1. *L. squamaria* (Tooth-wort).—The only British species. The *stem* is branched below the surface of the ground or withered leaves among which it grows ; it is of a lightish hue, and thickly clothed with tooth-like *scales* ; each branch bears a one-sided cluster of drooping purplish *flowers*, with rather broad bracts at the base of each. Grows in woods and thickets on the roots of Hazel.— Fl. April, May. Perennial.

NATURAL ORDER LVIII

SCROPHULARIACEÆ.—FIG-WORT TRIBE

Calyx 4 to 5-lobed, not falling off ; *corolla* irregular, often 2-lipped ; *stamens* usually 4, 2 long and 2 short (didynamous), sometimes 2 or 5 ; *ovary* 2-celled ; *style* 1 ; *stigma* 2-lobed ; *capsule* 2-celled, 2 to 4-valved, or opening by pores. A large and important Order, containing nearly two thousand species, of which some are shrubs, but the greater number are herbaceous, inhabiting all parts of the world, from the arctic regions to the tropics. The general character of the species is acrid and bitterish, and some have power-

P

ful medicinal properties. The powdered leaves of Foxglove (*Digitalis purpurea*) lower the pulse, and, if taken in large doses, are poisonous. *Euphrasia* (Eye-bright), the " Euphrasy " of Milton, makes a useful eye-water. Among foreign species, *Gratiola* is said to be the active ingredient in the famous gout medicine, " Eau medicinale." Fox-glove, Snapdragon, Mullein, and Toad-flax have showy and ornamental flowers ; and several kinds of Speedwell (*Veronica*) are deservedly admired for their small but elegant blue flowers.

Stamens 4, 2 long and 2 short

1. DIGITALIS (Foxglove).—*Calyx* in 5 deep, unequal segments ; *corolla* irregularly bell-shaped, with 4–5 shallow lobes ; *capsule* egg-shaped. (Name from the Latin *digitale*, the finger of a glove, which its flowers resemble.)

2. ANTIRRHINUM (Snapdragon).—*Calyx* 5-parted ; *corolla* personate, swollen at the base (not spurred), its mouth closed by a palate ; *capsule* oblique, opening by pores at the top. (Name in Greek signifying *opposite the nose*, from the mask-like appearance of the flowers.)

3. LINARIA (Toad-flax).—Like *Antirrhinum*, except that the *corolla* is spurred at the base. (Name from *Linum*, Flax, which the leaves of some species resemble.)

4. SCROPHULARIA (Fig-wort).—*Calyx* 5-lobed ; *corolla* nearly globose, with two short lips, the upper 2-lobed, with a small scale within, the lower 3-lobed ; *capsule* opening with 2 valves, the edges of which are turned in. (Name from the disease for which the plant was formerly thought a specific.)

5. LIMOSELLA (Mud-wort).—*Calyx* 5-cleft ; *corolla* bell-shaped, 5-cleft, equal ; *capsule* globose, 2-valved. (Name from the Latin, *limus*, mud, from the character of the places in which the plant grows.)

6. MELAMPYRUM (Cow-wheat).—*Calyx* tubular, with 4 narrow teeth ; *corolla* gaping, *upper lip* flattened vertically, turned back at the margin ; *lower lip* 3-cleft ; *capsule* oblong, obliquely pointed, flattened ; *seeds* 1 or 2 in each cell. (Name in Greek signifying *black wheat*, the seeds, when ground and mixed with flour, being said to make it black.)

7. PEDICULARIS (Red-rattle).—*Calyx* inflated, its segments somewhat leafy ; *corolla* gaping ; *upper lip* arched, flattened vertically ; *lower lip* plane, 3-lobed ; *capsule* flattened, oblique ; *seeds* angular. (Name in allusion to the disease produced in sheep which feed in places where it grows.)

8. RHINANTHUS (Yellow-rattle).—*Calyx* inflated, 4-toothed ; *corolla* gaping ; *upper lip* flattened vertically ; *lower lip* plane, 3-

PLATE LXVIII.

Lesser Snapdragon   Toadflax   Figwort
Ivy-leaved Linaria   Pale Linaria

lobed; *capsule* flattened, blunt; *seeds* numerous, flat, and bordered. (Name in Greek signifying *nose-flower*, from its peculiar shape.)

9. BARTSIA.—*Calyx* tubular, 4-cleft; *corolla* gaping, with a contracted throat; *upper lip* arched, entire; *lower lip* 3-lobed, lobes bent back; *capsule* flattened, pointed; *seeds* numerous, angular. (Name in honour of *John Bartsch*, a Prussian botanist.)

10. EUPHRASIA (Eye-bright).—*Calyx* tubular, 4-cleft; *corolla* gaping; *upper lip* divided; *lower lip* in 3 nearly equal lobes; *anthers* spurred at the base; *capsule* flattened, blunt, or notched; *seeds* numerous, ribbed. (Name from the Greek, *Euphrosyne*, gladness, from the valuable properties attributed to it.)

11. SIBTHORPIA (Cornish Money-wort).—*Calyx* in 5 deep, spreading segments; *corolla* wheel-shaped, 5-cleft, nearly regular; *capsule* nearly round, flattened at the top. (Name in honour of Dr. *Sibthorp*, formerly professor of botany at Oxford.)

12. MIMULUS (Monkey-flower).—*Calyx* 5-lobed; *corolla* 2-lipped, gaping; *seeds* numerous. (Name from the Greek, *mimo*, an ape, from a supposed resemblance which the flower bears to that fantastic quadruped.)

Stamens 2

13. VERONICA (Speedwell).—*Corolla* wheel-shaped, unequally 4-cleft, lower segment the narrowest. (*Veronica* is the name of a saint in the Romish Church, but why given to this plant is unknown.)

Stamens 5

14. VERBASCUM (Mullein).—*Calyx* 5-parted; *corolla* wheel-shaped, 5-cleft, irregular; *stamens* hairy. (Name from the Latin, *barba*, a beard, from the shaggy leaves of some species.)

1. DIGITALIS (*Foxglove*)

1. *D. purpurea* (Purple Foxglove).—The only British species. A stately plant 2-6 feet high, with large wrinkled, somewhat downy *leaves* and a tall *stem*, bearing a long raceme of numerous purple bell-shaped *flowers*, which droop after expansion. On the inside the flowers are beautifully spotted, and occasionally an elegant white variety is found. The name *Foxglove* is a corruption of *folk's-glove*; that is, *Fairies' gloves*. The powdered leaf, though poisonous in large doses, is a valuable medicine in cases where it is desired to lower the pulse. Common in dry, hilly places and in woods, but never on limestone.—Fl. June, July. Biennial.

2. ANTHIRRHINUM (*Snapdragon*)

1. *A. majus* (Great Snapdragon).—*Leaves* narrow, tapering; *spikes* many-flowered; *sepals* egg-shaped, blunt, much shorter than

the corolla. A handsome plant, with numerous leafy *stems*, each of which bears a spike of large, erect, personate flowers of a purple hue, sporting to rose colour or white. The garden varieties are innumerable, and range through splendid shades of crimson, pink, white, and yellow, not to mention the curiously veined and colour-flecked forms. Children derive much amusement from pinching the flowers between the finger and thumb, when the palate opens, as if in imitation of the fabulous monster from which it derives its name. This plant, though not indigenous, is not uncommonly found naturalized in limestone quarries, chalk-pits, and on old walls. —Fl. June to August. Perennial.

2. *A. orontium* (Lesser Snapdragon).— *Leaves* very narrow, tapering ; *spikes* few-flowered ; *sepals* much longer than the corolla. Smaller and more slender than the last, seldom above a foot high, and at once distinguished by its small flowers which grow in the axils of the upper leaves, the petals of which are pink, and the sepals long and narrow. Cornfields chiefly in the south ; not uncommon. —Fl. July to September. Annual.

3. LINARIA (*Toad-flax*)

1. *L. vulgaris* (Yellow Toad-flax).—An erect herbaceous plant 1–2 feet high, with numerous grass-like *leaves* of a glaucous hue, and dense spikes or clusters of yellow *flowers* which are shaped like those of the *Snapdragon*, but spurred at the base. A variety is sometimes found with a regular, 5-spurred corolla, but it is rare. Hedges ; common.—Fl. August, September. Perennial.

2. *L. elatine* (Sharp-pointed Fluellen).—A small prostrate plant, with downy *stem* and downy halbert-shaped *leaves ; flowers* small, solitary, axillary, the upper lip deep purple, the lower yellow, and the spur straight. Cornfields ; frequent.—Fl. July to September. Annual.

3. *L. spuria* (Round-leaved Toad-flax).—Resembling the last so closely that it might be mistaken for a luxuriant specimen. The *flowers* are the same colour, but larger, and with the *spur* recurved ; and the *leaves* are always rounded at the base, not halbert-shaped. Similar situations with the last, but less frequent.—Fl. July to September. Annual.

4. *L. cymbalaria* (Ivy-leaved Toad-flax).—*Leaves* kidney-shaped, 5-lobed, smooth ; *stem* creeping. Not a native species, but quite naturalized, growing freely from seed, and extending widely by help of its long, rooting stems. The flowers are small, solitary, and pale lilac ; the leaves somewhat fleshy, and of a purple hue on the under side. So rapidly does it increase in some places that it has been given the name of "*Mother of Thousands.*" On old garden walls ; common.—Fl. nearly all the year round. Perennial.

PLATE LXIX.

Foxglove   Common Speedwell   Yellow Mimulus

Brooklime   Germander Speedwell

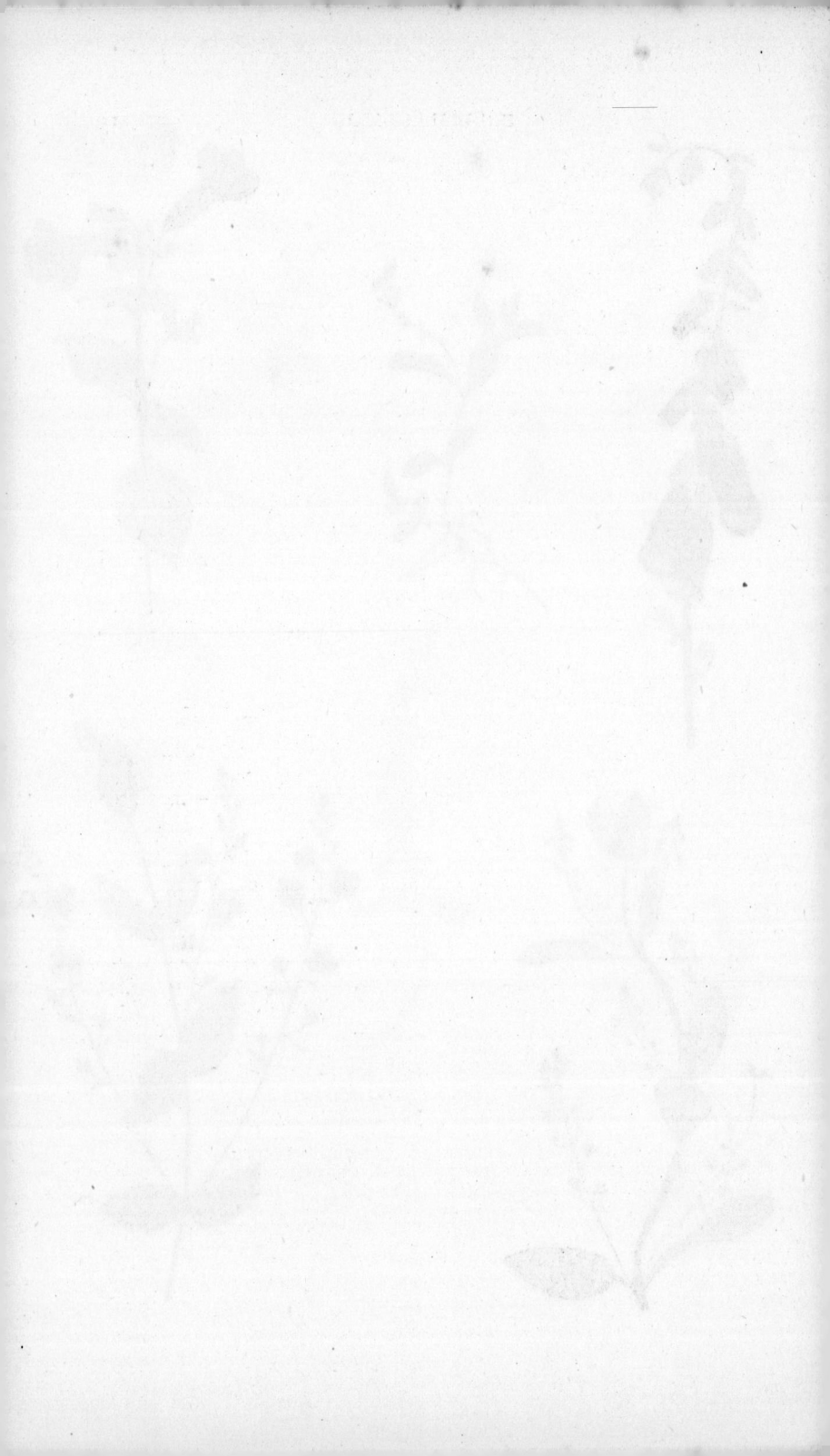

5. *L. repens* (Pale blue Toad-flax).—A slender, erect plant 1–2 feet high, with glaucous, very narrow *leaves* and veined, purplish blue *flowers* growing in spiked clusters. Stony calcareous places, rare.—Fl. July to September   Perennial.

6. *L. minor* (Least Toad-flax).—A small, erect, much-branched plant, with narrow viscid, downy *leaves* and solitary, small lilac *flowers*, with a blunt spur. A cornfield weed, not uncommon.— Fl. May to October   Annual.

Several other species occur as weeds in gardens and growing on ballast near the sea, but they have no claim to be considered natives.

4. Scrophularia (*Fig-wort*)

1. *S. nodosa* (Knotted Fig-wort).—A tall herbaceous plant 3–4 feet high ; *stem* square, with the angles blunt ; *leaves* smooth, heart-shaped, tapering to a point ; *flowers* in repeatedly forked, loose panicles, dingy greenish-purple. The plant has a strong, unpleasant smell. Damp bushy places ; common.—Fl. June, July. Perennial.

2. *S. aquatica* (Water Fig-wort).—*Stem* square, with the angles winged ; *leaves* smooth, heart-shaped, oblong, blunt ; *flowers* in close panicles. Resembling the last, but at once distinguished by the winged angles of its stems, which, though hollow and succulent, are rigid when dead, and prove very troublesome to anglers, owing to their lines becoming entangled in the withered capsules. Sides of streams and ditches ; common.—Fl. July, August. Perennial.

SCROPHULARIA AQUATICA
(*Water Fig-wort*)

3. *S. Scorodonia* (Balm-leaved Fig-wort). —Very like the last, but distinguished by its downy, wrinkled *leaves ;* the *stems* also are not winged. Found only in Cornwall, Ireland, and the Channel Islands. —Fl. July, August. Perennial.

4. *S. vernalis* (Yellow Fig-wort).—Well distinguished by its re- markably bright green *foliage* and yellow *flowers*. It appears early in spring, and is the only species found in Britain which can be called ornamental. It is of local occurrence, but not indigenous. —Fl. April to June. Perennial.

5. LIMOSELLA (*Mud-wort*)

LIMOSELLA AQUATICA
(*Common Mud-Wort*)

1. *L. aquatica* (Common Mud-wort).—
The only British species. A small plant,
throwing up from the *roots* a number
of smooth *leaves* on long stalks, and
several minute, pale rose-coloured or
white *flowers*, which are overtopped by
the leaves. Watery places; not common.—Fl. July, August. Annual.

6. MELAMPYRUM (*Cow-wheat*)

1. *M. pratense* (Common Yellow Cow-
wheat).—A common plant 6–12 inches high,
with opposite pairs of straggling *branches*
below; *leaves* in distant pairs, narrow,
tapering, smooth; and long-tubed axillary
yellow *flowers* in pairs, all turning one way;
corolla four times as long as the calyx; *lower
lip* longer than the *upper*. Cows are said to
be fond of it, and according to Linnæus, the
best and yellowest butter is made where
it abounds. The name *pratense* (growing
in meadows) is misleading, as it is practically never found in such situations. Woods,
common.—Fl. June to August. Annual.

MELAMPYRUM PRATENSE
(*Common Yellow Cow-
wheat*)

2. *M. sylvaticum* (Small Cow-wheat).—
Very like the last, but smaller; the *flowers*
are deeper yellow, the *corolla* only twice as
long as the calyx, and the *lips* are equal.
Mountainous woods in Scotland and the
north of England.—Fl. July, August. Annual.

3. *M. arvense* (Purple Cow-wheat).—*Flowers* in oblong spikes;
corolla-tube pink, *throat* yellow, and *lips* red; flowers almost buried
among the long bracts, which are of a rosy pink, and very much
cut and toothed. Cornfields in Norfolk, and a few places in South-
Eastern England; rare.—Fl. July, August. Annual.

4. *M. cristatum* (Crested Cow-wheat).—Plant about a foot high;
leaves narrow; *flowers* in 4-sided spikes; *corolla* yellow and purple,
the floral bracts broad and toothed and of a beautiful pink. Woods
and thickets in the eastern counties; rare.—Fl. August, September.
Annual.

PLATE LXX.

Red Bartsia

Penny-royal

Yellow Rattle

Red and White Lousewort

Common Yellow Cow-wheat

7. PEDICULARIS (*Red-rattle*)

1. *P. palustris* (Marsh Red-rattle).—
An herbaceous plant 12–18 inches high ;
stem solitary, erect, branched throughout, of a purple tinge ; *leaves* deeply
cut ; *calyx* downy, with 2 deeply-cut
lobes ; *flowers* large, crimson. It is a
conspicuous plant in marshes and bogs,
where it often overtops the surrounding
herbage with its somewhat handsome
flowers. Common.—Fl. June to September. Perennial.

PEDICULARIS PALUSTRIS
(*Marsh Red-rattle*)

2. *P. sylvatica* (Dwarf Red-rattle,
Louse-wort).—*Stems* several from the
same root, prostrate, unbranched ; *calyx*
smooth, with 5 unequal, leaf-like lobes.
Distinguished from the last by its humbler growth and rose-coloured flowers
with smooth calyces. A white variety
is occasionally found. Damp meadows
and heathy places ; common.—Fl. June
to August. Perennial.

8. RHINANTHUS (*Yellow-rattle*)

1. *R. Crista-galli* (Cock's-comb, Yellow-rattle).—An erect, somewhat rigid plant 12–18 inches high, composed of a single *stem* and
terminating in a loose *spike* of yellow *flowers*. *Leaves* narrow,
oblong, tapering to a point, serrated ; *flower-bracts* egg-shaped,
deeply serrated ; *calyces* inflated. " When the fruit is ripe the
seeds rattle in the husky capsule, and indicate to the Swedish
peasantry the season for gathering in their hay. In England, Mr.
Curtis well observes, haymaking begins when the plant is in full
flower " (Sir W. J. Hooker). In cultivated land ; common.—
Fl. June. Annual.

A variety, *R. major* (Large bushy Yellow-rattle), which is of local
occurrence, bears the *flowers* in crowded *spikes ;* it is a larger and
more branching plant, and at the base of each flower is a yellowish
bract ending in a fine point.

9. BARTSIA

1. *B. viscosa* (Yellow Viscid Bartsia).—An erect plant, from a few
inches to a foot or rather more high. *Leaves* narrow, tapering,
deeply serrated, lower opposite, upper alternate. Somewhat resembling Yellow-rattle, but at once distinguished by its solitary

axillary, not spiked yellow *flowers*, and by being covered with clammy down. Marshes and wet places in the south and south-west.—Fl. June to September. Annual.

2. *B. odontites* (Red Bartsia).— A much-branched herbaceous plant 6–12 inches high, with narrow, tapering, serrated *leaves* of a dingy purplish-green, and numerous one-sided *spikes* of small pink *flowers*. While flowering the spikes usually drop towards the ends. Cornfields ; abundant.—Fl. July to September. Annual.

3. *B. Alpina* (Alpine Bartsia).—An erect plant, approaching *B. viscosa* in habit, 6–8 inches high. *Leaves* all opposite, ovate, crenate ; *flowers* dull purple in a leafy *spike*. High mountains in Scotland and the north of England ; rare.—Fl. July, August. Perennial.

10. EUPHRASIA (*Eye-bright*)

EUPHRASIA OFFICINALIS
(*Common Eye-bright*)

1. *E. officinalis* (Common Eye-bright). — The only British species. An elegant little plant 2–6 inches high, with deeply cut *leaves* and loose, leafy *spikes* of numerous white or purplish *flowers*, variegated with yellow. On the mountains and near the sea the stem is scarcely branched, and the leaves are fleshy ; but in rich soil it assumes the habit of a minute shrub. The *roots* are said to be parasitic on grasses. An infusion of this plant makes a useful eye-water.—Fl. July, August. Annual.

11. SIBTHORPIA (*Cornish Money-wort*)

1. *S. Europæa* (Cornish Money-wort).—The only British species. An elegant little plant, with slender, thread-like *stems*, which creep along the ground in tangled masses ; and small, delicate green, downy, orbicular, notched *leaves* on slender stems. The *flowers* very small, pink and yellow, on axillary stalks. It is found clothing the banks of springs and rivulets in most parts of Cornwall, and occasionally met with in some of the other southern counties. —Fl. June to September. Perennial.

SIBTHORPIA EUROPÆA
(*Cornish Money-Wort*)

12. MIMULUS (*Monkey-flower*)

1. *M. luteus* (Yellow Monkey-flower).—*Stems* hollow, about a foot high, shortly creeping ; *leaves* ovate, toothed, smooth ; *flowers* large, yellow, often marked inside with reddish spots. A pretty plant, with showy yellow flowers. Native of North America, and not uncommonly found naturalized by streams and in marshy meadows. The cultivated garden varieties are often very handsomely spotted and blotched with red-brown.—Fl. June to September. Perennial.

13. VERONICA (*Speedwell*)

1. *V. spicata* (Spiked Speedwell).—*Stems* erect, about 6 inches high, woody below ; *leaves* roundish, downy ; flowers in a dense *spike*, bright blue or pale pink ; *petals* narrow. Chalk downs in Suffolk and Cambridge ; rare.—Fl. July. Perennial.

2. *V. saxatilis* (Rock Speedwell).—*Stems* 4–5 inches high, slender, woody ; *leaves* entire, oblong, small, and tough ; *flowers* large, brilliant blue, in a short panicle ; *capsules* egg-shaped. Almost the entire plant is glabrous. A rare species, found only on one or two mountains in Scotland.—Fl. July, August. Perennial.

V. fruticulosa (Flesh-coloured Speedwell) is a variety of *V. saxatilis*, with small pink *flowers*, and is extremely rare.

3. *V. Alpina* (Alpine Veronica).—A slightly hairy little plant, with simple, ascending *stems*, 2-5 inches high (not woody), bearing *leaves* a little larger than in *V. serpyllifolia*, and a crowded *raceme* of 4 or 5 deep blue *flowers* with very short *styles*. A rare species, found only near the summits of the Highland mountains.—Fl. July, August. Perennial.

4. *V. serpyllifolia* (Thyme-leaved Veronica).—A small plant, with branched, prostrate, or slightly ascending *stems ;* smooth, egg-shaped, or elliptical, slightly notched *leaves*, nearly sessile, and less than half an inch in length. The *flowers*, which grow in somewhat crowded *spikes*, are small, very light blue, and striped with dark blue veins. *Capsules* inversely heart-shaped, with a long *style*. Waste ground ; common.—Fl. May to July. Perennial.

A somewhat downy variety, with rather larger flowers, is found high up in the Scotch mountains, and is apt to be taken for a distinct species.

5. *V. officinalis* (Common Speedwell).—A hairy plant with prostrate *stems*, rooting at the *nodes*, varying from 2–6 inches in length ; *leaves* oblong, serrated, astringent, sometimes made into tea ; *flowers* rather small, pale blue, in hairy, axillary *spikes* or *racemes*. Heaths and dry pastures ; common.—Fl. May to August. Perennial.

6. *V. anagallis* (Water Speedwell).—A smooth, erect plant, 6–18 inches high, sometimes rather fleshy ; *leaves* narrow, tapering, serrated, sessile ; *flowers* small, pale blue or flesh-coloured, in opposite axillary *racemes*. Streams and ditches, common.—Fl. June to August. Perennial.

✕ 7. *V. beccabunga* (Brooklime).—A succulent plant about a foot high, with elliptical, blunt, slightly serrated *leaves*, and short axillary, opposite clusters of small bright blue *flowers ; stems* rooting at the base. Whole plant smooth. Brooks and ditches ; common. —Fl. June to August. Perennial.

8. *V. scutellata* (Marsh Speedwell).—Smooth, or sometimes slightly downy ; *leaves* linear, slightly toothed ; *clusters* short, alternate ; *fruit-stalks* bent back ; *capsules* flat, deeply notched. A weak, straggling plant, well distinguished by its very narrow leaves and large flat capsules. Flowers pale pink. Marshes ; not uncommon.—Fl. June to August. Perennial.

9. *V. montana* (Mountain Speedwell).—*Stem* hairy all round ; *leaves* stalked ; *clusters* few-flowered ; *capsule* flat, much longer than the calyx. Approaching the last in habit, but well distinguished by the above characters and by its smaller light blue flowers. Woods ; common.—Fl. May, June. Perennial.

10. *V. chamædrys* (Germander Speedwell).—*Stems* with two hairy, opposite lines ; *leaves* very shortly stalked, deeply serrated, hairy ; *clusters* very long, axillary ; *capsule* shorter than the 4-cleft calyx. A well-known plant, which under the popular names of *Blue Speedwell* and *Bird's-eye* is a favourite with everyone. No one can have walked in the country in spring without admiring its cheerful bright blue flowers, but few perhaps have remarked the singular pair of hairy lines which traverse the whole length of the stem, shifting from side to side whenever they arrive at a fresh pair of leaves. Hedge banks ; abundant.—Fl. May, June. Perennial.

11. *V. hederifolia* (Ivy-leaved Speedwell).—A common weed, with stalked 5 to 7-lobed *leaves,* and bearing in the axil of each leaf a pale blue *flower,* the *stalk* of which is bent back when in fruit ; *sepals* heart-shaped, fringed. The *capsule* is composed of 2 muchswollen lobes, each of which contains 2 large black *seeds.* Waste places ; common.—Fl. all the summer. Annual.

12. *V. agrestis* (Field Speedwell).—A common weed, with several branched, prostrate *stems* and stalked, heart-shaped, deeply serrated *leaves,* the lower ones of which are opposite, the upper alternate, and in the axils of each of these is a small blue *flower* on a slender pedicle nearly as long as the leaf. The *capsule* is composed of 2 swollen, keeled lobes, and each *cell* contains about 6 *seeds.* Waste places ; very common.—Fl. all the summer. Annual.

V. agrestis varies considerably, especially in the shape of the *sepals* and size and colour of the *corolla*, and two of the more distinct forms have been named. *V. polita.*—Rounded *sepals;* *corolla* large and blue; *leaves* small. *V. opaca.*—*Sepals* spoon-shaped; *seeds* few.

13. *V. Buxbaumii* (Buxbaum's Speedwell).—Not unlike the last, but a stouter plant, with large blue *flowers* on *pedicles* longer than the leaves; *capsules* sharply keeled, twice as broad as long.. Cultivated ground; common. Probably introduced with agricultural seeds at some time.—Fl. all the summer. Annual.

14. *V. arvensis* (Wall Speedwell).—A small plant, with inconspicuous light blue *flowers*, which are almost concealed among the upper *leaves* or *bracts;* *lower leaves* egg-shaped, heart-shaped at the base, crenate, stalked; *upper leaves* sessile, longer than the flowers. The whole plant is downy, and a great collector of dust. Walls and fields; common.—Fl. April to September. Annual.

15. *V. verna* (Vernal Speedwell).—A small plant, 2–3 inches high, much resembling the last, but distinguished by its *leaves* being cut into 3–7 pinnatifid lobes. Sandy fields in Norfolk and Suffolk.—Fl. May to July. Annual.

16. *V. triphyllos* (Finger-leaved Speedwell).—A rare species, distinguished by its 3–7 fingered *leaves* and loose *racemes* of a few dark blue *flowers*. Sandy places in Norfolk, Suffolk, and Yorkshire.—Fl. April to July. Annual.

14. VERBASCUM (*Mullein*)

1. *V. Thapsus* (Great Mullein).—A stout herbaceous plant with a simple or branched *stem*, 2–5 feet high, remarkable for its large flannel-like *leaves*, woolly on both sides, running down the stem. The *flowers* are yellow, and borne in dense club-shaped spikes. Two of the 5 *stamens* are longer than the rest, and hairy; the remaining 3 are smooth. This plant, together with Foxgloves, is a picturesque object if planted broadly in the wilder parts of a garden.—Fl. July, August. Biennial.

VERBASCUM
THAPSUS
(*Great Mullein*)

2. *V. Blattaria* (Moth Mullein). — A tall, somewhat slender plant, simple or branched, smooth or nearly so, with shining, crenate *leaves*, the lower ones stalked, often lobed at the base, those half-way up the stem sessile, and the upper ones clasping or running down the stem; *flowers* large and handsome, yellow or sometimes white, in

loose tufts on a long, interrupted spike. The *stamens* are covered with purple hairs. Banks; rare, except in the south-west of England, where it is not unfrequent.—Fl. July, August. Biennial.

3. *V. virgatum* (Primrose-leaved Mullein).—Allied to the preceding ; but the *lower leaves* are downy, and the *flowers* are on shorter stalks. Banks, rare.—Fl. August, September. Biennial.

4. *V. nigrum* (Dark Mullein).—A handsome plant 2–3 feet high. *Leaves* slightly downy on both sides, especially below ; lower ones oblong, heart-shaped, stalked ; upper ones small and sessile. The *flowers*, in dense tufts on a long, crowed spike, are bright yellow, and the *stamens* are covered with purple hairs. Hedges and roadsides, but of local occurrence.—Fl. July to September. Biennial.

5 *V. Lychnitis* (White Mullein).—*Stems* 2–3 feet high ; *leaves* smooth above, under sides of leaves and stems covered with powdery down ; *flowers* small, cream-coloured or white ; *filaments* covered with white hairs. Chiefly on chalky soil ; rare.—Fl. July, August. Biennial.

6. *V. pulverulentum* (Hoary Mullein).—*Stem* 2–3 feet high ; *panicle* of smallish yellow *flowers*, branched ; *filaments* covered with white hairs. Remarkable for the mealy down which clothes both sides of the *leaves*. Found in Norfolk and Suffolk.—Fl. July. Biennial.

Natural Order LIX
LABIATÆ.—Labiate Tribe

Calyx tubular, regular, or 2-lipped ; *corolla* irregular, mostly 2-lipped (*labiate*), the lower lip largest and 3-lobed ; *stamens* 4, 2 longer than the others, or sometimes wanting ; *ovary* deeply 4-lobed ; *style* 1 ; *stigma* 2-cleft ; *fruit* of 4 seeds, each of which is enclosed within a distinct shell or rind. A large and strongly-marked Natural Order, comprising some 2500 species of herbs and shrubs, which all agree in having square stems, opposite leaves, labiate, or 2-lipped flowers, and a 4-lobed ovary with a single style arising from the base of the lobes. They are most abundant in temperate climates, and are remarkable for not possessing injurious properties in any single instance. Many are fragrant and aromatic. *Patchouli* is a favourite perfume, both in its natural state and when distilled. Lavender contains a fragrant volatile oil, which is valued both for its fragrance, and as a medicine for its stimulant properties. Several kinds of mint, as Peppermint and Penny-royal, are much used in medicine. Spear-mint, Basil, Thyme, Marjoram, Savory, and Sage, are commonly used as pot-herbs, furnishing both agreeable and wholesome condiments. Horehound, Ground-Ivy, and Balm are in rural districts popular remedies for chest complaints. Rosemary is remarkable for its undoubted power of encouraging the growth ot the hair, and curing baldness, and is the active ingredient in most good pomatums ; an infusion of it prevents the hair from uncurling in damp weather ; and it is one of the plants used in the preparation of Hungary water and eau de Cologne. The admired flavour of Narbonne honey is ascribed to the bees feeding on the flowers of this plant, as that of the honey of Hymettus is indebted for its flavour to Wild Thyme. Several species of Sage (*Salvia*) are also cultivated for the beauty of their flowers. The Japanese plant, *Stachys tuberifera*, is grown for the sake of its tubers, which are known as Chinese Artichokes, and are a most delicate vegetable.

Stamens 2

1. LYCOPUS (Gipsy-wort).—*Calyx* 5-toothed ; *corolla* 4-cleft, nearly regular. (Name in Greek signifying a *Wolf's-foot*, from a fancied resemblance in the leaves.)

2. SALVIA (Sage).—*Calyx* 2-lipped ; *corolla* gaping ; *filaments* forked. (Name in the Latin, *salveo*, to be well, from the healing properties of the genus.)

Stamens 4

Corolla nearly regular, its tube scarcely longer than the calyx.

3. MENTHA (Mint).—*Calyx* equal, 5-toothed ; *corolla* 4-cleft, with a very short tube. (Name, the Latin name of the plant.)

Corolla 2-lipped, lips nearly equal in length

4. THYMUS (Thyme).—*Calyx* 2-lipped, 10- to 13-ribbed, the *throat* hairy ; *corolla* with the upper lip notched, the lower 3-cleft ; *flowers* in heads or whorls. (Name, the Latin name of the plant.)

5. ORIGANUM (Marjoram).—*Calyx* 5-toothed, 10- to 13-ribbed, the *throat* hairy ; *flowers* in spikes, which are imbricated with bracts. (Name from the Greek, *oros*, a mountain, and *ganos*, joy, from the favourite station of the family.)

Corolla with the upper lip very short, or wanting

6. AJUGA (Bugle).—*Calyx* 5-cleft ; *corolla* with a long tube, the upper lip very short, lower 3-cleft. (Name said to be corrupted from the Latin, *abiga*, an allied plant.)

7. TEUCRIUM (Germander).—*Calyx* 5-cleft ; *corolla* with the upper lip deeply 2-cleft, lower 3-cleft. (Name from *Teucer*, who is said to have been the first to use it in medicine.)

*Corolla 2-lipped, lips unequal ; calyx 5-toothed ; stamens
longer than the tube of the corolla*

8. BALLOTA (Black Horehound).—*Calyx* funnel-shaped, with
5 sharp equal teeth ; *corolla* with the upper lip erect, concave ;
lower 3-lobed, the middle lobe largest, heart-shaped ; two front
stamens the longest.   (Name in Greek signifying *rejected*, from the
offensive smell of the plant.)

9. LEONURUS (Motherwort).—*Calyx* with 5 prickly teeth ; *corolla*
with the upper lip nearly flat, very hairy above ; *anthers* sprinkled
with hard, shining dots ; two front *stamens* the longest.   (Name
in Greek signifying a *Lion's tail*, from some fancied resemblance in
the plant.)

10. GALEOPSIS (Hemp Nettle).—*Calyx* bell-shaped, with 5 prickly
teeth ; *corolla* with an inflated throat ; upper lip arched, lower
3-lobed, with 2 teeth on its upper side ; two front *stamens* the
longest.   (Name in Greek denoting that the flower bears some
resemblance to a *weasel*.)

11. LAMIUM (Dead-nettle).—*Calyx* bell-shaped or tubular, with
5 teeth ; *corolla* with an arched upper lip, and 3-lobed lower lip ;
two front *stamens* the longest.   (Name from the Greek, *laimos*,
a throat, from the shape of the corolla tube.)

12. STACHYS (Woundwort).—*Calyx* with 5 or 10 ribs, and 5 equal
teeth ; tube of the *corolla* as long or longer than the calyx ; upper
lip arched, lower 3-lobed, the side lobes bent back before withering ;
two front *stamens* the longest.   (Name in Greek signifying a *bunch*,
from the mode of flowering.)

13. NEPETA (Cat-mint).—*Calyx* tubular, oblique, 5-toothed ;
tube of the *corolla* longer than the calyx ; upper lip flat, notched,
lower 3-lobed, two front *stamens* the shortest.   (Name of doubtful
origin.)

*Corolla 2-lipped, lips unequal ; calyx 5 to 10-toothed ;
stamens shorter than the tube of the corolla*

14. MARRUBIUM (White Horehound).—*Calyx* with 5 or 10 teeth,
the throat hairy ; tube of the *corolla* longer than the calyx ; upper
lip straight, very narrow, deeply 2-cleft, lower 3-lobed.   (Name of
doubtful origin.)

Corolla 2-lipped, the lips unequal ; calyx 2-lipped

15. CALAMINTHA (Calamint, Wild Basil, Basil Thyme).—*Calyx*
13-nerved, tubular, swollen underneath ; upper lip 3-cleft ; lower
2-cleft, throat mostly hairy ; tube of the *corolla* straight ; upper
lip nearly plane, lower spreading, 3-cleft.   (Name, the Greek name
of some allied plant.)

16. **Melittis** (Wild Balm).—*Calyx* bell-shaped, much wider than the tube of the corolla, variously lobed; upper lip of the *corolla* nearly flat, entire, lower with 3 rounded, nearly equal lobes. (Name from the Greek, *melitta*, a bee, from the quantity of honey contained in the tube.)

17. **Prunella** (Self-heal).—*Calyx* flattened, and closed when in fruit; *filaments* 2-forked. (Name from a German word for the *quinsy*, for which complaint it was considered a specific.)

18. **Scutellaria** (Skull-cap).—Upper lip of the *calyx* bulged outward about the middle, and finally closing down like a lid over the fruit; tube of the *corolla* much larger than the calyx. (Name from the Latin, *scutella*, a little cup, which the calyx somewhat resembles.)

1. Lycopus (*Gipsy-wort*)

1. *L. Europæus* (Common Gipsy-wort).—An aquatic plant, with erect, scarcely branched *stems*, 2 feet high, deeply cut lanceolate *leaves*, and small, pale flesh-coloured *flowers*, growing in crowded whorls in the axils of the upper leaves. The only British species. On the banks of rivers and ditches; frequent.—Fl. July, August. Perennial.

L. Europæus
(*Common Gipsy-wort*)

Salvia Verbenaca
(*Wild Sage*)

2. Salvia (*Sage*)

1. *S. verbenaca* (Clary, or Wild Sage).—An aromatic, herbaceous plant, 1–2 feet high, with oblong, blunt *leaves*, heart-shaped at the

base, wavy at the edge and crenate ; it is rendered conspicuous by its long spikes of purple-blue *flowers*, the calyces of which are much larger than the corolla. At the base of each flower are 2 heart-shaped, fringed, acute *bracts*. Dry pastures, especially near the sea, or on a chalky soil.—Fl. June to August. Perennial.

2. *S. pratensis* (Meadow Clary).—This is not considered a native, but occurs in Kent, Cornwall, and Oxford. It is distinguished by its handsome spikes of blue *flowers ;* the *corolla* twice as long as the *calyx*. Dry pastures ; rare.—Fl. June to August. Perennial.

3. MENTHA (*Mint*)

1. *M. sylvestris* (Horse Mint).—A strong-scented plant, usually growing in masses 1–2 feet high, with egg-shaped *leaves* tapering to a point, serrated, downy, and very white with down beneath ; and dense, rather slender spikes of lilac *flowers*, which are often interrupted below ; *bracts* awl-shaped. A doubtful native ; damp waste ground, more frequent in the south than the north of England.—Fl. August, September. Perennial.

2. *M. rotundifolia* (Round-leaved Mint).—*Leaves* sessile, broadly elliptical, blunt, much wrinkled, nearly smooth above, shaggy beneath ; *flowers*, pale lilac or white, in dense cylindrical spikes. The spikes of this species are more slender than in the last, the stem is somewhat woody, and the leaves are much wrinkled and remarkably blunt ; the scent is strong and aromatic, but scarcely agreeable. Waste ground ; not common.—Fl. August, September. Perennial.

MENTHA HIRSUTA
(*Hairy Mint*)

3. *M. hirsuta* (Hairy Mint).—The commonest of the mints, 1–4 feet high, growing in extensive masses in wet places, and well - distinguished by its stalked egg-shaped, serrated *leaves*, which are downy on both sides, and whorls of lilac *flowers*, which, towards the summit of the stem, are crowded into heads ; hairy ; the scent is strong and unpleasant. A very variable plant. Banks of rivers and marshes ; abundant.—Fl. August, September. Perennial.

4. *M. arvensis* (Corn Mint).—A branched downy plant, 6–12 inches high, with stalked, egg-shaped, serrated, hairy *leaves*, and distant whorls of small lilac *flowers ; calyx* bell-shaped. The plant has a strong unpleasant smell. Cornfields ; common. —Fl. August, September. Perennial.

PLATE LXXI.

Ground Ivy

Water Mint

Common Marjorum

Wild Basil

Greater Skull-cap

5. *M. palegium* (Penny-royal).—*Stem* prostrate ; *leaves* egg-shaped, nearly smooth ; *flowers* in distant whorls ; *calyx* downy, its mouth closed with hairs. The smallest of the family, and very different in habit from any of the others ; the stems are prostrate, the flowers purple, and the whole plant of an agreeable perfume and flavour. It is commonly cultivated in cottage gardens for the sake of being made into tea, which is a favourite remedy for colds. Wet, heathy places ; not common.—Fl. July, August. Perennial.

Several other species and varieties of Mint are described by botanists, some of which are scarcely distinct from the preceding ; others, such as Pepper-Mint, Spear-Mint, and Bergamot-Mint, are not really wild, but have escaped from cultivation.

THYMUS SERPYLLUM
(*Wild Thyme*)

4. THYMUS (*Thyme*)

1. *T. serpyllum* (Wild Thyme).—The only British species. A well known and favourite little plant, with much-branched, almost woody *stems*, small fringed *leaves*, and numerous heads of purple *flowers*. The whole plant diffuses a fragrant, aromatic perfume, which, especially in hot weather, is perceptible at some distance. Dry, heathy places ; common. Besides the common type, which has terminal heads of flowers borne on stems ascending from the prostrate ones, a very distinct form is found, known as *T. chamædrys*, having axillary flower heads, and ascending stems springing from the root. — Fl. June to August. Perennial.

5. ORIGANUM (*Marjoram*)

1. *O. vulgare* (Common Marjoram),—The only British species. Growing 1-2 feet high, and distinguished by its egg-shaped, downy *leaves*, and heads of purple *flowers*, which are crowded into the form of a cyme. The *bracts* are longer than the flowers, and tinged with the same colour, both being, while the plant is in bud, of a deep red hue. The whole plant is fragrant and aromatic, and is frequently cultivated as a pot-herb. Dry bushy places, especially on chalk or limestone ; frequent.—Fl. July, August. Perennial.

6. AJUGA (*Bugle*)

1. *A. reptans* (Common Bugle).—*Stem* erect, with creeping scions at the base ; *lower leaves* stalked, *upper* sessile ; *flowers* whorled,

Q

crowded into a spike. Well marked by its solitary tapering flower-stalk, 4–9 inches high, and creeping scions. The flowers are blue, and the upper bract-like leaves tinged with the same colour. White and flesh-coloured varieties are occasionally found. Moist meadows and woods ; common.—Fl. May, June. Perennial.

2. *A. chamæpitys* (Yellow Bugle, Ground Pine).— A tufted, much-branched plant, 4–6 inches high, with reddish-purple, viscid *stems*, and hairy *leaves*, divided into three narrow lobes, the outer ones sometimes again divided. The *flowers* are yellow, spotted with red, in axillary pairs. Its habit is very different from that of the preceding. Sandy fields in Kent, Essex, and Surrey.—Fl. May, June.—Perennial.

3. *A. pyramidalis* (Pyramidal Bugle).—A rare Highland species, distinguished from Common Bugle by being without *scions*, and by bearing its *whorls* of *flowers* crowded into 4-sided *spikes*.—Fl. May, June. Perennial.

7. Teucrium (*Germander*)

1. *T. scorodonia* (Wood-Germander, Wood-sage).— *Root-stock* creeping ; *stem* erect ; *leaves* heart-shaped, oblong, stalked, wrinkled ; *flowers* in 1-sided, spike-like clusters. A common woodland plant, 2 feet high, with sage-like leaves, and several one-sided clusters of small greenish-yellow flowers. The whole plant is very bitter, and has been used as a substitute for hops. Woods and hedges ; common.—Fl. June to August. Perennial.

2. *T. scordium* (Water Germander).— A rare species, growing in marshy places. It is only a few inches high, has creeping *scions*, and bears its *flowers*, which are purplish red, in distant *whorls*. This plant was formerly employed in medicine as a tonic and a protection against infectious diseases ; now, however, it is scarcely used, except by rustic practitioners. Wet, marshy places ; rare.—Fl. July, August. Perennial.

3. *T. chamædrys* (Wall Germander).— Another rare species ; *stem* scarcely branched, woody below, 6–8 inches high ; *flowers* purple, with dark lines, large and handsome, growing in whorls of 2–6 ; *leaves* ovate, toothed, hairy. Found in a few places as a garden escape on old walls.—Fl. July, August. Perennial.

4. *T. botrys* (Cut-leaved Germander).—A rare species, with *stems* 4–9 inches high ; with stalked *leaves*, ovate in outline, deeply divided into narrow lobes, and downy ; *flowers* pink, in axillary whorls of 4–6. Found in Surrey ; very rare.—Fl. August. Annual.

PLATE LXXII.

Marsh Woundwort

Hedge Woundwort

Red Hemp-nettle

Betony

Black Horehound

8. BALLOTA (*Black Horehound*)

1. *B. Nigra* (Black Horehound).—The only British species. A coarse, bushy plant, 2–3 feet high, erect and branching, with ovate or heart-shaped, downy, wrinkled, and crenate *leaves*, and numerous one-sided clusters or whorls of purple *flowers*. The odour of the whole plant is peculiarly strong and offensive. Waste ground ; common. —Fl. July to September. Perennial.

9. LEONURUS (*Motherwort*)

1. *L. cardiaca* (Common Motherwort) —The only British species. Distinguished from all other British plants of the Order by its *leaves*, which are deeply cut into 5 or 3 narrow, pointed segments, and by the prickly *calyx-teeth* of its *flowers*, which grow in whorls. When not in flower it resembles Mugwort (*Artemisia vulgaris*) in habit. The *stems* are 2–3 feet high, branched, principally below ; the upper leaves are very narrow and entire ; the *flowers* light purple. Hedges and waste places ; not common, and perhaps not indigenous.—Fl. August. Perennial.

LEONURUS CARDIACA
(*Common Motherwort*)

10. GALEOPSIS (*Hemp-nettle*)

1. *G. tetrahit* (Common Hemp-nettle).— An erect, slender plant, 2 feet high, with a bristly *stem*, swollen below the joints, opposite, spreading *branches*, and bristly, serrated *leaves*. The *flowers*, which are variegated with light purple and yellow, or sometimes white, grow in whorls in the axils of the upper leaves, and are rendered conspicuous by the long sharp *calyx-teeth*. Cornfields ; common.—Fl. July to September. Annual.

G. versicolor is a variety of *G. tetrahit*, which it resembles in general character ; the *flowers* are large, yellow, with usually a broad purple spot upon the *lower lip*. In both the variety and the type the size of the flowers varies a good deal.

GALEOPSIS TETRAHIT
(*Common Hemp-nettle*)

2. *G. ladanum* (Red Hemp-nettle).—*Stem* and *leaves* downy with soft hair ; stem not swollen below the joints. Resembling the last, but only about 8 or 9 inches high. The *flowers* are purple, mottled with crimson. Gravelly and sandy fields ; not uncommon. —Fl. August, September. Annual.

3. *G. ochroleuca* (Downy Hemp-nettle).—Resembles *G. Ladanum*, but more downy. The *flowers* are larger and pale yellow. Culti-vated fields ; rare.—Fl. July, August. Annual.

11. LAMIUM (*Dead-nettle*)

1. *L. album* (White Dead-nettle).—*Leaves* heart-shaped, taper-ing to a point, serrated, stalked. A common, but not inelegant weed, well marked by its large pure white *flowers* and black *stamens*. So closely does the foliage of this plant resemble that of the Stinging Nettle that many persons are afraid to handle it, supposing it to be a Nettle in flower. The flowers of the latter, however, are green, and so small that they would be passed unnoticed but for their growing in spiked panicles near the summit of the stem. The square stem of the Dead-nettle is enough to distinguish it at any stage of its growth. Hedges and waste ground ; abundant.— Fl. all the summer. Perennial.

2. *L. purpureum* (Red Dead-nettle).—*Leaves* heart- or kidney-shaped, blunt, crenate, the *lower* ones on long, the *upper* on short stalks. A com-mon weed of spreading habit, distinguished by the purple tinge of its foliage, crowded upper leaves, and small purple flowers. A variety with deeply cut leaves is occasionally found, and is known as *L. incisum* (Cut-leaved Dead-nettle). Cultivated ground and by waysides ; common. —Fl. all the summer. Annual.

LAMIUM PUPUREUM
(*Purple Dead-nettle*)

3. *L. maculatum* (Spotted Dead-nettle).—Very nearly allied to *L. Album*, but distinguished by its *leaves* each having a white blotch, and by its large purple flowers. A somewhat uncommon garden escape. —Fl. summer. Perennial.

4. *L. amplexicaule* (Henbit-nettle).—From a few inches to a foot high, and of low, branching habit. *Leaves* round and deeply cut, lower ones on long stalks, floral ones sessile. The *flowers*, which are of a purplish red, are borne in from 1–3 whorls. A common weed. —Fl. almost all the year round. Perennial.

5. *L. Galeobdolon* (Yellow Dead-nettle, Archangel, Weasel-snout). —Resembling in habit the common White Dead-nettle, but rather taller ; the *leaves* are narrow and more pointed, and the *flowers*,

PLATE LXXIII.

White dead-nettle   Wood Sage

Red dead-nettle   Common Bugle   Archangel

which grow in close whorls and are large and handsome, are yellow blotched with red. Damp woods and hedges; not uncommon.— Fl. May to July. Perennial.

12. STACHYS (*Wound-wort*)

1. *S. Betonica* (Wood Betony).—A common and very pretty woodland plant, about 2 feet high, bearing an interrupted *head* or *spike* of light purple *flowers*, on a long and slender *stem*. There are always 2 or 3 pairs of oblong crenate sessile *leaves* beneath the divisions of the spike; the lower leaves are all stalked. Whole plant softly hairy. Woods and hedges; common.—Fl. July, August. Perennial.

2. *S. sylvatica* (Hedge Wound-wort). — A branched, hairy plant, 2–4 feet high, with spikes of dull purple *flowers* arranged in whorls of 6–10. *Stem* erect; *leaves* heart-shaped, crenate, stalked. When in seed the *calyx-teeth* are rigid. The plant has a strong, unpleasant smell. Woods and hedges; common.—Fl. July, August. Perennial.

STACHYS BETONICA
(*Wood Betony*)

3. *S. palustris* (Marsh Wound-wort).—Much like the last, but distinguished by its taller and stouter *stem*, softer *hairs*, narrower tapering *leaves*, heart-shaped at the base, and more crowded spikes of light purple *flowers*, 6–8 in a whorl. The smell is less offensive. Marshes; common.—Fl. July, August. Perennial. The form *S. ambigua*, which is distinguished by having broader leaves, on longer stalks, is said to be a hybrid. It is of local occurrence.

4. *S. arvensis* (Corn Wound-wort).—*Flowers* 2–6 in a whorl; *stem* spreading; *leaves* heart-shaped, obtuse; *corolla* scarcely longer than the *calyx*. A small plant, 6–8 inches high, occurring abundantly as a weed in cultivated land; distinguished from the preceding by its smaller size, and from the other *labiate* flowers which grow in similar situations, by its whorls of light purple flower. Common as a weed of cultivation.—Fl. July to September. Annual.

5. *S. Germanica* (Downy Wound-wort).—*Stem* erect, branching, 1–3 feet high; *leaves* tapering, heart-shaped at the base, short-stalked; whole plant remarkable for being covered with soft, silky *hairs; flowers* in spikes of crowded whorls. It is found on chalky soil in Oxfordshire, Bedfordshire, and Berkshire, but is a doubtful native.—Fl. July, August. Perennial.

13. NEPETA (*Cat-mint*)

1. *N. cataria* (Cat-mint). — *Stem* erect, branched, 2–3 feet high, white with mealy down ; *leaves* whitish beneath ; the *flowers*, which are small and whitish or bluish, dotted with crimson, grow in dense whorls, which towards the summit of the stem are so close as almost to form a spike. The whole plant has a strong aromatic odour, resembling Pennyroyal, and peculiarly grateful to cats, whence it derives its name. Hedges and waste ground ; not common.—Fl. July, August. Perennial.

2. *N. glechoma* (Ground Ivy).—*Stem* trailing ; *flowers* 3 or 4 together, axillary. A favourite spring flower, with creeping *stems*, kidney-shaped, crenate, roughish *leaves*, and bright purple-blue flowers, which mostly grow in threes in the axils of the leaves. The whole plant has a strong aromatic odour, which, though scarcely fragrant, is far from being disagreeable. In rural districts the leaves are often dried and made into tea. Described by some botanists under the name of *Glechoma hederacea*. Hedges and waste ground ; abundant.—Fl. April to June. Perennial.

NEPETA CATARIA
(*Cat-Mint*)

14. MARRUBIUM (*White Horehound*)

1. *M. vulgare* (White Horehound).—The only British species. Well distinguished by its bushy *stems*, 1–2 feet high, which are covered with woolly down, by its wrinkled *leaves*, and its dense whorls of small white *flowers*, of which the *calyx-teeth* are sharp and hooked. The whole plant is aromatic and bitter, and is a common remedy for coughs. Waste ground ; not common.—Fl. August. Perennial.

15. CALAMINTHA
(*Calamint, Basil Thyme, Wild Basil*)

1. *C. vulgaris* (Basil Thyme).—*Stem* ascending, branched ; *leaves* oblong, on short stalks, serrated, acute. A small bushy herb, 6–8 inches high, with hairy, egg-shaped leaves

MARRUBIUM VULGARE
(*White Horehound*)

and purple flowers, which grow in whorls as well as at the summit of the stem. The *calyx* is distinctly 2-lipped, the *lower lip* bulged at the base. Dry gravelly places ; not common.—Fl. July, August. Perennial.

2. *C. officinalis* (Common Calamint). — *Leaves* stalked, egg-shaped, slightly serrated ; *flowers* stalked, in forked axillary cymes. An erect, bushy plant, with downy stems and foliage, and numerous light purple flowers, which have small pointed bracts in the forks of their stalks. The whole plant has a sweet aromatic flavour, and makes a pleasant tea. Waysides and hedges ; not uncommon.—Fl. July, August. Perennial.

CALAMINTHA OFFICINALIS (*Common Calamint*)

3. *C. clinopodium* (Wild Basil).—*Calyx* scarcely bulged at the base ; *leaves* egg-shaped, stalked ; *flowers* in crowded compound whorls. A straggling, hairy plant, 1–2 feet high, with egg-shaped leaves, several bristly whorls of stalked purple flowers, and numerous long, pointed bracts. Aromatic and fragrant. Bushy places ; frequent.—Fl. July, August. Perennial.

MELITTIS MELISSOPHYLLUM (*Wild Balm*)

16. MELITTIS (*Wild Balm*)

1. *M. melissophyllum* (Wild Balm).— The only British species. A very handsome plant, 12–18 inches high, with large heart-shaped, hairy, serrated *leaves* and conspicuous white *flowers* blotched with bright rose-colour. The foliage while fresh has an offensive smell, but in drying acquires the flavour of new hay or Woodruff. Woods in the south and west of England.—Fl. June, July. Perennial.

17. PRUNELLA (*Self-heal*)

1. *P. vulgaris* (Self-heal). — The only British species. Well distinguished by its flattened *calyx* and whorls of purplish blue *flowers*, which are collected into a head, having a pair of *leaves* at the base and two taper-pointed *bracts* beneath each whorl. The *stems* are creeping, and the erect *flowering stems* from 3–9 inches high. Pastures and dry ground ; very common.—Fl. July, August. Perennial.

PRUNELLA VULGARIS (*Self-heal*)

18. SCUTELLARIA (*Skull-cap*)

1. *S. galericulata* (Greater Skull-cap).—*Leaves* oblong, tapering, heart-shaped at the base, notched; *flowers* in pairs, axillary. A handsome plant, 12–18 inches high, with rather large bright blue *flowers*, the *tube* of which is much longer than the *calyx*. Soon after the *corolla* has fallen off, the upper lip of the *calyx* closes on the lower, and gives it the appearance of a capsule with a lid ; when the seed is ripe it opens again. Banks of rivers and ponds; frequent.—Fl. July to September. Perennial.

2. *S. minor* (Lesser Skull-cap).—A small bushy herb, 4–6 inches high, with egg-shaped *leaves*, of which the lower ones are often toothed at the base ; the *flowers* are small, of a dull purple colour ; the *calyx* is the same as in the last. It grows in bogs, but is not common, except in the west of England.

SCUTELLARIA
MINOR
(*Lesser
Skull-cap*)

NATURAL ORDER LX

VERBENACEÆ.—VERVAIN TRIBE

Calyx tubular, not falling off ; *corolla* irregular, with a long tube ; *stamens* 4 ; 2 longer than the others, rarely 2 only; *ovary* 2- or 4-celled ; *style* 1 ; *stigma* 2-cleft ; *seeds* 2 or 4, adhering to one another. A tribe of plants closely allied to the *Labiatæ*, comprising trees, shrubs, and herbaceous plants, having opposite leaves and irregular flowers, which usually grow in spikes or heads. Many are aromatic and fragrant, and some few are employed as medicines, but are not highly valued. Great virtues were, in ancient times, attributed to the common *Vervain*, insomuch that it was accounted an holy plant, and was used to sweep the tables and altars of the gods. It is now little thought of. *Aloysia citriodora*, formerly called *Verbena triphylla*, is the Lemon-plant, or Lemon Verbena of gardens, well known for the delicious fragrance of its rough, narrow leaves. Many varieties of *Verbena* are also cultivated for the sake of their ornamental flowers, which for brilliancy of colouring are scarcely surpassed. But by far the most remarkable plant of this Order is the Teak-tree (*Tectoria grandis*), which inhabits the mountainous parts of Eastern Asia. The trunk of this tree sometimes attains the height of two hundred feet, and its leaves are twenty inches long by sixteen broad. The timber somewhat resembles mahogany in colour, but is lighter and stronger. For ship-building it rivals Oak.

1. VERBENA (Vervain).—*Calyx* 5-cleft ; *corolla* unequally 5-cleft ; *stamens* shorter than the tube of the corolla. (Name, the Latin name of the plant.)

1. VERBENA (*Vervain*)

1. *V. officinalis* (Common Vervain).—The only British species. A slender plant 1–2 feet high, with but few *leaves*, which are roughish, 3-cleft, or simply cut. The *flowers*, which are very small, are lilac, and grow in terminal, very slender *spikes*. Waste ground; common.—Fl. July, August. Perennial.

NATURAL ORDER LXI
LENTIBULARIACEÆ.—BUTTERWORT TRIBE

Calyx divided, not falling off; *corolla* irregular, 2-lipped; *stamens* 2, sometimes 4, 2 long and 2 short; *ovary* 1-celled; *style* 1, very short; *stigma* 2-lipped, the *lower lip* smallest; *capsule* 1-celled, 2-valved, many-seeded. Herbaceous aquatic plants, bearing either undivided leaves, which spring directly from the root, or compound root-like leaves, with numerous small bladders or air-vessels. There are but four genera in the Order, two of which contain British examples—Butterwort (*Pinguicula*), small plants with handsome purple flowers and concave leaves, of a texture which resembles greasy parchment; and Bladderwort (*Utricularia*), submersed plants with finely divided leaves, bearing minute bladders and yellow flowers, which rise above the surface of the water to open. Both Butterwort and Bladderwort are carnivorous, in that small insects become caught by sticking to the greasy leaves of the former, and minute water insects, entering the bladders of *Utricularia* by trap doors, with which they are furnished, likewise become prisoners.

" *Pinguicula vulgaris* (Common Butterwort) has the property of giving consistence to milk, and of preventing its separating into either whey or cream. Linnæus says that the solid milk of the Laplanders is prepared by pouring it, warm from the cow, over a strainer on which fresh leaves of *Pinguicula* have been laid. The milk, after passing among them, is left for a day or two to stand, until it begins to turn sour; it throws up no cream, but becomes compact and tenacious, and most delicious in taste. It is not necessary that fresh leaves should be used after the milk is once turned; on the contrary, a small portion of this solid milk will act upon that which is fresh, in the manner of yeast " (Lindley).

1. PINGUICULA (Butterwort).—*Calyx* 2-lipped, *upper lip* 3-cleft, *lower* 2-cleft; *corolla* gaping, spurred. (Name from the Latin, *pinguis*, fat, the leaves being greasy to the touch.)

2. UTRICULARIA (Bladderwort).—*Calyx* of 2 equal sepals; *corolla* personate, spurred. (Name from the Latin, *Utriculus*, a little bladder, from the little air-bladders which grow among the leaves.)

1. PINGUICULA (*Butterwort*)

1. *P. vulgaris* (Common Butterwort).—*Spur* tapering ; segments of the *corolla* very unequal, entire. A singular and very beautiful plant. The leaves, which spring all from the roots, have the edges rolled in ; they are of a peculiar yellowish-green hue, and have a frosted appearance. The flowers are large, purple, very handsome, and grow in a nodding manner, each on the summit of a delicate stem, 3–4 inches high, which springs directly from the root. The root is fibrous, and has a very loose hold on the soft ground in which it grows. Bogs and heaths, principally in the north.—Fl. June. Perennial. A variety known as *P. grandiflora* has larger *flowers*, and is distinguished by having the middle segment and *spur* of the *corolla* notched. It is found in the counties of Cork and Kerry in Ireland.

2. *P. Lusitanica* (Pale Butterwort).—*Spur* cylindrical, obtuse, curved downwards ; segments of the *corolla* nearly equal ; *leaves* and *flower-stalks* covered with short hairs. Of the same habit as *P. vulgaris*, but much smaller. The leaves are greenish-white and veined ; the flowers of a pale lilac, with a yellow throat. Bogs in the western parts of England, in the west of Scotland, and in Ireland.—Fl. July to September. Perennial.

PINGUICULA
LUSITANICA
(*Pale
Butterwort*)

3. *P. Alpina* (Alpine Butterwort).—Smaller than the last ; the *flower-stalks* are smooth, and the *flowers* small and yellowish. Very rare, and found only in bogs in Ross-shire and Skye.—Fl. May, June. Perennial.

2. UTRICULARIA (*Bladderwort*)

1. *U. vulgaris* (Common Bladderwort).— Submersed. *Leaves* divided into numerous hair-like segments, and bearing small air-bladders ; *lips* of the *corolla* about equal in length ; *spur* conical. Before flowering, the stem and leaves float in the water by help of the minute bladders, which are then filled with air ; the flowers, which grow in clusters of 6–8 together, are large and bright yellow, and are raised several inches out of the water. After flowering, the bladders become filled with water, and the whole plant sinks to the bottom. Ditches and deep pools ; not very common.—Fl. June, July. Perennial.

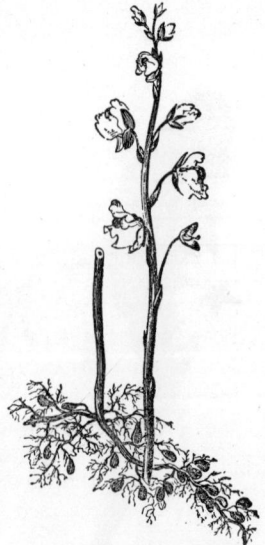

UTRICULARIA VULGARIS
(*Common Bladderwort*)

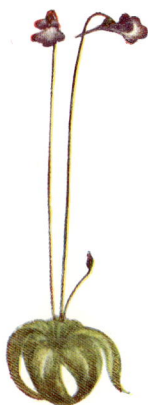

PLATE LXXIV.

Common Verbena

Common Butterwort

Primrose

Bird's-eye Primrose

Cowslip

2. *U. minor* (Lesser Bladderwort).—Smaller than the last in all
its parts ; *flowers* small, yellow, with a short blunt *spur*. Similar
situations to the last ; rare.—Fl. June to August. Perennial.

3. *U. intermedia* (Intermediate Bladderwort).—Distinguished
from *U. vulgaris* by having the upper lip of the corolla much longer
than the lower, and by bearing its air-bladders on branched stalks
distinct from the leaves. Rare.—Fl. July to September. Perennial.

Natural Order LXII
PRIMULACEÆ.—Primrose Tribe

Calyx 5-cleft, rarely 4-cleft (in *Trientalis* 7-cleft), regular, not
falling off ; *corolla* of as many lobes as the *calyx* (in *Glaux* wanting) ;
stamens equalling in number the lobes of the corolla, and opposite
to them ; *ovary* 1-celled ; *style* 1 ; *stigma* capitate ; *capsule* 1-
celled, opening with valves ; *seeds* numerous, attached to a central
column. Herbaceous plants, mostly of humble growth, inhabiting,
principally, the colder regions of the northern hemisphere, and in
lower latitudes ascending to the confines of perpetual snow. In
this Order are found several of our favourite British plants.
The Primrose, as its name indicates (*prima rosa*, the first rose), is
the most welcome harbinger of spring ; the Cowslip is hardly less
prized for its pastoral associations than for its elegance and fragrance ; Pimpernel, or " Poor man's weather-glass," is as trusty a
herald of summer weather as the Primrose of spring. Nor is it only
as *Flowers of the Field* that the plants of this tribe are valued. The
Polyanthus and Auricula equally grace the cottager's garden, and
the collections of the florist ; and several species of Cyclamen are
commonly found in conservatories. Some species possess active
medicinal properties ; the flowers of Cowslip are made into a pleasant soporific wine ; and the leaves of the Auricula (*Primula
auricula*) are used in the Alps as a remedy for coughs. The flowers
of Pimpernel and roots of Cyclamen are acrid.

1. Primula (Primrose).—*Calyx* tubular, 5-cleft ; *corolla* salver- or
funnel-shaped, with a long cylindrical tube ; *stamens* 5, enclosed
within the tube of the corolla ; *capsule* 5-valved, with 10 teeth.
(Name from the Latin, *primus*, first, from the early appearance of
the flowers.)

2. Hottonia (Water Violet).—*Calyx* 5-cleft almost to the base ;
corolla salver-shaped, with a short tube ; *stamens* 5 ; *capsule* opening
with 5 teeth. (Named after *Professor Hotton*, of Leyden.)

3. Cyclamen (Sow-bread).—*Calyx* bell-shaped, cleft half-way
down into 5 segments ; *corolla* wheel-shaped, the lobes reflexed ;
stamens 5 ; *capsule* opening with 5 teeth. (Name in the Greek,
cyclos, a circle, either from the reflexed lobes of the corolla, or from
the spiral form of the fruit-stalks.)

4. ANAGALLIS (Pimpernel).—*Calyx* 5-cleft to the base ; *corolla* wheel-shaped ; *stamens* 5, hairy ; *capsule* splitting all round. (Name in Greek, denoting that the plant excites pleasure.)

5. LYSIMACHIA (Loosestrife).—*Calyx* 5-cleft to the base ; *corolla* wheel-shaped ; *stamens* 5, not hairy ; *capsule* opening by valves. (Name in Greek, having the same meaning as the English name.)

6. CENTUNCULUS (Chaffweed).—*Calyx* 5-cleft to the base ; *corolla* with an inflated tube ; *stamens* 4 ; *capsule* splitting all round. (Name of doubtful etymology.)

7. TRIENTALIS (Chickweed Winter-green).—*Calyx* 7-cleft to the base ; *corolla* wheel-shaped ; *stamens* 7 ; *capsule* opening with valves. (Name of doubtful etymology.)

8. GLAUX (Sea-milkwort).—*Calyx* 0; *corolla* bell-shaped, 5-lobed ; *stamens* 5 ; *capsule* 5-valved, with 5–10 seeds. (Name in Greek, denoting the sea-green colour of the foliage.)

9. SAMOLUS (Brookweed).—*Calyx* 5-cleft, adhering to the lower half of the capsule, not falling off ; *corolla* salver-shaped, with 5 scales at the mouth of the tube ; *stamens* 5 ; *capsule* opening with 5 reflexed teeth. (" Named, some say, from the Island of Samos, where Valerandus, a botanist of the 16th century, gathered our *Samolus Valerandi*."—Sir W. J. Hooker.)

1. PRIMULA (*Primrose*)

1. *P. vulgaris* (Primrose).—*Flowers* each on a separate stalk ; *leaves* oblong, egg-shaped. Among the most welcome of spring flowers, and too well known to need any description. The colour of the flower is so peculiar as to have a name of its own ; artists maintain that primrose-colour is a delicate green ; white, purple, and lilac varieties are not uncommon. Banks and woods ; abundant. —Fl. March to May. Perennial.

2. *P. elatior* (Oxlip).—*Flowers* in a stalked umbel, salver-shaped ; *calyx* tubular ; *leaves* egg-shaped, contracted below the middle. Distinguished from the *Primrose* by its umbellate yellow flowers and by its leaves, which become suddenly broader above the middle, and from the *Cowslip* by its tubular, not bell-shaped calyx, and flat, not concave, corolla. Woods and pastures ; not common.— Fl. April, May. Perennial.

3. *P. veris* (Cowslip, Paigle).—*Flowers* in a stalked umbel, drooping, funnel-shaped ; *calyx* bell-shaped ; *leaves* egg-shaped, contracted below the middle. Among the many pleasing purposes to which these favourite flowers are applied by children none is prettier than that of making *Cowslip Balls*. The method, which may not be known to all, is as follows : The umbels are picked off as close as possible to the top of the main stalk, and from fifty to sixty are

made to hang across a string stretched between the backs of two
chairs. The flowers are then carefully pressed together and the
string is tied tightly, so as to collect them into a ball. Care should
be taken to choose such heads or umbels only as have all the flowers
open, or the surface of the ball will be uneven. Pastures; common.
—Fl. April, May. Perennial.

4. *P. farinosa* (Bird's-eye Primrose).—A very beautiful little
plant, with a rosette of small *leaves* covered on the under side with
a white powdery meal, as also are the slender *stalks* and *calyces*.
The *flowers*, which grow in a compact umbel, are of a delicate lilac-
pink with a yellow eye. Mountainous pastures ; not uncommon in
the north of England and south of Scotland.—Fl. June, July.
Perennial. A white variety is sometimes found, but is extremely
rare and beautiful. Another smaller form, with broader leaves and
flowers of a deeper shade of colour, known as *P. scotica*, is found in
the Orkneys and a few places in the north of Scotland.

2. HOTTONIA (*Water Violet*)

1. *H. Palustris* (Water Violet).—The only
British species. An aquatic plant, with finely
divided, submersed *leaves ; flowers* large,
handsome, pinkish, with a yellow eye, arranged in whorls around a leafless *stalk*,
which rises several inches out of the water.
Ponds and ditches ; not very common.—
Fl. May, June. Perennial.

3. CYCLAMEN (*Sow-bread*)

1. *C. hederæfolium* (Ivy - leaved Sow -
bread).—The only species found in Britain,
and probably not a native. Remarkable
for its globular brown *root* and nodding pink
or white *flowers*, the lobes of which are bent
upwards. As the *fruit* ripens the flower-stalk

HOTTONIA
(*Water Violet*)

curls spirally and buries it in the earth. The root is intensely
acrid. Found established in woods in Kent, Sussex, and Surrey.—
Fl. autumn.

4. ANAGALLIS (*Pimpernel*)

1. *A. arvensis* (Scarlet Pimpernel).—*Leaves* egg-shaped, dotted
beneath, sessile ; *petals* crenate. A pretty little prostrate plant,
with bright scarlet *flowers*, which expand only in fine weather, and
have consequently gained for the plant the name of *Poor man's
weather-glass*. The colour of the flowers occasionally varies to flesh-
colour or white, with a red eye. A bright blue variety, which some
botanists consider a distinct species, is more unfrequent. Cultivated
ground ; abundant.—Fl. June to September. Annual.

2. *A. tenella* (Bog Pimpernel).—*Stem* creeping ; *leaves* roundish, stalked, shorter than the *flower-stalks*. A beautiful little prostrate plant, with slender stems 4–6 inches long, small leaves which are arranged in opposite pairs, and erect rose-coloured flowers, larger than those of the *Scarlet Pimpernel*. Boggy ground and sides of rivulets ; common.—Fl. June to August. Perennial.

5. LYSIMACHIA (*Loosestrife*)

1. *L. nummularia* (Money-wort, Herb-twopence, Creeping Jenny).—*Stem* creeping ; *leaves* roundish, slightly stalked ; *flowers* solitary, axillary. A very pretty plant, well marked by its opposite, shining leaves and large yellow flowers. The stems grow from 1–2 feet in length, and hang from the banks of rivers in a very graceful way. This plant is much used to ornament rock gardens. Banks of rivers and damp meadows ; common.—Fl. June, July. Perennial.

2. *L. nemorum* (Wood Loosestrife, Yellow Pimpernel).—*Stem* spreading ; *leaves* egg-shaped, acute, on short *stalks ; flowers* solitary, axillary. Approaching the Scarlet Pimpernel in habit, but somewhat larger ; the flowers are bright yellow and very pretty. Woods ; common.—Fl. June to August. Perennial.

3. *L. vulgaris* (Great Yellow Loosestrife).—*Stem* erect, branched, downy ; *leaves* tapering to a point, opposite, or 3–4 in a whorl ; *flowers* in terminal panicles. Very different in habit from either of the preceding, growing quite erect, 2–3 feet high, with terminal panicles of rather large yellow flowers. Banks of rivers ; common. —Fl. July. Perennial.

4. *L. thyrsiflora* (Tufted Loosestrife).—Resembles *L. vulgaris* in habit, but bears its *flowers*, which are small and yellow, in numerous dense *clusters*. It grows in the north of England and parts of Scotland, but is rare.—Fl. June, July.

6. CENTUNCULUS (*Chaffweed*)

CENTUNCULUS
MINIMUS
(*Chaffweed*)

1. *C. minimus* (Chaffweed). — The only British species. One of the smallest among British plants, rarely exceeding an inch in height, and often much less. It is nearly allied to the *Pimpernel*, and at the first glance might be taken for a stunted specimen of the common species. The *leaves* are egg-shaped, acute; the *flowers* sessile, axillary. It is sometimes branched, but very frequently consists of a single stem, 6 or 8 leaves, and as many inconspicuous flowers. It grows in damp gravelly places, especially where water has stood during the winter.— Fl. June to August. Annual.

PLATE LXXV.

Thrift

Loosestrife

Money-wort

Yellow Pimpernel

7. TRIENTALIS (*Chickweed, Winter-green*)

1. *T. Europæa* (European Chickweed, Winter-green).—The only British species. A pretty plant with an unbranched *stem* 4–6 inches high, bearing a few lanceolate *leaves* near its summit, from which rise one or more slender *flower-stalks*, each bearing a delicate white *flower*. The number of *stamens* varies from 7–9. Abundant in many parts of the Highlands of Scotland, and occasionally found in the north of England.—Fl. June. Perennial.

8. GLAUX (*Sea-Milkwort*)

1. *G. maritima* (Sea-Milkwort).—The only species. A fleshy marine plant 3–6 inches high, growing in thick patches, with numerous egg-shaped, glaucous *leaves*, and axillary pink *flowers*. In habit it resembles *Honckenya peploides*. Sea-shore and salt marshes; common.—Fl. June to August. Perennial.

GLAUX MARITIMA
(*Sea Milk-wort*)

9. SAMOLUS (*Brookweed*)

1. *S. Valerandi* (Brookweed).—A smooth, pale green, herbaceous plant, with blunt, fleshy *leaves*, and one or more clusters of very small white *flowers*, which in their early stage are crowded, but finally become distant, resembling in this respect the habit of the Cruciform Tribe. Watery places, common, and, like many other aquatic plants, widely diffused over the world.—Fl. July to September. Annual.

SAMOLUS VALERANDI
(*Brookweed*)

NATURAL ORDER LXIII
PLUMBAGINACEÆ.—THRIFT TRIBE

Calyx tubular, plaited, chaffy, not falling off, often coloured; *corolla* 5-cleft, nearly to the base; *stamens* 5, opposite the *petals; ovary* of 5 carpels, 1-celled; *styles* 5; *fruit* 1-seeded. Herbaceous or shrubby plants, with undivided, fleshy leaves, and flowers of a thin texture, approaching that usually called everlasting, collected into heads or growing in panicles. They inhabit salt marshes and the seashore of most temperate regions, and some are also found in mountainous districts.

Their properties are various—some are tonic, some intensely acrid, and many contain iodine. The root of *Statice Caroliniana* is one of the most powerful astringents known ; several species of *Plumbago* are so acrid that the fresh root is used to raise blisters. Thrift (*Armeria*) and several kinds of Sea-Lavender (*Statice*) grow on the seashores of Britain, and are very pretty plants. Other species are cultivated in gardens and conservatories, to which they are highly ornamental. It has been remarked that plants of this Order, like many other marine plants, when growing at a distance from the sea, lose the peculiar salts which they contain in their natural localities. Thrift, for example, as a marine plant contains iodine and soda, but as a mountain or garden plant exchanges these two salts for potash. Some species of Plumbago are grown as garden plants on account of their great beauty, and the British genera, *Armeria* and *Statice*, give us exquisite subjects for our hardy herbaceous borders.

1. ARMERIA (Thrift).—*Flowers* in heads ; *styles* hairy. (Name from the French, *armoires*, wardrobes, though in what connection is uncertain.)

2. STATICE (Sea Lavender).—*Flowers* panicled ; *styles* smooth. (Name from the Greek, *statizo*, to stop, from its astringent medicinal properties.)

1. ARMERIA (*Thrift*)

1. *A. maritima* (Thrift).—*Leaves* linear, fleshy, forming dense tufts or balls ; *flower-stalks* springing directly from the roots, leafless, downy, 3–6 inches high, and bearing each a roundish head of rose-coloured *flowers ;* the summit of the flower-stalk is cased in a brown membranous sheath, and the flowers are intermixed with chaffy *bracts*, or *scales ;* the *fruit* is almost winged by the dry, chaffy calyx. Sea-shores and the tops of mountains ; common.— Fl. July, August. Perennial.

2. *A. plantaginea* (Plantain Thrift).—Much like the last, but larger, and with broader *leaves*, marked with 3 or 5 veins. Found in Jersey.—Fl. July, August. Perennial.

2. STATICE (*Sea Lavender*)

1. *S. Limonium* (Sea Lavender).—*Leaves* oblong, 1-ribbed, tipped with a point ; *flower-stalk* from the root, leafless, 6–18 inches high, branched near the summit into many spreading, spike-like clusters of thin lavender-blue, scentless flowers. Muddy sea-coast ; not unfrequent.—Fl. July, August. Perennial.

2. *S. spathulata* (Spathulate Sea-Lavender).—In some respects resembling the last, but distinguished by its *leaves* being smaller, oblong near the base, and wider above (*spathulate*), and by its

flower-stalks being branched below the middle into several erect tufts of blue *flowers*. Not uncommon on the rocky sea-coast. —Fl. July, August. Perennial.

3. *S. reticulata* (Matted Sea-Lavender).—Smaller than either of the last; the *flower-stalks* are divided almost from the base into numerous zigzag branches, of which the lower ones are barren. Salt marshes in Norfolk, Lincoln, Suffolk, and Cambridge.—Fl. July, August. Perennial.

NATURAL ORDER LXIV
PLANTAGINACEÆ.—PLANTAIN TRIBE

Calyx 4-parted; *corolla* 4-parted, chaffy, not falling off; *stamens* 4, alternate with the segments of the *corolla*, and having very long, thread-like *filaments*, and lightly attached *anthers*; *ovary* 2-, rarely 4-celled; *style* 1; *stigma* hairy; *capsule* splitting transversely; *seeds* 1, 2, or many in each *cell*. Herbaceous plants of humble growth, with many ribbed or fleshy leaves spreading horizontally from the root. The flowers, which are made conspicuous by their long stamens, grow in spikes. Several species are common in Great Britain as wayside, meadow, and marine plants, and as troublesome lawn weeds. The Order is distributed over most parts of the world. The leaves are slightly bitter and astringent; the seeds abound in a tasteless mucilage, which is used in medicine as a substitute for Linseed, and is said to be employed in France to stiffen muslin.

1. PLANTAGO (Plantain).—*Calyx* 4-cleft, the segments bent back; *corolla* tubular, with 4 spreading lobes; *stamens* very long; *capsule* splitting all round, 2- to 4-celled. (Name of doubtful origin.)

2. LITTORELLA (Shore-weed).—*Stamens* and *pistils* in different flowers; *barren flower*, stalked; *stamens* very long; *fertile flower* sessile; *bracts* 3; *corolla* tubular, contracted at both ends; *style* very long; *capsule* 1-seeded. (Name in Latin having the same meaning as the English name.)

1. PLANTAGO (*Plantain*)

1. *P. major* (Greater Plantain).—*Leaves* broadly egg-shaped on long, channelled stalks; *flowers* in spikes, 2–6 inches long, the stem of which is cylindrical; *cells* of the *capsule* many-seeded. Well known for its spikes of green flowers, the seeds of which are a favourite food of canary birds. Borders of fields and waysides; abundant.—Fl. June, July. Perennial.

2. *P. media* (Hoary Plantain).—*Leaves* broadly elliptical on short, flat stalks; *flowers* in a close cylindrical spike, 1–2 inches long, the stalk of which is also cylindrical; *cells* of the capsule 1-seeded.

R

The leaves spread horizontally from the crown of the root, and lie so close to the ground as to destroy all vegetation beneath, or to leave the impression of their ribs on the ground; the spike, which is shorter than in *P. major*, grows on a longer stalk, and the flowers, which are fragrant, are rendered conspicuous by their light purple anthers. Meadows; common.—Fl. June, July. Perennial.

3. *P. lanceolata* (Ribwort Plantain).—*Leaves* narrow, tapering; *flowers* in a short spike, the stalk of which is angular; *cells* of the *capsule* 1-seeded. Under the name of Cocks and Hens this plant is well known to children, who amuse themselves by striking the heads one against another until the stalk breaks. The flowers are dark brown.

Meadows; abundant.—Fl. June, July. Perennial.

4. *P. maritima* (Sea plantain).—Easily distinguished from the rest of the genus by its long, linear, fleshy *leaves*, which are grooved and woolly at the base. Seashores, and in the north on the tops of mountains.—Fl. June to September. Perennial.

PLANTAGO LANCEOLATA
(*Ribwort Plantain*)

5. *P. coronopus* (Buck's-horn Plantain).—*Leaves* pinnatifid; *capsule* imperfectly 4-celled, 4-seeded. The only British species which has divided leaves; these are more or less downy, and usually prostrate. Waste ground; common.—Fl. June, July. Annual.

2. LITTORELLA (*Shore-weed*)

1. *L. lacustris* (Shore-weed).—The only species. Not unlike *Plantago maritima* in habit, but at once distinguished by its solitary *barren flowers*, raised each on a stalk 2–4 inches high; the *fertile flowers* are sessile among the leaves. Marshes and banks of lakes.—Fl. June to September. Perennial.

LITTORELLA LACUSTRIS
(*Shore-weed*)

Sub-class IV

MONOCHLAMYDEÆ

Flowers having a calyx or corolla, or neither—never both. In this Sub-class it is often doubtful whether the leaves which enclose the stamens and pistils of a flower should be called a *calyx* or *corolla ;* the term *perianth* (from the Greek, *peri*, around, and *anthos*, a flower) is therefore used to denote this organ, and must be taken to mean all the leaves, whether resembling *sepals* or *petals*, which enclose the other parts of fructification. Used in this sense, and applied to the preceding Sub-classes, the calyx and corolla would be correctly called a double *perianth*.

Natural Order LXV

CHENOPODIACEÆ.—Goose-foot Tribe

Perianth 5-lobed, not falling off ; *stamens* 5, rarely 1 or 2, from the base of the perianth and opposite its lobes ; *ovary* 1, superior or adhering to the tube of the perianth ; *style* 2- or 4-cleft, rarely simple ; *stigma* undivided ; *fruit* 1-seeded, enclosed in the perianth, which often becomes enlarged or fleshy. Herbaceous or somewhat shrubby plants, with leaves which are more or less inclined to be fleshy ; the flowers are small and inconspicuous, the perianth decidedly partaking of the characters of a calyx, which sometimes, as in *Atriplex*, has a tendency to become enlarged when in fruit. Some plants have flowers bearing pistils only, others stamens only, and others again both pistils and stamens. They are common weeds in many temperate climates, and are most abundant in salt marshes and on the sea-shore. Many of the plants of this tribe are used as esculent vegetables—as Spinach, Beet, and Orache. Beet is cultivated extensively in France for making sugar, and a variety of it affords valuable food for cattle under the name of Mangold Wurzel. In Peru the leaves of *Chenopodium Quinoa*, a plant growing at a great elevation, are a common article of food. Many of those kinds which grow in salt marshes and on the sea-shore afford an immense quantity of soda. According to some naturalists, *Salvadora Persica*, belonging to this Order, is the Mustard Tree of Scripture. It bears a juicy fruit, having the flavour of cress, and its seeds are very small. The Mangold Wurzel, the White Sugar Beet of France, and the red garden Beetroot, are all said to have originated from the wild *Beta maritima* of sea-shores. Popular garden flowers belonging to this Order are *Love-lies-bleeding, Prince's-feather*, and *Cock's-comb*.

1. CHENOPODIUM (Goose-foot).—*Perianth* deeply 5-cleft, remaining unaltered, and finally closing over the single seed ; *stamens*

5 ; *stigmas* 2 ; *leaves* flat. (Name in Greek having the same meaning as the English name.)

2. SUÆDA (Sea Blite).—*Perianth* deeply 5-cleft, often fleshy ; *stamens* 5 ; *stigmas* 2–3 ; *leaves* semi-cylindrical. (Name from *suæd*, soda, in which the plants abound.)

3. ATRIPLEX (Orache).—*Stamens* and *pistils* for the most part in separate flowers, sometimes united ; *barren flower, perianth* deeply 5-cleft ; *stamens* 5 ; *fertile flower, perianth* of 2 valves ; *stigmas* 2 ; *fruit* 1-seeded, covered by the enlarged perianth ; *leaves* flat. (Name from the Greek, *a*, not, and *trephein*, to nourish.)

4. BETA (Beet).—*Perianth* deeply 5-cleft ; *stamens* 5 ; *stigmas* 2 ; *fruit* 1-seeded, adhering to the tube of the fleshy perianth ; *leaves* flat. (Name, the Latin name of the plant.)

5. SALSOLA (Saltwort).—*Perianth* deeply 5-cleft ; *stamens* 5 ; *stigmas* 2 ; *fruit* 1-seeded, crowned by the shrivelled lobes of the perianth ; *leaves* cylindrical. (Name from the Latin, *sal*, salt, from the soda in which it abounds.)

6. SALICORNIA (Glasswort).—*Perianth* top-shaped, fleshy, undivided ; *stamens* 1–2 ; *style* very short ; *stigma* 2-cleft ; *fruit* enclosed in the dry perianth ; *stem* jointed ; *leaves* none. (Name from the Latin, *sal*, salt, and *cornu*, a horn, from the soda in which it abounds, and the horn-shaped branches.)

1. CHENOPODIUM (*Goose-foot*)
Leaves undivided

1. *C. olidum* (Stinking Goose-foot).—*Stem* spreading ; *leaves* egg-shaped, with a triangular base, fleshy, mealy ; *flowers* in dense clustered spikes. Distinguished by its fishy smell, which is disgusting in the extreme. Waste places, especially near the sea ; not common.—Fl. August, September. Annual.

2. *C. polyspermum* (Many-seeded Goose-grass).—*Stem* spreading, branched ; *leaves* egg-shaped, sessile ; *flowers* in branched, somewhat leafy, slender spikes ; *seeds* flattened horizontally, shining, minutely dotted. Varying in size from 4–12 inches in height ; the stems and leaves usually have a red tinge, and the plant, when in flower, has a not inelegant appearance from the number of shining, brown fruits, which are not concealed by the perianth. Waste ground ; not common.—Fl. August to October. Annual.

Leaves toothed, angled, or lobed

3. *C. Bonus Henricus* (Good King Henry).—*Leaves* triangular, arrow-shaped ; *flowers* in compound, leafless spikes. A dark green, succulent plant, about a foot high, with large, thickish leaves, which are used as *Spinach*. Waste places near villages ; common. —Fl. May to August. Perennial.

PLATE LXXVI.

Good King Henry

Buck Wheat   Snake Weed

4. C. album (White Goose-foot).—*Leaves* egg-shaped, with tri-angular base, bluntly toothed, *upper* ones narrow, entire ; *flowers* in dense clustering spikes. The whole plant succulent ; leaves more or less fleshy, and covered with a whitish, mealy powder. This is perhaps the commonest species ; it grows 1–3 feet high. Waste places and cultivated ground ; common.—Fl. July to September. Annual.

There are several other British species of this uninteresting family, some of which have nothing but their rarity to recommend them, and others are remarkable only for the tendency of their leaves to assume a triangular outline, the margin being variously lobed and toothed. The characters of most are difficult of discrimination, so that botanists are agreed neither as to the number of species nor names.

2. SUÆDA (*Sea Blite*)

1. S. maritima (Annual Seaside Goose-grass).—*Styles* 2 ; *stem* herbaceous. A low, straggling plant, 2 or 3–12 inches high, with short, fleshy, semi-cylindrical leaves, and small, inconspicuous, green flowers. Muddy sea-shores ; common.—Fl. July, August. Annual.

2. S. fruticosa (Shrubby Sea Blite).—*Styles* 3 ; *stem* shrubby. Larger than the last, 2–3 feet high, with a shrubby stem, and having 3 styles in each flower. Rarer than the last, and local on the southern and eastern coast of England.—Fl. September, October. Perennial.

3. ATRIPLEX (*Orache*)

1. A. patula (Common Orache).—*Stem* spreading, often with the *central branch* erect ; *leaves* triangular, with 2 spreading lobes at the lower angles, toothed, the *upper leaves* narrow, entire ; *flowers* in tufted spikes ; *perianth* of the fruit warty and black. A common weed, with straggling, furrowed stems, often tinged with red ; distinguished from the Goose-foot family by the solitary seed being shut in between two triangular, leaf-like valves. The main stem is usually erect, the rest are prostrate, appearing as if they had been bent down by force. Cultivated and waste ground, and on the seashore ; abundant.—Fl. July to October. Annual.

2. A. laciniata (Frosted Sea Orache).—*Stems* spreading ; *leaves* with three angles, wavy at the edge, and toothed, mealy beneath. Distinguished from the preceding by its mealy leaves, and the whitish hue of the whole plant. Sea-shore, not uncommon.—Fl. July, October. Annual.

Several other species are described by botanists, but the remark annexed to the preceding family applies equally well to this.

4. BETA (*Beet*)

1. *B. maritima* (Sea-Beet).— The only British species. A tall, succulent plant, about 2 feet high, with large, fleshy, glossy, *lower leaves*, and narrower *upper leaves ;* angular *stems*, and numerous leafy spikes of green *flowers*, which are arranged 1 or 2 together, with a small leaf at the base of each. The root-leaves when boiled are quite as good as *Spinach*. Sea-shore ; common.— Fl. June to October. Perennial.

5. SALSOLA (*Saltwort*)

1. *S. kali* (Prickly Saltwort).— The only British species. A small plant, hairy and glaucous, with prostrate, angular, branched *stems*, 6–12 inches high, and succulent awl-shaped *leaves*, each of which terminates with a sharp prickle; the *flowers* are solitary, and have 3 *bracts* at the base of each. The whole plant abounds in alkali salt, whence its name. Sandy sea-shore; common. — Fl. July. Annual.

BETA MARITIMA
(*Sea-Beet*)

6. SALICORNIA (*Glasswort*)

1. *S. herbacea* (Jointed Glasswort).—*Stem* herbaceous, jointed ; *leaves* o. A singular plant, 4–8 inches high, consisting of a number of fleshy joints, each of which is fitted into the one below, entirely destitute of leaves, and bearing between every two joints of the terminal branches 3 inconspicuous green flowers. Salt marshes ; abundant.—Fl. August, September. Annual.

2. *S. radicans* (Rooting Glasswort).—*Stems* prostrate, rooting, woody, and usually of a browner hue. Both species, on account of the soda which they contain, were at one time used in the manufacture of glass—hence the name Glasswort. *S. herbacea* is also made into a pickle. Sea-coasts; uncommon.—Fl. August, September. Perennial.

NATURAL ORDER LXVI
SCLERANTHACEÆ.—THE KNAWEL TRIBE

Perianth tubular, 4- or 5-cleft; *stamens* 5–10, inserted into the mouth of the tube; *ovary* 1, superior, 1-celled; *styles* 2 or 1, notched at the summit; *fruit* enclosed within the hardened tube of the perianth. Only one British genus belongs to this Order, containing but two species, which are small, inconspicuous weeds, with wiry, much-branched stems, scanty foliage, and small, greenish flowers, remarkable only for the chaffy edge of the perianth.

1. SCLERANTHUS (Knawel).—*Calyx* 5-cleft, contracted at the mouth of the tube; *petals* 0; *stamens* 10, rarely 5; *styles* 2; *fruit* 1-seeded, covered by the hardened calyx. (Name from the Greek, *scleros*, hard, and *anthos*, a flower, from the hardness of the calyx.)

1. SCLERANTHUS (*Knawel*)

1. *S. annua* (Annual Knawel).—*Calyx*, when in fruit, spreading, acute, with a narrow, whitish margin; *root* annual. A small plant, 2–4 inches high, with numerous tangled stems, awl-shaped leaves, and green flowers, which grow either in the forks of the stems or in terminal tufts. Cornfields, especially on gravelly soil; common. —Fl. July to November. Annual.

2. *S. perennis* (Perennial Knawel).—*Stems* prostrate; *calyx-leaves* blunt, with a broad margin. Dry, sandy fields in the south and east of England; very rare. Perennial.

SCLERANTHUS ANNUA
(*Annual Knawel*)

NATURAL ORDER LXVII
POLYGONACEÆ.—THE PERSICARIA TRIBE

Flowers often bearing *stamens* only, or pistils only. *Perianth* deeply 3–6 parted, often in two rows; *stamens* 5–8, from the base of the perianth; *ovary* 1, not attached to the perianth; *styles* 2 or 3; *fruit*, a flattened or triangular nut. Herbaceous plants, distinguished by the above characters and by bearing alternate leaves, furnished at the base with membranous stipules, which encircle the stalk. The perianth is often coloured; and as the flowers, though not large, are numerous, and grow in spikes or panicles, many of them are handsome plants. Others, as the Dock, are unsightly weeds; they are found in all parts of the world, from the Tropics to the Poles, and at all altitudes. The properties residing in the leaves and roots are very different, the former being acid and astringent, and sometimes of an agreeable flavour, the latter nauseous and purgative. The powdered root of several species of *Rheum* affords the valuable medicine, Rhubarb, and the leaf-stalks of the same plants are much used for making tarts ; the sharp taste is attributed to the presence of oxalic, nitric, and malic acids. Two native kinds of Sorrel, and several of Dock, belong to the genus, *Rumex.* Sorrel (*R. acetosa*) is sometimes used in the same way as Rhubarb-stalks, but the species mostly employed in cookery is *R. scutata.* To the genus *Polygonum* belongs *P. fagopyrum*, Buck-wheat. In some countries the flour derived from its seeds is made into bread, but in England it is not much cultivated, except as food for pheasants, which are very partial to it. *P. tinctorum* is extensively cultivated in France and Flanders for the sake of the blue dye afforded by its herbage, and several other species are used in medicine. *Triplaris Americana* attains the dimensions of a tree, and is remarkable for being infested by ants, which excavate dwellings for themselves in the trunk and branches.

1. POLYGONUM (Persicaria).—*Perianth* deeply 5-cleft, not falling off ; *stamens* 5-8 ; *styles* 2 or 3 ; *fruit*, a triangular or flattened nut. (Name in Greek signifying having many knees, or joints, from the numerous joints of the stem.)

2. RUMEX (Dock).—*Perianth* deeply 6-cleft, in two rows, the interior segments large ; *stamens* 6 ; *styles* 3 ; *fruit*, a triangular nut, covered by an enlarged inner perianth. (Name, the Latin name of the plant.)

3. OXYRIA (Mountain Sorrel).—*Perianth* deeply 4-cleft, in two rows, the interior segments large ; *stamens* 6 ; *styles* 2 ; *fruit*, a flattened nut with a membranous wing. (Name from the Greek, *oxys*, sharp, from the acid flavour of the stem and leaves.)

1. POLYGONUM (*Persicaria*)

1. *P. aviculare* (Common Knot-grass).—*Stem* branched, 1-2 feet long, prostrate, or, when growing with tall plants, erect ; *leaves* narrow, elliptical, small ; *flowers* in axillary clusters of 2-5 ; *styles* 3 ; *fruit* triangular. A common weed, with leaves which are furnished with white chaffy stipules, and with minute flesh-coloured or greenish-white flowers. Varies greatly in size. Waste ground and roadsides ; abundant.—Fl. all the summer. Annual.

2. *P. maritimum* (Sea Knot-grass). — A variable plant, distinguished by its large-nerved *stipules* and long shining *fruits*, which project from the perianth ; *stems* shrubby, thicker than in the last ; *leaves* usually thicker, and glaucous ; and *flowers* also larger. South coast.—Fl. August, September. Perennial.

3. *P. convolvulus* (Climbing Persicaria).
— *Stem* twining ; *leaves*, heart - arrow -
shaped ; segments of the *perianth* bluntly
keeled ; *fruit* triangular, roughish. A mischievous weed, with the habit of the
Field Convolvulus, twining round the stems
of corn and other plants, and bearing
them down by its weight. The flowers
are greenish - white, and grow in loose
axillary clusters about 4 together. Cultivated ground ; abundant. — Fl. July,
August. Annual.

4. *P. dumetorum* (Copse Buck - wheat).
—Distinguished from the last by its more
luxuriant growth, its winged *perianth*, and
shining *fruit*. By some botanists classed
as a variety of the last. It grows in
bushy places in the south of England.
—Fl. August, September. Annual.

POLYGONUM CONVOLVULUS
(*Climbing Persicaria*)

5. *P. viviparum* (Viviparous Bistort).—*Stem* simple, erect, bearing
a single, loose spike, which has in the lower part small bulbs in
place of flowers ; *perfect flowers* with 3 *styles*, and producing triangular *fruits ; leaves* very narrow, their margins rolled back.
A slender plant, 6–8 inches high, remarkable for its tendency to
propagate itself by small, red bulbs, which supply the place of
flowers in the lower part of the spike ; the flowers are light flesh-
coloured. Mountain pastures in the highlands of Scotland, and
the north of England.—Fl. June, July. Perennial.

6. *P. bistorta* (Bistort Snake-root).— A rather handsome plant,
with a large twisted *root*, and several simple, erect *stems*, 12–18
inches high, each of which bears a cylindrical spike of flesh-coloured
flowers ; leaves egg-shaped, the radicle ones on long stalks, and
sometimes as much as 6 inches long. Moist meadows, chiefly in
the north ; not common.—Fl. June. Perennial.

7. *P. amphibium* (Amphibious Persicaria).—*Stem* erect, or supported in the water by the floating *leaves ; flowers* in oblong spikes ;
stamens 5 ; *styles* 2 ; *fruit* flattened ; *leaves* oblong, heart-shaped
at the base. So different are the forms assumed by this plant when
growing in water and on land that the varieties might well be taken
for two distinct species. In the water the stems are 2–3 feet long,
being supported by long-stalked, floating, smooth leaves ; on land
the stems are about a foot high, and the leaves narrow and rough.

In both forms of the plant the spikes of flowers are rose-coloured
and handsome. Ditches and banks of pools ; frequent.—Fl. July
to September. Perennial.

8. *P. Persicaria* (Spotted Persicaria).—*Stem* erect, branched ;
leaves narrow, tapering, often spotted ; *flowers* in spikes ; *stamens*
6 ; *styles* forked ; *stipules* fringed. A common weed, 1–2 feet
high, distinguished by its rather large leaves, stained with a purple
blotch, and numerous oblong spikes of greenish- or pinkish-white
flowers. Waste and damp ground ; abundant.—Fl. July, August.
Annual.

9. *P. lapanthifolium* (Pale-flowered Persicaria).—Closely resembles the last, and by some considered only a variety. Distinguished by having 2 distinct, instead of forked *styles,* and by
not having the *stipules* fringed ; in both species the *leaves* are
sometimes white with silky down. Waste and damp ground ;
not uncommon.—Fl. July to September. Annual.

10. *P. hydropiper* (Water-Pepper).—*Stem* erect ; *leaves* narrow,
tapering ; *flowers* in loose, drooping spikes ; *stamens* 6. Well
distinguished by its slender drooping spikes of greenish flowers.
The fresh juice is acrid, but not of an unpleasant flavour, and is
said to cure pimples on the tongue. Ditches and places where
water has stood during winter ; abundant.—Fl. August, September.
Annual.

11. *P. minus* (Slender Persicaria).—By some classed as a variety
of the last. Distinguished by its smaller size, close, slender, upright *spikes,* narrower *leaves,* nearly undivided *styles,* and lack of
acrid taste. Not common.—Fl. July to September. Annual.

2. Rumex (*Dock Sorrel*)

Flowers having both stamens and pistils ; herbage not acid

1. *R. hydrolapathum* (Great Water-Dock).— *Leaves* narrow,
elliptical, tapering at both ends, the *lower* ones heart-shaped at
the base ; enlarged segments of the *perianth* bluntly triangular,
tubercled. A picturesque plant, 4–6 feet high, with exceedingly
large leaves, and several stems, which bear numerous green flowers
in almost leafless whorls. River banks ; frequent.—Fl. July,
August. Perennial.

There are about ten other species of *Dock,* some of which are
rarely to be met with, others far too common. The most abundant
kind is *R. obtusifolius* (Broad-leaved Dock), too well known to need
any description. *R. crispus* (Curled Dock) has acute curled leaves,
and is also common. *R. sanguineus* (Bloody-veined Dock) has
the veins of its leaves tinged of a beautiful crimson. The other
species are less frequent, and unlikely to interest beginners.

PLATE LXXVII.

Sheep's Sorrel.   Spotted Persicaria

Stamens and pistils on different plants ; herbage acid

2. *R. acetosa* (Common Sorrel).—*Leaves* oblong, slightly arrow-shaped at the base. A slender plant, about 2 feet high, with juicy stems and leaves, and whorled spikes of reddish-green flowers. Well known for the grateful acidity of its herbage. Meadows ; abundant.—Fl. June, July. Perennial.

3. *R. acetosella* (Sheep's Sorrel).—*Leaves* tapering to a point, produced at the base into long, arrow-shaped barbs. Much smaller than the last, and often tinged, especially towards the end of summer, with a deep red hue. Dry, gravelly places ; abundant.—Fl. May to July. Perennial.

RUMEX ACETOSA
(*Common Sorrel*)

3. OXYRIA (*Mountain Sorrel*)

1. *O. reniformis* (Mountain Sorrel).— The only species. Approaching the *Common Sorrel* in habit, but shorter and stouter. The *leaves* are all from the root, and kidney-shaped ; the *flowers* are green, and grow in clustered spikes ; the herbage has a grateful acid flavour. Damp places, near the summit of high mountains ; frequent.—Fl. June to August. Perennial.

NATURAL ORDER LXXVIII

ELÆAGNACEÆ.—OLEASTER TRIBE

Stamens and *pistils* on separate plants ; *barren flowers* in catkins ; *perianth* tubular ; *stamens* 3–8, sessile on the throat of the perianth ; *fertile flowers* solitary, tubular, not falling off ; *ovary* 1-celled ; *style* short ; *stigma* awl-shaped ; *fruit*, a single nut, enclosed within the fleshy perianth. Trees and shrubs, with leaves which have no stipules, but are covered with scurfy scales. They are found in all parts of the Northern Hemisphere. The fruit of several species of Elæagnus is eaten in the East, and the flowers are highly fragrant and abound in honey, which, in some parts of Europe, is considered a remedy for malignant fevers. The only British species is the Sea Buckthorn (*Hippophaë Rhamnoides*).

1. HIPPOPHAË (Sea Buckthorn).—*Stamens* and *pistils* on separate plants ; *barren flowers* in small catkins ; *perianth* of 2 valves ; *stamens* 4, with very short *filaments ; fertile flowers* solitary ; *perianth* tubular, cloven at the summit ; *style* short ; *stigma* awl shaped ; *fruit*, a 1-seeded nut, enclosed in the fleshy perianth (Name of doubtful etymology.)

1. Hippophaë (*Sea buckthorn*)

1. *H. rhamnoides* (Sea Buckthorn, Sallow-Thorn). — The only species. A thorny shrub, 4–5 feet high, with very narrow, silvery *leaves*, small greenish *flowers*, which appear with the leaves in May, and numerous orange-coloured *berries*, which are of an acid flavour and very juicy. The stems, roots, and foliage, are said to impart a yellow dye. Sandhills and cliffs on the eastern coast of England. —Fl. May. Shrub.

Natural Order LXIX
THYMELACEÆ.—Daphne Tribe

Calyx tubular, coloured, 4- rarely 5-cleft, occasionally having scales in its mouth ; *stamens* 8, 4, or 2, inserted in the tube of the perianth ; *ovary* 1-celled ; *style* 1 ; *stigma* undivided ; *fruit*, a 1-seeded nut or drupe. Shrubs with undivided laurel-like leaves, remarkable for their tough bark, which is of a highly acrid nature, causing excessive pain if chewed, and raising a blister if applied to the skin. Both bark and root of Mezereon (*Daphne Mezereon*) are used in medicine ; they are of a very violent effect, whether taken inwardly or applied externally. The berries of Spurge-Laurel are poisonous to all animals except birds. In the East the bark of several species is manufactured into ropes and paper. The inner bark of *Lagetta lintearia*, when macerated and cut into thin pieces, assumes a beautiful net-like appearance, whence it has received the name of Lace-bark. In the south of Europe two plants belonging to this tribe are used to dye wood yellow. The seeds of *Inocarpus edulis* are eaten when roasted, and have the taste of Chestnuts. *Daphne Japonica*, or *Indica*, with its varieties, is commonly cultivated in conservatories and gardens for the sake of the delicious fragrance of its flowers. The only British genus belonging to this Tribe is—

1. Daphne (Spurge-Laurel).—Characters given above. (Name, the Greek for a Laurel, which it resembles in the character of its foliage.)

1. Daphne (*Spurge-laurel*)

1. *D. laureola* (Spurge-Laurel). — *Flowers* in drooping, axillary clusters ; *leaves* evergreen. A low shrub, about 2 feet high, very little branched, and remarkable for its smooth, erect stems, which are bare of leaves, except at the summit. The leaves are smooth, shining, and evergreen ; the flowers are green, and in mild weather fragrant ; the berries, which are egg-shaped and nearly black, are, as has been noted above, poisonous. From the tendency of this plant to bear its proportionally large leaves only on the summit of the stem, it has some resemblance to a group of Palms. It is used

PLATE LXXVIII.

Spurge Laurel   Wood Spurge

by nurserymen as a stock upon which to graft the delicious *D. Indica*
of greenhouses. Woods ; not unfrequent.—Fl. March. Shrub.

2. *D. Mezereum* is occasionally found in situations where it is
apparently wild ; but it is not considered a native ; its purple,
fragrant flowers appear before the leaves, and are sessile on the
branches ; the leaves are not evergreen ; berries red.

Natural Order LXX
SANTALACEÆ.—Sandal-wood Tribe

Perianth attached to the ovary, 4- or 5-cleft, valvate when in
bud ; *stamens* as many as the lobes of the perianth, and opposite
to them ; *ovary* 1-celled ; *style* 1 ; *stigma* often lobed ; *fruit,* a
hard, dry drupe. The plants of this group are found in Europe
and North America, in the form of obscure weeds ; in New Holland,
the East Indies, and the South Sea Islands, as large shrubs, or small
trees. Some are astringent, others yield fragrant wood. Sandal-
wood is the produce of *Santalum album,* an East Indian tree, and
is used both medicinally and as a perfume. In New Holland and
Peru the seeds of some species are eaten. The only British plant
belonging to this tribe is—

1. THESIUM (Bastard Toad-flax).—Characters given above.
(Name of doubtful origin.)

1. THESIUM (*Bastard Toad-flax*)

1. *T. linophyllum* (Bastard Toad-flax).—The only British species.
A rather small plant, with a woody *root ;* nearly prostrate stems,
6–12 inches high ; very narrow, pointed *leaves,* and leafy clusters
of whitish *flowers.* Chalky hills in the south of England ; not
common.—Fl. July. Perennial.

Natural Order LXXI
ARISTOLOCHIACEÆ.—Birth-wort Tribe

Perianth attached to the ovary below, tubular above, with a
wide mouth ; *stamens* 6–12, inserted on the ovary ; *ovary* 3 to
6-celled ; *style* 1 ; *stigmas* rayed, as many as the cells of the ovary ;
fruit 3- to 6-celled, many-seeded. Herbs or shrubs, often climbing,
with simple leaves, and solitary, axillary flowers, very abundant in
the warmer parts of South America, but rare elsewhere. The
plants of this Order are generally bitter, tonic, and stimulant.
The dried and powdered leaves of Asarabacca (*Asarum Europæum*)
are used in the preparation of cephalic snuffs, exciting sneezing,
and giving relief to headache and weak eyes. Virginian Snake-
root (*Aristolochia serpentaria*) and other allied species are used as

antidotes to snake bites. The juice extracted from the root of a South American species is said to have the power of stupefying serpents if placed in their mouths. Other African species are said to be used by the Egyptian jugglers to stupefy the snakes with which they play tricks during the exhibition of their art. The wood of *Aristolochia* is remarkable for not being arranged in concentric layers, but in wedges. A thin slice is a beautiful object for examination under a microscope of low power.

1. ARISTOLOCHIA (Birth-wort).—*Perianth* tubular, curved, swollen at the base, the *mouth* dilated on one side ; *anthers* 6, inserted on the style ; *stigma* 6-lobed ; *capsule* 6-celled. (Name in Greek denoting the supposed medicinal virtues of the plant.)

2. ASARUM (Asarabacca).—*Perianth* bell-shaped, 3-cleft ; *stamens* 12, inserted at the base of the style ; *stigma* 6-lobed ; *capsule* 6-celled. (Name from the Greek, *a*, not, and *seira*, a wreath, denoting that the plant was by the ancients excluded from garlands.)

1. ARISTOLOCHIA (*Birth-wort*)

1. *A. clematitis* (Birth-wort).—The only species found growing in wild situations in Britain. A singular plant, with creeping *roots*, slender, unbranched, erect *stems*, and large heart-shaped *leaves ;* the *flowers*, which grow several together, are of a dull yellow colour, swollen at the base, contracted above, and expanding into an oblong lip with a short point. Woods, and among ruins in the east and south of England ; rare.—Fl. July, August. Perennial.

2. ASARUM (*Asarabacca*)

1. *A. Europæum* (Asarabacca).—The only species found in Britain, and a doubtful native. A curious plant, consisting of a very short *stem*, bearing two large, shining, kidney-shaped *leaves*, and a solitary dingy, brown-green *flower*. Woods in the north ; rare.—Fl. May. Perennial.

NATURAL ORDER LXXII

EMPETRACEÆ.—CROW-BERRY TRIBE

Stamens and *pistils* on separate plants ; *perianth* of several scales arranged in 2 rows, the inner resembling petals ; *stamens* equal in number to the inner scales, and alternate with them ; *ovary* of 3, 6, or 9 cells, on a fleshy disk ; *style* 1 ; *stigma* rayed ; *fruit* fleshy, with long cells ; *seeds* 1 in each cell. Small heath-like evergreen shrubs, with minute axillary flowers, chiefly inhabiting Europe and North America. The leaves and fruit slightly acid. The berries of the Crow-berry (*Empetrum nigrum*), though of an unpleasant flavour, are eaten in Arctic regions, and are considered as a preventive of scurvy.

1. EMPETRUM (Crow-berry).—*Perianth* of 3 outer and 3 inner scales. (Name in Greek signifying growing *on a rock*.)

1. EMPETRUM (*Crow-berry*)

1. *E. nigrum* (Black Crow-berry, Crake-berry).—The only British species. A small, prostrate shrub, with the habit of a Heath. The *stems* are much branched ; the *leaves* are oblong, very narrow, and have their margins so much recurved as to meet at the back ; the *flowers* are small and purplish, growing in the axils of the upper leaves. The *berries*, which are black, are much eaten by moor-fowl. Abundant on mountainous heaths in the north.—Fl. May. Perennial.

NATURAL ORDER LXXIII
EUPHORBIACEÆ.—SPURGE TRIBE

Stamens and *pistils* in separate flowers ; *perianth* lobed, with various scales or petal-like appendages ; *stamens* varying in number and arrangement ; *ovary* mostly 3-celled, with as many *styles* and *stigmas ; fruit* generally 3-celled and 3-seeded. A large Order, very difficult to be defined, even by the experienced botanist, and, therefore, very likely to puzzle the beginner, who must not be disheartened if he is a long while in reducing to their place in the system those plants belonging to it which he first meets with. The Order contains nearly 200 genera, and it is necessary to examine many of these before the relation can be traced between those families which most differ. The number of species is thought to be not less than 2500, which are distributed over most of the tropical and temperate regions of the globe, especially the warmer parts of America. They are either trees, shrubs, or herbs, and some kinds have the external habit of the cactus tribe. Among so numerous an assemblage of plants we should expect to find a great dissimilarity of properties, which, indeed, exists to a certain extent, yet nearly all agree in being furnished with a juice, often milky, which is highly acrid, narcotic, or corrosive, the intensity of the poisonous property being usually proportionate to the abundance of the juice. Of the genus *Euphorbia*, Spurge, which gives its name to the Order, ten or twelve species are natives of Britain. The British Spurges are all herbaceous, and remarkable for the singular structure of their green flowers and their acrid milky juice, which exudes plentifully when either the stems or leaves are wounded. The roots of several of the common kinds enter into the composition of some of the quack fever medicines, but they are too violent in their action to be used with safety. The Irish

Spurge is extensively used by the peasants of Kerry for poisoning, or rather stupefying fish. So powerful are its effects that a small creel, or basket, filled with the bruised plant, suffices to poison the fish for several miles down a river. *Euphorbia Lathyris* is sometimes, though erroneously, called in England the Caper-plant. Its unripe seeds are pickled, and form a dangerous substitute for the genuine capers, which are the unexpanded flower-buds of *Caparis epinosa*, a shrub indigenous to the most southern countries of Europe. Among the foreign Spurges, some species furnish both the African and American savages with a deadly poison for their arrows. Another, called in India *Tirucalli*, furnishes an acrid juice, which is used in its fresh state for raising blisters. Other kinds are used in various parts of the world as medicines, but require to be administered with caution. The gum resin, *Euphorbium*, of chemists, is procured from the species growing in Africa and the Canaries, by wounding the stems and collecting in leathern bags, the sap which exudes. It is an acrid poison, and highly inflammable, and so violent in its effects as to produce severe inflammation of the nostrils if those who are employed in powdering it do not guard themselves from its dust. Pliny relates that the plant was discovered by King Juba, and named by him after his chief physician, Euphorbus. The Manchineel tree (*Hippomane Mancinella*) is said to be so poisonous that persons have died from merely sleeping beneath its shade. Its juice is pure white, and a single drop of it falling upon the skin burns like fire, forming an ulcer, often difficult to heal. The fruit, which is beautiful and looks like an apple, contains a similar fluid, but in a milder form ; the burning it causes in the lips of those who bite it guards the careless from the danger of eating it. *Jatropha Manihot*, or Manioc, is a shrub about six feet high, indigenous to the West Indies and South America, abounding in a milky juice of so poisonous a nature that it has been known to occasion death in a few minutes. The poisonous principle, however, may be dissipated by heat, after which process the root may be converted into the most nourishing food. It is grated into a pulp and subjected to heavy pressure, until the juice is drained off. The residue, called *cassava*, requires no further preparation, being simply baked in the form of thin cakes on a hot iron hearth. This bread is so palatable to those who are accustomed to it as to be preferred to that made from wheaten flour, and Creole families, who have changed their residence to Europe, frequently supply themselves with it at some trouble and expense. The fresh juice is highly poisonous, but if boiled with meat and seasoned, it makes an excellent soup, which is wholesome and nutritious. The heat of the sun even is sufficient to dissipate the noxious properties, for if it be sliced and exposed for some hours to the direct rays of the sun, cattle may eat it with perfect safety. The roots are sometimes eaten by the

Indians, simply roasted, without being previously submitted to the process of grating and repressing the juice. They also use the juice for poisoning their arrows, and were acquainted with the art of converting it into an intoxicating liquid before they were visited by Europeans. By washing the pulp in water and suffering the latter to stand, a sediment of starch is produced, which, under the name of tapioca, is extensively imported into Europe, where it is used for all the purposes to which arrowroot and sago are applied. Caoutchouc, or India-rubber, is a well-known elastic gum, furnished in greater or less abundance by many plants of this Order, but especially by a South American tree, *Siphonia* or *Hevea elastica*.

The fragrant aromatic bark called cascarilla is produced by a shrub belonging to this Order, *Croton Eleutheria*, a native of the Bahamas, and by other species of *Croton* indigenous to the West Indies and South America. Croton oil is the product of *Croton Tiglium*, and is so violent a medicine as to be rarely administered until all other remedies have failed. Castor oil is expressed from the seeds of *Ricinus communis*, an African tree, frequently grown in English gardens as an annual, on account of its handsome leaves. *Poinsetia*, some of the *Crotons*, and *Euphorbias* are a good deal grown in greenhouses. The Box is the only British tree belonging to this Order, of the poisonous properties of which it partakes, though to a limited extent. In some parts of Persia it is very abundant, and in these districts it is found impossible to keep camels, as the animals are very found of browsing on the leaves, which kill them. The Dog-mercury (*Mercurialis perennis*) is an herbaceous plant, common in our woods, and an active poison. Another species, *M. annua*, is less frequently met with, and, though poisonous, is not so virulent as the other species.

1. EUPHORBIA (Spurge).—*Perianth* or *involucre* bell-shaped, containing 12 or more *barren flowers* or *stamens*, and 1 *fertile flower* or *pistil ; ovary* 3-lobed ; *styles* 3 ; *stigmas* 2-cleft ; *capsule* 3-celled, 3-seeded. (Name from *Euphorbus*, physician to Juba, an ancient king of Mauritania, who first employed the plant as medicine.)

2. MERCURIALIS (Mercury).—*Stamens* and *pistils* on different plants. *Perianth* 3-cleft to the base ; *barren flower ; stamens* 9, or more ; *fertile flower, styles* 2 ; *ovary* 2-lobed ; *capsule* 2-celled, 2-seeded. (Name in honour of the heathen god, *Mercury*.)

3. BUXUS (Box).—*Stamens* and *pistils* in separate flowers, but on the same plant. *Perianth* 4-cleft to the base ; *barren flower* with 1 *bract ; stamens* 4 ; *fertile flower* with 3 *bracts ; styles* 3 ; *capsule* with 3 horns, 3-celled ; *cells* 2-seeded. (Name, the Latin name of the tree.)

S

1. Euphorbia (*Spurge*)

1. *E. peplis* (Purple Spurge).—Grows quite flat to the ground, sending out several branches at right angles to the root, in a circular manner, about 6 inches across. Smooth and glaucous, and of a beautiful glaucous hue ; flower-heads small. Peculiar to the sandy sea-shore in South Wales and south of England.—Fl. August, September. Annual.

2. *E. helioscopia* (Sun Spurge).—*Umbel*, of 5 rays, which are often repeatedly forked ; *leaves* oblong, tapering towards the base, serrated above ; *capsule* smooth. Varying in size from 6–12 inches in height, but easily distinguished by the golden-green hue of its spreading umbel, which is large in proportion to the size of the plant, and has several serrated leaves at its base. Cultivated ground ; abundant.—Fl. July, August. Annual.

3. *E. peplus* (Petty Spurge).—A very common garden weed, 3–9 inches high, distinguished by its pale hue, its 3-rayed and forked *umbel* of numerous *flowers*, the *involucres* of which are crescent-shaped, with long horns.—Fl. summer. Cultivated ground. Annual.

4. *E. exigua* (Dwarf Spurge). — A slender species, from 1 or 2–8 inches high, with ascending *stems* and narrow, glaucous *leaves*. Cultivated land ; common.—Fl. June to September. Annual.

5. *E. Lathyris* (Caper Spurge).—A tall, herbaceous species, 2–4 feet high, remarkable for the glaucous hue of its *foliage*, its heart-shaped, taper-pointed *bracts*, and very large *capsules*, which abound to a great degree, as well as the rest of the plant, in the milky, acrid fluid found throughout the family. The leaves also, unlike those of other Euphorbias, are all opposite. Common in cottage gardens ; not unfrequent as an escape, and perhaps truly wild in one or two localities.—Fl. June, July. Biennial.

6. *E. paralias* (Sea Spurge).—A stout, shrubby plant, 6–12 feet high ; *stems* leafless below, and with numerous glaucous, leathery, imbricated leaves above. Sandy sea-shores; uncommon.—Fl. August to October. Perennial.

7. *E. segetalis* (Portland Spurge).—Distinguished from the last by its less robust habit and the red fringe of its stems and leaves, and by its leaves being thinner. South and west coasts ; uncommon.—Fl. June to September. Perennial.

8. *E. amygdaloides* (Wood Spurge.)—*Stem* branched above in an umbellate manner into about 5 rays ; *rays* 2-forked ; *bracts* perfoliate ; *leaves* narrow, egg-shaped, hairy beneath ; glands of the *involucre* crescent-shaped. A common plant, with somewhat shrubby stems, 1–2 feet high, conspicuous in spring and summer

with its golden-green leaves and flowers, and in autumn with the red tinge of its stems and leaves.   Woods ; abundant.—Fl. March, April.   Perennial.

9. *E. platyphyllos* (Broad-leaved Spurge).—An erect, slender, slightly-branched plant, 6–18 inches high, smooth or hairy, with the *upper leaves* broad and heart-shaped, and 3–5 rayed *umbels*, which are again forked.   *Capsules* small and warted.   Cultivated ground in the south ; rare.—Fl. July to September.   Annual or biennial.

10. *E. Hiberna* (Irish Spurge).—A smooth, or sometimes downy species, 12–18 inches high, with oblong *leaves*, 2–4 inches in length ; *umbel* 5-rayed ; *capsules* large and warted.   In Ireland and in Devonshire.—Fl. May, June.   Perennial.

Two other species are found in Britain, viz. *E. pilosa* (Hairy Spurge).—A tall, leafy, slightly hairy perennial, with glandular capsules.   Found established in woods near Bath and one or two other places, but probably not indigenous ; very rare.   And—

E. esula (Leafy Spurge).—A very rare species, found only in Scotland, and not indigenous.   It grows 12–18 inches high, and is best distinguished by its many-rayed umbel.

2. MERCURIALIS (*Mercury*)

1. *M. perennis* (Dog's Mercury).—A common woodland, herbaceous plant, sending up from its creeping *roots* numerous simple *stems*, 6–12 inches high.   Each stem bears in the upper part several pairs of stalked, rather large, roughish *leaves*, ovate-lanceolate and serrated, and among the uppermost of these grow the small green *flowers*, the *barren* on long stalks, the *fertile* sessile.   Woods and shady places ; abundant.—Fl. April, May.   Perennial.

MERCURIALIS PERENNIS
(*Dog's Mercury*)

2. *M. annua* (Annual Mercury).—Taller than the last, and distinguished by its branched *stems*, and smaller, smooth, *leaves*, which are of a light green hue.   *Barren* and *fertile flowers* are sometimes found on the same plant.   Waste places ; not common.— Fl. August.   Annual.   Two forms are found, one with stalked leaves, the other with sessile.

3. Buxus (*Box*)

1. *B. sempervirens* (Common Box-tree).—A small, well-known tree, growing in great abundance, and apparently wild, on Box-hill in Surrey, where it ripens its seeds. In a natural state it attains a height of 8 or 10 feet; in gardens it is often clipped into various shapes, and a dwarf variety is commonly used as an edging to beds.— Fl. April. Small tree.

Natural Order LXXIV

CALLITRICHACEÆ.—Water Star-wort Tribe

Flowers in different parts of the same plant, axillary, solitary, very minute, imperfect, with two white *bracts* at the base; *calyx* and *corolla* absent; *barren flower*, with one *stamen*, or very rarely two; *filament* thread-like, bearing a 1-celled *anther*, which opens at the summit by two transverse valves; *fertile flower*, ovary 4-angled, 4-celled; *styles* 2, awl-shaped; *stigma* simple; *fruit* 4-celled, 4-lobed, 4-seeded, flattened laterally, not opening. Small aquatic, herbaceous plants, with long, weak, tangled *stems*, which are usually submerged, opposite simple entire *leaves*, of which the upper alone float on the surface of the water, and long, thread-like silvery *roots*, which proceed from the joints of the stem, and are either attached to the soil below or are suspended in the water.

BUXUS SEMPERVIRENS (*Common Box-tree*)

1. CALLITRICHE (Water Star-wort).—Characters given above.

1. CALLITRICHE (*Water Star-wort*)

1. *C. verna* (Vernal Water Star-wort).—*Leaves* in pairs, united at the base; *flowers* in the axils of the leaves; *carpels* bluntly keeled at the back. An aquatic plant, with long slender stems, which send out shining roots from the joints; either growing in running water, when the leaves are usually very narrow, or in stagnant water, when the upper leaves are broader, and float on the surface, crowded into a starry

CALLITRICHE VERNA (*Vernal Water Star-wort*)

form, the stamens being the only parts of the plant actually raised above it. Streams and stagnant water; everywhere.—Fl. May to July. Annual.

2. *C. autumnalis* (Autumnal Water Star-wort).—*Carpels* winged at the back. Resembling the last, and growing in similar situations, but rare. In this species the whole plant is submerged ; all the leaves are narrow and abrupt, and of a deeper green.—Fl. June to October. Annual.

Four other British forms of *Callitriche* are described by botanists, which vary in a slight degree from the preceding ; but they are not of common occurrence, and are on other accounts scarcely deserving of a separate notice in a volume of the present scope.

NATURAL ORDER LXXV

URTICACEÆ.—NETTLE TRIBE

Stamens and *pistils* generally in separate flowers, and often on different plants ; *perianth* divided, not falling off, sometimes wanting ; *stamens* equal in number to the lobes of the perianth, and opposite to them ; *anthers* curved inwards in the bud, and often bursting with elasticity ; *ovary* 1, simple ; *fruit*, a hard and dry 1-seeded capsule. A difficult Order, the limits of which are variously assigned by different botanists. In its widest extent it contains some 1500 species, among which are a number of valuable fruits, as the famous Bread-fruit and Jack-fruit (*Artocarpus incisifolia* and *A. integrifolia*), the Fig, Mulberry, and Sycamore of the Scriptures. The Upas-tree of Java and Palo-de-vaca, or Cow-tree of Demerara, are arranged in the same Order, with many others. In its more limited extent the Nettle Tribe contains 23 families, comprising, almost entirely, rough-leaved plants, which, though they occasionally acquire the stature of trees, have, nevertheless, little more than an herbaceous texture, their wood being remarkable for its lightness and sponginess. They are found in most parts of the world, occurring as weeds in the temperate and colder regions, and attaining a larger size in hot climates. The British species of Nettle (*Urtica*) are well known for the burning properties of the juice contained in the stings (formic acid), with which their foliage is plentifully armed. But, painful as are the consequences of touching one of our common nettles, they are not to be compared with the effects of incautiously handling some of the East Indian species. A slight sensation of pricking is followed by a burning heat, such as would be caused by rubbing the part with a hot iron ; soon the pain extends, and continues for many hours, or even days, being attended by symptoms such as accompany lock-jaw or influenza. A Java species produces effects which last for a whole year, and are even said to cause death. In some species the fibre is so strong that cordage is manufactured from it. The burning property of the juice is dissipated by heat, the young shoots of the common nettle being often boiled and eaten as a

vegetable. Besides the use to which Hops are put in the manufacture of beer, the young shoots may also be boiled, when they
form a delicious vegetable.

1. URTICA (Nettle).—*Stamens* and *pistils* in separate flowers, on
the same or different plants ; *barren flower, perianth* of 4 leaves,
stamens 4 ; *fertile flower, perianth* of 2 leaves, 1-seeded. (Name
from the Latin, *uro*, to burn, from its stinging properties.)

2. PARIETARIA (Pellitory).—*Stamens* and *pistils* in the same
flower ; *perianth* 4-cleft ; *stamens* 4 ; *filaments* at first curved inwards, finally spreading with an elastic spring ; *fruit* 1-seeded.
(Name from the Latin, *paries*, a wall, where these plants often
grow.)

3. HUMULUS (Hop).—*Stamens* and *pistils* on different plants ;
barren flower, perianth of 5 leaves ; *stamens* 5 ; *fertile flower*, a
catkin composed of large concave *scales,* each of which has at its
base two *styles* and 1 *seed*. (Name from the Latin, *humus*, rich
soil, in which the plant flourishes.)

1. URTICA (*Nettle*)

1. *U. dioica* (Great Nettle). — *Roots* creeping ; *stems* 2–3 feet
high ; *lower leaves* heart-shaped at the base, tapering to a point ;
upper leaves narrower ; *flowers* in long, branched clusters. A
common weed, too well known to need further description.—
Fl. July, August. Perennial.

2. *U. urens* (Small Nettle).—*Leaves* elliptical ; *flowers* in short,
nearly simple clusters. Smaller than the last, but closely resembling it in habit and properties. Waste places ; abundant.—
Fl. July to October. Annual.

3. *U. pilulifera* (Roman Nettle).—Taller than the last, about
2 feet high, with ovate, heart-shaped *leaves*, and globular heads of
flowers. Local and not indigenous.—Fl. July to October. Annual.

2. PARIETARIA (*Pellitory-of-the-wall*)

1. *P. officinalis* (Common Pellitory-of-the-wall).—The only
British species. A much-branched, bushy, herbaceous plant, with
narrow, hairy *leaves*, reddish, brittle *stems*, and small, hairy *flowers*,
which grow in clusters in the axils of the *leaves*. The *filaments* are
curiously jointed and elastic, so that if touched before the expansion
of the flower, they suddenly spring from their incurved position
and shed their pollen. In rural districts an infusion of this plant
is a favourite medicine.—Fl. all the summer. Perennial.

PLATE LXXIX.

Hop   Stinging Nettle

Pellitory of the Wall   Lesser Stinging Nettle

3. HUMULUS (*Hop*)

1. *H. lupulus* (Common Hop).—A beautiful climbing plant, commonly cultivated for the sake of its catkins, which are used to give a bitter flavour to beer, and naturalized in many places.— Fl. July. Perennial.

NATURAL ORDER LXXVI

ULMACEÆ.—ELM TRIBE

Stamens and *pistils* in the same or different flowers ; *perianth* bell-shaped, often irregular ; *stamens* equalling in number, and opposite to, the lobes of the perianth ; *ovary* not attached to the perianth, 2-celled ; *styles* and *stigmas* 2 ; *fruit* 1- or 2-celled, not bursting, drupe-like, or furnished with a leafy border. Trees or shrubs with rough leaves and clustered flowers (never in catkins) inhabiting temperate climates, and often forming valuable timber trees.

1. ULMUS (Elm).—*Perianth* bell-shaped, 4- to 5-cleft, persistent ; *stamens* 5 ; *styles* 2 ; *capsule* thin and leaf-like, containing a single seed. (Name, the Latin name of the tree.)

1. ULMUS (*Elm*)

1. *U. montana* (Scotch or Wych Elm).—A tall tree, with almost stalkless *leaves*, which are obliquely ovate and edged with double teeth ; *fruit* ovate, green, slightly notched at the top, and with the seed about the centre ; no suckers from the roots. Chiefly found in the north.—Fl. March. Tree.

2. *U. campestris* (Common Elm).—A tall tree, very near the last. *Fruit* deeply notched, and *seed* in the upper half, near the notch. Growth usually more upright that in *U. montana.* A variety with somewhat pendulous branches is sometimes erroneously called Wych Elm. A variety is not unfrequent in hedges with rough, corky bark on stems and twigs. Hedges, parks, etc. ; common.—Fl. March. Tree.

NATURAL ORDER LXXVII

AMENTACEÆ.—CATKIN-BEARING TRIBE

Stamens and *pistils* in separate flowers, and often on different plants ; *barren flowers* in heads or catkins, composed of scales ; *stamens* 1-20, inserted on the scales ; *fertile flower*, clustered, solitary, or in catkins ; *ovary* usually simple ; *stigmas* 1 or more. An extensive Order, containing a large number of trees which are highly valued for their fruit, timber, bark, and other minor productions. They are most abundant in temperate climates, comprising a large proportion of our English forest trees. They have been subdivided by botanists into several Sub-orders, or groups, four of which contain British specimens. The first Sub-order, SALICINEÆ (the Willow group), is distinguished by bearing all its flowers in catkins, the fruit being a 2-valved capsule, containing numerous seeds tufted with down. In the Sub-order, MYRICEÆ (Sweet-Gale group), the flowers are all in catkins, and the ripe fruit assumes a drupe-like appearance, from being invested by the fleshy scales of the catkin. In BETULINEÆ (Birch group) the flowers are all in catkins, and the fruit is thin and flattened, containing 1 or 2 seeds, which are not tufted with down. In CUPULIFERÆ the fertile flowers grow in spikes or tufts, the barren flowers in catkins, and the fruit is either wholly or partially invested with a tough case, termed a cupula. By some modern botanists these groups are severally treated as distinct Orders, under the names of SALICACEÆ, MYRICACEÆ, BETULACEÆ, and CUPULIFERÆ; but it has been thought expedient to retain the few examples described in this volume under the comprehensive Order AMENTACEÆ.

Sub-order I. SALICINEÆ.—Willow Group

1. SALIX (Willow).—*Stamens* and *pistils* on different plants (*diœcious*); *scales* of the catkin imbricated, entire; *stamens* 1–5; *stigmas* 2; *capsule* of 2 valves, 1-celled; *seeds* numerous, tufted with cottony down. (Name, the Latin name of the plant.)

A very large genus, widely distributed from the tropics to the Arctic regions, and found both in low-lying lands and at great altitudes. This is perhaps the most puzzling family with which the student will meet. Not only do many confusing natural hybrid forms occur, but botanists often find it difficult to " pair " the male and female forms of the same species. As many as thirty British species have been described, but the truly distinct forms are probably about half that number. For a detailed description of the species the student is referred to Bentham and Hooker's " British Flora," or John's " Forest Trees of Britain."

2. POPULUS (Poplar).—*Stamens* and *pistils* on different plants; *scales* of the catkin jagged; *stamens* 8–30; *stigmas* 4 or 8; *capsule* of 2 valves, obscurely 2-celled; *seeds* numerous, tufted with cottony down. (Name from the Latin, *populus*, and signifying *the tree of the people*, which it was considered to be at Rome and in France during the revolutions.)

The three principal British species are—

P. alba (White Poplar, Abele).—A tall growing tree, with smooth ash-grey bark; ovate-cordate, lobed leaves, white, with cottony down on the under side; buds downy; the roots send up many suckers. Perhaps indigenous and much planted.

PLATE LXXX.

Silver Birch
Elm
Common Alder
Sweet Gale

P. tremula (Aspen).—Smaller than the last; leaves smaller, orbicular, toothed, not cottony beneath, borne on slender stems, and therefore agitated by the least breath of air; suckers from the root.

POPULUS (*Poplar*)

P. nigra (Black Poplar).—A tall tree of pyramidal growth. Leaves rhomboid, serrated, not cottony beneath; buds sticky; no suckers from the root. Not indigenous, but common by streams and rivers.

The Lombardy Poplar is not indigenous, having been introduced from the East.

Sub-order II. MYRICEÆ.—*Sweet-Gale Tribe*

3. MYRICA (Sweet-Gale).—*Stamens* and *pistils* on different plants ; *scales* of the catkin concave ; *stamens* 4–8 ; *stigmas* 2 ; *fruit* drupe-like, 1-seeded. (Name, the Greek name of the *Tamarisk*.) The only British species is *M. Gale* (Sweet-Gale).—A low shrub, about 3 feet high, which has a sweet resinous smell when bruised. Leaves ovate-lanceolate, toothed towards the upper end. The catkins appear before the leaves in the spring. Found in bogs in Scotland and the north of England, and occasionally in the south.

Sub-order III. BETULINEÆ.—*Birch Group*

4. BETULA (Birch).—*Stamens* and *pistils* in separate flowers (*monœcious*) ; *scales* of the barren catkins in threes ; *stamens* 10–12 ; *scales* of the fertile catkin 3-*lobed*, 3-*flowered* ; *stigmas* 2 ; *fruit* flattened, 1-seeded, winged. (Name, the Latin name of the tree.) There are two British species, viz.—

B. alba (Common, White, or Silver Birch).—A very graceful tree, with silvery-white bark, which peels from the trunk in a curious manner. The branches are slender and somewhat pendulous, and the leaves, borne on long stalks, are broadly ovate, pointed, and serrate. A common forest tree.

B. nana (Dwarf Birch).—A mountain shrub or small tree, with wiry branches, and numerous rounded, notched leaves, which are beautifully veined.   Scotland and the north of England.

5. ALNUS (Alder).—*Stamens* and *pistils* in separate flowers; *scales* of the barren catkin 3-lobed, 3-flowered ; *stamens* 4 ; *scales* of the fertile catkin 2-flowered, permanent, becoming hard and dry ; *stigmas* 2 ; *fruit* flattened, not winged.   (Name, the Latin name of the tree.)   *A. glutinosa* (Common Alder) is the only British species belonging to this family.   It is a smallish tree, with dingy bark, and short-stalked leaves, broadly ovate, wavy at the edge, and toothed ; catkins two or thee together, barren ones long ; fertile ones roundish, hard, woody, hanging for a long time on the tree.   A widely diffused tree, growing in swampy ground in most of the temperate regions of the globe.

Sub-order IV.   CUPULIFERÆ.—*Mast-bearing Group*

Stamens and pistils in separate flowers (*Monœcious*)

6. FAGUS (Beech).—*Barren flowers* in a globose catkin ; *stamens* 5–15 ; *fertile flowers* 2 together, within a 4-lobed, prickly involucre ; *stigmas* 3 ; *nuts* 3-cornered, enclosed in the enlarged involucre. (Name in Greek, *phegos*, a species of Oak ; in Latin, *fagus*, a Beech.)

F. sylvatica (Common Beech). — The only British species. A large, handsome tree, with smooth, greyish bark, and short-stalked, ovate leaves, silky when young, and rather thin, smooth texture when fully expanded.   The three-cornered masts or nuts are much appreciated by squirrels and children.   Indigenous, and a largely planted forest tree.

7. CASTANEA (Chestnut).—*Barren flowers* in a very long, spike-like catkin ; *stamens* 10–20 ; *fertile flowers* 3 together, within a 4-lobed, very prickly involucre ; *stigmas* 6 ; *nuts* not distinctly 3-cornered, enclosed in the enlarged involucre.   (Latin, the name of the tree.)   *C. sativæ* (Sweet, or Spanish Chestnut).—A handsome tree, with perpendicularly furrowed bark, and smooth, narrow, sharply serrated leaves.   The male catkins are 4 or 5 inches long, and have a heavy sickly smell.   The nuts, though frequently produced in England, are usually small ; but in some parts of Southern Europe they form the chief article of food of the inhabitants.   Not indigenous, but frequently planted.

8. QUERCUS (Oak).—*Barren flowers* in a long, drooping catkin ; *stamens* 5–10 ; *fertile flowers* with a cup-shaped, scaly involucre ; *stigmas* 3 ; *fruit,* an acorn.   (Name, the Latin name of the tree.) *Q. Robur* (British Oak).—One of our most splendid forest trees, too well known to need much description.   The leaves, which often hang on the trees till very late into the winter, are very variable

PLATE LXXXI.

Hazel

Beech

Spanish Chestnut

in general outline, with usually sinuate, bluntly-lobed edges, sometimes almost pinnately lobed. The excellence of the timber has become almost proverbial ; the bark is used for tanning ; the galls, which form from the attacks of certain insects, have been used in the manufacture of ink ; and the acorns are relished by swine.— Fl. in spring, when the leaves are expanding.

9. CORYLUS (Hazel).—*Barren flowers* in a long, drooping, cylindrical catkin ; *scales* 3-cleft ; *stamens* 8 ; *fertile flowers*, several, enclosed in a bud-like involucre ; *stigmas* 2 ; *nut* enclosed in the enlarged, jagged involucre. (Name, the Latin name of the tree.)

C. avellana (Common Hazel).—A shrub or small tree, with coarse, rounded, serrated leaves. The *barren catkins*, which form in the autumn, expand early in spring before the leaves appear ; the *fertile flowers* may be recognized by their crimson stigmas ; nuts edible.

10. CARPINUS (Hornbeam). —*Barren flowers* in a long cylindrical catkin ; *scales* roundish ; *fertile flowers* in a loose catkin ; scales large and leaf-like, 3-lobed ; stigmas 2 ; nut strongly ribbed. (Name, the Latin name of the tree.) A small tree, with ovate, doubly serrate leaves, somewhat downy beneath. The tough wood is used for making cog-wheels. Indigenous to the south of England and Wales. — Fl. when the leaves are expanding in spring.

CARPINUS BETULUS
(*Common Hornbeam*)

NATURAL ORDER LXXVIII
CONIFERÆ.—FIR TRIBE

Stamens and *pistils* in separate flowers, and often on different trees. *Stamens* collected in sets around a common stalk ; *fertile flowers* in cones, destitute of *styles* and *stigmas ; fruit*, a cone, composed of hardened *scales* or *bracts*, bearing, at the base of each, naked *seeds*, which are often winged. A large Order of trees, represented in all parts of the globe. They vary from mere stunted bushes to the gigantic Redwood trees of California. Only three species are natives of Britain, but a large number are planted both as forest trees and as ornamental garden trees and bushes.

1. PINUS (Fir).—*Barren flowers*, in clustered, scaly catkins, the upper scales bearing sessile *anthers* ; *fertile flowers* in an egg-shaped catkin, which finally becomes a woody *cone ; seeds* winged. (Name, the Latin name of the tree.)

P. sylvestris (Scotch Fir).—A tall, picturesque tree, with reddish bark, and a dense, tufted head. *Leaves* in pairs, about 2 inches long, surrounded by scales, evergreen. The *cones* are small, sessile, and grow 1–3 together. *Wings* of the seeds 2 or 3 times as long as the *seeds*. Indigenous in the Highlands of Scotland, and largely planted elsewhere.

2. JUNIPERUS (Juniper).—*Barren flowers* in scaly catkins ; *anthers* attached to the base of the scales ; *fertile flowers* in cat-kins of a few united *scales*, which finally become a fleshy *berry*, containing 3 *seeds*. (Name, the Latin name of the tree.)

J. communis (Common Juniper) is a native of all the northern parts of Europe, and in Great Britain is generally found on hills and heathy downs, especially in the north, and where the soil is chalky. The berries are much used to flavour hollands or geneva, a spirit distilled from corn.

JUNIPERUS COMMUNIS
(*Common Juniper*)

3. TAXUS (Yew).—*Barren flowers* in oval catkins, which are scaly below ; *stamens* numerous ; *fertile flowers* solitary, scaly below ; *fruit*, a naked seed, surrounded at the base by the enlarged pulpy scales. (Name, the Latin name of the tree.)

T. baccata (Common Yew).—The only British yew, is an evergreen tree, remarkable for its longevity. The foliage is poisonous, but the red pulp of the berries is said to be in-nocuous, being often eaten by chil-dren without ill effect. The hard stone, however, should not be swal-lowed. The variety called Irish Yew has erect, instead of spreading branches.

TAXUS BACCATA
(*Common Yew*)

PLATE LXXXII.

Scotch Fir

Oak   Sallow

Class II

MONOCOTYLEDONOUS PLANTS

In the plants belonging to this class the *embryo* of the seed is accompanied by a single *cotyledon*. The stem consists of *woody fibre, cellular tissue,* and *spiral vessels* ; but there is no true *bark* nor *pith,* nor is the *wood* arranged in concentric layers. The stem increases in density (scarcely at all in diameter) by deposits at or near the centre ; hence plants of this class are called ENDOGENOUS (increasing by additions on the inside). As new substance is deposited, the old layers of wood are pressed outwards, and thus the hardest part is near the circumference. The growth of the stem is usually produced by a single terminal *bud,* without the aid of buds in the axils of the leaves ; there are, however, exceptions to this rule, and the stem is often hollow. The principal *veins* of the *leaves* are parallel, not forming a complicated network. The *flowers* are furnished with *stamens* and *pistils,* 3, or some multiple of 3, being the predominating number of the parts of fructification. A large number are destitute of *petals,* the place of which is supplied by *scales* or *chaff* (glumes).

Sub-Class I

PETALOIDEÆ

Flowers furnished with *petals,* arranged in a circular order, or without petals.*

Natural Order LXXIX

HYDROCHARIDACEÆ.—Frog-bit Tribe

Flower-buds enclosed in a sheath ; *sepals* 3, green ; *petals* 3 ; *stamens* 3, 9, 12, or more ; *ovary* inferior, 1 or many-celled ; *style* 1 ; *stigmas* 3–9 ; *fruit* dry or juicy, not bursting, 1 or many-celled. A tribe of aquatic plants, often floating, among which the most remarkable is *Valisneria spiralis,* the flower of which grows at the extremity of a long, spiral stalk. As the bud expands the spire partially uncoils, allowing the flower to float on the surface for a few hours, and then contract again, drawing the seed-vessel beneath the surface, there to ripen its seeds. The number of species is

---

* Sub-Class II, GLUMACEÆ, contains plants which have, instead of petals, chaffy scales, or *glumes,* which are not arranged in a circular order, as is the case with *Petaloideæ,* but are imbricated, such as the GRASSES or SEDGES.

small, and only two are natives of Britain. A species of comparatively recent introduction is *Anacharis Alsinastrum*, a submerged aquatic, having much the habit of *Potamogeton densus*,
from which it may be at once distinguished by bearing its leaves
three and sometimes four in a whorl. It increases so rapidly that
in some places it has seriously impeded canal navigation, and it is
a troublesome pond weed. It is a native of North America, but
how it was introduced into this country is unknown.

ANACHARIS ALSINASTRUM   HYDROCHARIS MORSUS-RANÆ
                                                    (*Frog-bit*)

1. HYDROCHARIS (Frog-bit).—*Stamens* and *pistils* on different
plants; *stamens* 9–12; *ovary* 6-celled; *stigmas* 6. (Name from
the Greek, *hydor*, water, and *charis*, elegance, the plants being
showy aquatics.)

2. STRATIOTES (Water-soldier).—*Stamens* and *pistils* on different
plants; *stamens* about 12, surrounded by many imperfect ones;
ovary 6-celled; *stigmas* 6. (Name, the Greek for a soldier, from
its rigid, prickly, sword-shaped leaves.)

1. HYDROCHARIS (*Frog-bit*)

1. *H. Morsus-ranæ* (Frog-bit).—The only British species. A
floating aquatic, with creeping *stems*, roundish stalked *leaves*, and
delicate white *flowers*, which grow 2 or 3 together from a pellucid
2-leaved *sheath*. Ponds and ditches; not general.—Fl. July,
August. Perennial.

PLATE LXXXIII.

Early Purple Orchis

Broad-leaved Helleborine   White Helleborine   Marsh Helleborine

1. Stratiotes (*Water-soldier*)

1. *S. aloides* (Water-soldier).—The only
British species ; growing in ditches in the
east of England. The *roots* extend to
some distance into the mud, and throw
out numerous rigid, prickly *leaves,* like
those of an Aloe ; the *flower-stalk* is about
6 inches high, and bears at its summit a
2-leaved *sheath,* containing several delicate
white *flowers,* bearing *stamens,* or one
flower only, bearing *pistils.* It rises to the
surface before flowering, and then sinks to
the bottom.—Fl. July. Perennial.

Natural Order LXXX

ORCHIDACEÆ.—Orchideous Tribe

Sepals 3, often coloured ; *petals* 3, the
lowest unlike the rest, and frequently
spurred ; *stamens* and *style* united into a

Stratiotes Aloides
(*Water-soldier*)

central column ; *pollen* powdery or viscid, sometimes raised in masses
on minute stalks ; *ovary* 1-celled ; *stigma* a viscid hollow in front
of the column ; *fruit,* a 3-valved capsule, with 3 rows of seeds. A
very extensive tribe of perennial herbaceous plants, with fibrous or
tuberous roots, fleshy or leathery leaves, all the veins of which are
parallel, and flowers so variable in form as to defy general description, yet so peculiar that very slight experience will enable the
student to refer them to their proper tribe. British species have
for the most part two or more glossy sheathing leaves, and bear
their flowers in simple spikes or clusters. The colour of the flowers
is purple, mottled with various other tints—flesh-coloured, white,
or greenish. The structure of the lower lip of the corolla is in
many cases most singular, sometimes resembling in form, size, and
colour, insects which naturally frequent the places where the flowers
grow : such are the Bee, Fly, and Spider Orchis (*Ophrys apifera,
O. muscifera,* and *O. aranifera*). In other instances the same organ
presents a fantastic caricature of some more important subject of
the animal kingdom : such are the Man, and Monkey Orchis (*Aceras
anthropophora* and *Orchis macra*). The same mimicking extends
to foreign species. " So various are they in form," says Dr. Lindley,
" that there is scarcely a common reptile or insect to which some
of them have not been likened." Occasionally the structure is
more complex : in *Caleana nigrita* the column is a boat-shaped
box, resembling a lower lip ; the lip itself forms a lid that exactly
fits it, and is hinged on a claw, which reaches the middle of the
column ; when the flower opens the lip turns round within the

column and falls back, so that the flower being inverted, it stands fairly over the latter. The moment a small insect touches its point, the lip makes a sudden revolution, brings the point to the bottom of the column, and makes prisoner any insect which the box will hold. When it catches an insect, it remains shut as long as its prey continues to move about ; but if no capture is made, the lid soon recovers its position. The many strange forms found among the orchid tribe mostly hinge on the question of cross pollenization, and the ingenious devices which ensure this end are truly marvellous. Orchideous plants are to be found in all climates except the very coldest and driest ; they are most abundant in the hot, damp regions of the tropics, where they exist in the greatest profusion ; not, as in temperate countries, deriving their nourishment from the earth, but supported by the moisture that floats around them. Clinging to the trunks and branches of trees, to the stems of ferns, and even to the bare rock, they seem to adopt the habits of animals as well as to imitate their forms. In many cases the flowers only are conspicuous, the plant itself consisting of creeping, claw-like roots, and tufts of elliptical bulbs, from the summit of which spring a few tough leaves and wiry, jointed stems, which seem incapable of producing the curiously-shaped and finely coloured flowers they are shortly to bear. Of late years, great attention has been paid to the cultivation of exotic Orchideous plants, and by imitating as far as possible their natural condition great success may be obtained ; and if an orchid house be well managed, some one or other of these curious air plants, as they have been called, may be seen in bloom at all seasons of the year, some clinging to broken potsherds, some to logs of wood, some to cocoanut fibre, or simply suspended by wires from the roof of the house. It is somewhat remarkable that endless as are the varieties of form which the flowers of this tribe assume, their properties vary but little. They furnish few, if any, medicines of importance ; to the useful arts they contribute only a kind of cement or glue, which is recommended by no particular excellence ; a nutritious substance called Salep is prepared from the roots of *Orchis mascula* and other species, but this is not extensively used ; and though the flowers of many species are very fragrant, no perfume is ever extracted from them. With the exception of *Vanilla aromatica*, which is much used in flavouring chocolate and other sweetmeats, no plant in the Order can be said to be extensively used, either in the arts or sciences. On the other hand, Orchids may be almost called the precious stones of the plant world. So enthusiastic do cultivators become that they will often pay hundreds of pounds for a single specimen of a new or rare sort, and the adventures of Orchid-hunters in the tropics and the romance of the Orchid salerooms in London are an astounding testimony to the fascination of these strange plants.

PLATE LXXXIV.

Common Twayblade

Lady's Tresses   Spotted Orchis

The characters by which the families of this Order are distinguished are, owing to the curious structure of the flowers comprised in it, so peculiar, that they require to be attentively studied by reference to fresh specimens before any description of them can be understood. It has been thought necessary, therefore, in the case of the Orchideous Tribe, to depart from the method pursued in other parts of this work, and, instead of perplexing the student with a systematic detail of generic characters, to describe such species as are of common occurrence, attention being paid only to their more obvious characters. The student will thus be enabled to ascertain the names of most, if not all, of the species which are likely to excite his attention. He may then examine them with accuracy, and when he has made himself acquainted with their structure and peculiarities, he will be in a position to compare whatever new species may fall in his way with the descriptions given in works of higher pretention.

Orchis mascula (Early Purple Orchis). — A succulent plant, about a foot high, flowering in May and June, and abounding in woods and pastures wherever the Wild Hyacinth flourishes. The *root* consists of two roundish solid tubers; the *leaves* are of a liliaceous texture, stained with dark purple spots, oblong, and clasping the stem; the *stem* is solitary, and bears an erect cluster of purple *flowers*, mottled with lighter and darker shades; each flower rises from a somewhat twisted ovary, and has a long spur, which turns upwards. The colour of the flower, associated as it often is with Cowslips and Wild Hyacinths, is rich and beautiful, but the odour is strong and offensive, especially in the evening.

O. Morio (Green-winged Meadow Orchis).—Comes into flower about the same time with the last, and resembles it in habit. It is, however, a shorter plant, and bears fewer *flowers* in a cluster; it is best distinguished by the two lateral *sepals*, which are strongly marked with parallel green veins, and bent upwards, so as to form a kind of hood over the column. It grows in meadows, and is often very abundant.

Orchis pyramidalis (Pyramidal Orchis).—Grows about a foot high, has narrow, pointed *leaves*, and bears at the summit of its somewhat slender *stem* a dense cluster, broad at the base and tapering to a point, of small, deep rose-coloured *flowers*, which are remarkable for the length and slenderness of the *spur*. It usually grows on chalk or limestone, and flowers in July.

Orchis maculata (Spotted Orchis) may be distinguished from either of the preceding by its root, which consists of two flattened tubers, divided at the extremity into several finger-like lobes. Its *leaves* are spotted like those of *O. mascula*, and its *flowers* are light purple, curiously marked with dark lines and spots. It grows abundantly on heaths and commons, flowering in June and July.

T

Orchis latifolia (Marsh Orchis) is a taller plant than the last, but has, like it, palmated *roots;* the *leaves* are remarkably erect; *flowers* rose-coloured or purple, and the *bracts*, which taper to a fine point, are longer than the flowers. It grows abundantly in marshes and wet pastures, and blossoms in June and July. All the above species, especially *O. Morio*, occasionally bear white flowers.

O. militaris (Military Orchis) is a rather tall growing species, with purple, short-spurred *flowers*, found only in some of the south-eastern counties bordering the Thames.

O. ustulata (Dwarf Orchis).—A dwarf species, bearing dense spikes of purple *flowers*, which are small and very short-spurred; the unexpanded *flowers* are of a remarkably dark purple. Chalky hills; not common.

O. laxiflora (Loose Orchis). — Not unlike *O. mascula*, but the leaves are narrow and unspotted; *flowers* red, in a loose spike; *bracts* broad and veined. Found only in the Channel Isles.

O. hircina (Lizard Orchis).—A very rare species, found only in Kent and Suffolk. It grows 1–4 feet high, and is remarkable for its loose spike of greenish *flowers*, spotted with red, *lip* very long, and for its objectionable smell of goat.

Gymnadenia conopsea (Sweet-scented Orchis) somewhat resembles *Orchis maculata;* the *flowers* are rose-purple, but not spotted, and very fragrant; the *spur* is very slender, and twice as long as the *ovary*. It grows in dry, hilly, or mountainous pastures, and flowers in June and July.

Habenaria bifolia (Butterfly Orchis) is a singular plant, but not appropriately named, for the resemblance which its flowers bear to a butterfly is very slight. It bears two broad *leaves* immediately above the *root;* the *stem* is slender and angular, about a foot high, and bears a loose cluster of greenish-white *flowers*, which are remarkable for the length of the *spur* and for the strap-shaped lower lip of the *corolla*. It grows on heaths and the borders of woods, blooming in June. The flowers are fragrant in the evening.

H. viridis (Green Habenaria or Frog Orchis) and *H. albida* (Small White Habenaria) are small plants, from 6–8 inches high, the former with green, very short spurred *flowers;* the latter with *flowers* which are white and fragrant. Neither is very common.

H. intacta is a small species with often spotted *leaves*, and pink or purple, sometimes white, short spurred *flowers*. Found only in the west of Ireland.

Listera ovata (Twayblade) grows from 12–18 inches high, and is well marked by its bearing, about half-way up its cylindrical *stem*, two opposite, egg-shaped *leaves;* the *flowers* are small and green. It is not uncommon in woods and orchards, and flowers in June.

PLATE LXXXV.

Man Orchis
Fly Orchis

Bee Orchis
Butterfly Orchis

Listera cordata (Heart-leaved Twayblade) is a much smaller plant, with two heart-shaped *leaves*. It occurs in mountainous districts, chiefly in the north, and flowers from June to August.

Neottia nidus-avis (Bird's nest) is a pale, reddish-brown plant, about a foot high, entirely destitute of *leaves*, the place of which is supplied by numerous sheathing, brown *scales*. The *root* consists of many short fleshy fibres, for the extremities of which the young plants are produced. It is found sparingly in shady woods, flowering in June.

Spiranthus autumnalis (Autumn Lady's tresses).—A curious little plant, from 4–6 inches high, with tuberous *roots* and a spike of small white *flowers*, which are arranged in a single row, and in a spiral manner, in some specimens from left to right, in others from right to left, round the upper portion of the *stalk*. The *flowers* are fragrant in the evening. The *leaves* form a tuft just above the crown of the root, and wither before the flowers begin to expand. These are succeeded by a tuft of new leaves, which rise from the base of the old stems. Not uncommon in dry pastures, flowering in September and October. Two other species of *Spiranthes* occur, both exceedingly rare ; they are *S. æstivalis* (Summer Lady's tresses) and *S. Romazoviana* (Drooping Lady's tresses). The former is taller, and has larger *flowers* than *S. autumnalis*, and is found only in Hampshire and Worcestershire ; the latter is only found at Bantry Bay, in Ireland.

Ophrys apifera (Bee Orchis).—The distinctive character of the *flower* of this curious plant is given in its name, and the same may be said of *O. muscifera* (Fly Orchis) ; both species occur in considerable abundance in many of the limestone and chalk districts. No one who has heard that plants exist bearing these names can doubt their identity, should they fall in his way. The former of these flowers in June and July, the latter in May and June.

The Spider Orchis (*Ophrys aranifera*) is of rare occurrence.

Goodyera repens (Creeping Goodyera) is a small plant with creeping *roots*, and one-sided spikes of small, greenish white *flowers*, not unlike *Spiranthes*, but the spike not spiral. Rare and local ; found in Cumberland and in Scotland. Fir woods.—Fl. late summer.

Corallorhiza innata (Coral-root).—Well marked by its curiously-toothed *roots*, which in figure resemble branched coral ; the *stem* which bears *scales* in place of *leaves*, is some 9 inches high, and of a yellowish-green colour. *Flowers* small, greenish yellow. Confined to the east of Scotland ; damp woods.

Aceras anthropophora (Man Orchis) bears a long loose spike of greenish-yellow *flowers*, which bear a fancied resemblance to a man—the two upper side lobes of the *lip* representing the arms, the elongated, deeply-cleft, middle lobe the legs and body. Dry chalky places in Eastern England.

Malaxis paludosa (Bog Orchis).—The smallest British Orchideous plant, 2–4 inches high, and bears a spike of minute green *flowers*. Found in spongy bogs in many parts of Britain, but never common.

Liparis Loeselii (Two-leaved Liparis) is confined to the eastern counties, where it is rarely found in spongy bogs. It bears a spike of 6–12 yellowish *flowers* on a triangular stalk.

Cypripedium calceolus (Lady's Slipper). — Distinguished by its large inflated *lip*, occurs but rarely in the woods of the north of England, and is pronounced by Sir W. J. Hooker " one of the most beautiful and interesting of our native plants."

Natural Order LXXXI
IRIDACEÆ.—Iris Tribe

Perianth 6-cleft ; *stamens* 3, rising from the base of the *sepals ; ovary* inferior, 3-celled ; *style* 1 ; *stigmas* 3, often petal-like ; *capsule* 3-valved ; *seeds* numerous. Principally herbaceous plants, with tuberous or fibrous roots, long, and often sword-shaped, sheathing leaves, and showy flowers, which seldom last a long time. Chiefly natives of warm and temperate regions, and most abundant at the Cape of Good Hope, where, at the time of its discovery by the Portuguese, the natives mainly supported themselves on the roots of the plants of this tribe, together with such shell-fish as were left on the shore by the receding tide. *Iris, Crocus, Ixia,* and *Gladiolus* are favourite garden flowers. *Iris Pseud-acorus* (Yellow Iris or Flag) is one of our most showy marsh plants. Few species are used in the arts or sciences ; the roots of *Iris Florentina* afford Orrisroot, which, when dried, has a perfume resembling that of violets, and is used as an ingredient in tooth-powder. *Saffron,* the dried stigmas of *Crocus sativus,* was anciently much prized as a dye, and is still employed for the same purpose, as well as in medicine and cookery ; and the roots of a few species are used by barbarous nations as an occasional article of food.

1. Iris.—*Perianth* with the 3 *outer divisions* longer, and reflexed ; *stigmas* 3, petal-like, covering the *stamens*. (Name from Iris, the rainbow, from the beautiful colouring of the flowers.)

2. Romulea (Romulea).—*Perianth* in 6 equal, spreading divisions ; *tube* shorter than the limb ; *stigma* deeply 3-cleft, its *lobes* 2-cleft, slender. (Name from *Romulus,* who founded Rome.)

3. Crocus.—*Perianth* in 6 equal, nearly erect divisions ; *tube* very long ; *stigma* 3-cleft, its *lobes* inversely wedge-shaped. (Name from the Greek, *crocos,* saffron, and that from *croce,* a thread.)

4. Gladiolus.—*Perianth* in 6 nearly equal divisions, forming as it were two *lips ; 3 segments* in the upper, 2 in the lower ; *style* slender ; *lobes* of the *stigma* inversely wedge-shaped. (Name from the Latin, *gladius,* a sword, in reference to the shape of the leaves.)

PLATE LXXXVI.

Yellow Flag

5. SISYRINCHIUM.—*Flowers* several, in an umbel or head; *tube* of the *perianth* short; *stigmas* entire.

1. IRIS (*Flower-de-luce*)

1. *I. pseud-acorus* (Yellow Iris, Flag).—*Leaves* sword-shaped; *perianth* not fringed, its inner divisions smaller than the *stigmas.* A stout aquatic plant, with creeping, acrid roots, sword-shaped leaves 2–3 feet long, and large, handsome yellow flowers. The root yields a black dye, and the roasted seeds, it is said, may be used as a substitute for coffee. Marshes and banks of rivers; common.—Fl. June, July. Perennial.

2. *I. fœtidissima* (Stinking Iris).—*Leaves* sword-shaped; *perianth* not fringed, inner divisions about as large as the stigmas; *stem* slightly flattened. Resembling the last in habit, but smaller. The flowers are of a dull leaden hue, and the leaves so acrid as to leave a burning taste in the mouth, or even to loosen the teeth. The whole plant when bruised emits a disagreeable odour. The berry-like seeds, which are of a beautiful orange-scarlet colour, remain attached to the plant all through the winter, and a bunch of the pods, if cut with long stalks and hung inverted until quite dry, and then arranged in some quaint jar or vase (without water), remain a pleasing and decorative object throughout the winter. Woods and hedges in the west and south-west of England; not uncommon.—Fl. June to August. Perennial.

2. ROMULEA (*Romulea*)

1. *R. columnæ* (Common Romulea).—The only British species. A small, bulbous plant, 3–4 inches high, with very narrow *leaves*, and solitary, purplish *flowers*, tinged with yellow, partaking the characters of the *Iris* and *Crocus.* It grows only on a sandy pasture called the Warren, at Dawlish, Devon.— Fl. March, April. Perennial.

3. CROCUS

1. *C. sativus* (Saffron Crocus). *Leaves* appearing after the flowers, linear; *flower-stalks* enveloped with a double *sheath;* *stigma* long and drooping. Said to be naturalized at Saffron-Walden, in Essex, where it is largely cultivated for the sake of the saffron afforded by the dried stigmas, the only part of the plant which is used. The flowers are purple. — Fl. September. Perennial.

CROCUS SATIVUS
(*Saffron Crocus*)

4. GLADIOLUS (*Gladiolus*)

1. *G. communis* (Common Gladiolus).—The only British species.
Stem 1–2 feet high, with narrow, glaucous *leaves*, and bearing a
one-sided *spike* of 4–8 red *flowers*, each with two narrow *bracts* at
its base. Found only in the New Forest and the Isle of Wight;
rare.—Fl. June, July. Perennial.

5. SISYRINCHIUM (*Blue-eyed Grass*)

1. *S. angustifolium* (Blue-eyed Grass).—*Stems* 6–12 inches high,
2-edged and winged, and with sheathing, narrow *leaves ;* at the
summit of the *stalk* is a head of 1–6 blue *flowers*. Bogs near Kerry
and Galway in Ireland, and supposed to be indigenous.—Fl. July,
August. Perennial.

A species, *S. californicum*, with yellow flowers, was found in 1896
at Rosslare, Co. Wexford.

NATURAL ORDER LXXXII
AMARYLLIDACEÆ.—AMARYLLIS TRIBE

Perianth of 3 coloured *sepals* and 3 coloured *petals ; stamens* 6,
arising from the sepals and petals, sometimes united by the base
of their *filaments ; ovary* inferior, 3-celled ; *style* 1 ; *stigma* 3-lobed ;
fruit, a many-seeded *capsule* or a 1- to 3-seeded berry. An extensive
tribe, principally composed of herbaceous plants with bulbous roots,
sword-shaped leaves, and showy flowers, which are distinguished
from the true Lilies by their inferior ovary ; that organ in the
Lily tribe being superior, and enclosed within the corolla. Large
and beautiful species belonging to this Order are found in abundance in Brazil, the East and West Indies, and especially the Cape
of Good Hope. In the temperate regions they are less common,
and by no means so showy. In Great Britain it is doubtful whether
a single species is indigenous, though the number of varieties
cultivated in gardens, both in conservatories and in the open air,
is very great. The bulbous roots of many plants belonging to the
Amaryllis tribe are poisonous ; some, it is said, to such a degree
that deleterious properties are communicated to weapons dipped
in their juice. The roots of the Snowdrop and Daffodil are emetic,
and the flowers of the last (*Narcissus pseudo-narcissus*) are a
dangerous poison. The roots of some species, however, are nutritious, affording a kind of arrowroot.

From the juice of a kind of *Agave* (*A. Americana*) a fermented
liquor is made, which, under the name of " pulque," is in Mexico
a common beverage. This plant, called by the Mexicans " maguey,"
is cultivated over an extent of country embracing 50,000 square
miles. In the city of Mexico alone the consumption of pulque

PLATE LXXXVII.

Snowdrop

Daffodil

Summer Snowflake

amounts to the enormous quantity of eleven millions of gallons, and a considerable revenue is derived from its sale by Government. The plant attains maturity in a period varying from eight to fourteen years, when it flowers, and it is during the stage of flowering alone that the juice is extracted. The central stem, which encloses the flower-bud, is then cut off near the bottom, and a cavity or basin is discovered, over which the leaves are drawn close and tied. Into this reservoir the juice distils, which otherwise would have risen to nourish and support the flower. It is removed three or four times during the twenty-four hours, yielding a quantity of liquor, varying from a quart to a gallon and a half. The juice is extracted by means of a syphon, made of a species of gourd, and deposited in bowls. It is then placed in earthen jars, and a little old pulque is added, when it soon ferments, and is immediately ready for use. The fermentation occupies two or three days, and when it ceases it is in fine order. Old pulque has an unpleasant odour, which has been compared to that of putrid meat ; but when fresh it is brisk and sparkling. In time even Europeans prefer it to any other liquor. This *Agave* is popularly known in England by the name of American Aloe. It grows but slowly in this climate, and, as it rarely attains perfection, it is believed by many people to flower once in a hundred years. The roots and leaves of the species of *Agave* contain woody fibre (*pita thread*), useful for various purposes ; this is prepared by bruising and steeping in water, and afterwards beating. The Mexicans also make their paper of the fibres of *Agave* leaves, laid in layers. The expressed juice of the leaves is also stated to be useful as a substitute for soap.

1. NARCISSUS (Daffodil).—*Perianth* tubular at the base, terminating in a bell-shaped *crown* or *nectary*, which has 6 equal *sepals* and *petals* at its base. (Named after *Narcissus*, a fabulous youth, said to have been changed into a flower.)

2. GALANTHUS (Snowdrop). — *Perianth* bell-shaped; *sepals* 3 (white), spreading; *petals* 3, erect, notched. (Name in Greek signifying " milk-flower.")

3. LEUCOJUM (Snow-flake).—*Perianth* bell-shaped, of 6 equal *sepals* and *petals*, which are thickened at the point. (Name in Greek signifying " a white violet.")

1. NARCISSUS (*Daffodil*)

1. *N. pseudo-narcissus* (Common Daffodil, Lent Lily).—*Flower-stalk* hollow, 2-edged, bearing near its summit a membranous *sheath* and a single *flower ; nectary* notched and curled at the margin, as long as the *sepals* and *petals*. One of our most beautiful spring

flowers, in many places almost carpeting the woodlands with its splendid yellow trumpet-shaped flowers. The smell, unfortunately, is not pleasant, and the plant has poisonous properties. Woods and orchards ; common.—Fl. March and April. Perennial.

Several other species of Narcissus are occasionally found near houses, but they are invariably the outcast of gardens.

2. GALANTHUS (*Snowdrop*)

1. *G. nivalis* (Snowdrop).—Too well known to need any description. The Snowdrop, *G. plicatus*, which was introduced from the Crimea, differs mainly from the common species in having broader, plaited leaves, and somewhat larger flowers.—Fl. January to March. Perennial.

3. LEUCOJUM (*Snowflake*)

1. *L. æstivum* (Summer Snowflake).—A doubtful native, found occasionally in moist meadows in many parts of England. A bulbous plant, about 2 feet high, with narrow, keeled *leaves*, and 2-edged *flower-stalks* bearing an umbel of rather large white *flowers*, the *sepals* and *petals* of which are tipped with green. It is a common garden plant.—Fl. May. Perennial.

NATURAL ORDER LXXXIII

DIOSCOREACEÆ.—YAM TRIBE

Stamens and *pistils* on different plants (*diœcious*) ; *perianth* 6-cleft ; *stamens* 6, arising from the base of the *perianth* ; *ovary* inferior, 3-celled ; *style* deeply 3-cleft ; *fruit*, a dry, flat capsule, or (in *Tamus*, the only British species) a *berry*. Twining shrubs or herbs, approaching in habit some of the Dicotyledonous Orders, the leaves being decidedly stalked, and having netted veins ; the flowers are small, with 1–3 bracts each, and grow in spikes. The Order is a small one, and is, with the exception of *Tamus* (Black Bryony), confined to tropical regions. *Dioscorea*, the plant from which the Order takes its name, has large tuberous roots, which, under the name of " Yams," forms as important an article of food in tropical countries as the Potato in temperate climates. When growing it requires a support, like the Hop. There are several species, *D. sativa* and *D. alata* being natives of India. The Chinese *D. Batatas* is largely grown in France and Algeria, and may be grown in this country in the open, though it seldom is.

1. TAMUS (Black Bryony).—Characters described above. (Name, the Latin name of the plant.)

1. TAMUS (*Black Bryony*)

1. *T. communis* (Black Bryony).—The only British species. *Root* a large, solid tuber, black externally; *stem* slender, twining among bushes to the length of many feet, and clothed with numerous shining, heart-shaped *leaves*, and clusters of small green *flowers*, which are succeeded by elliptical scarlet *berries*. The leaves are reticulated with veins, somewhat like those of Dicotyledonous plants, but they are not jointed to the stem. Late in autumn they turn dark purple or bright yellow, when, assisted by the scarlet berries, they make a very showy appearance. In winter the stems die down to the ground.—Fl. May to July. Perennial.

NATURAL ORDER LXXXIV
TRILLIACEÆ.—HERB-PARIS TRIBE

Sepals and *petals* 6–8, coloured or green; *stamens* 6–10; *anthers* very long, their cells, one on each side of the filament; *ovary* superior, with 3–5 cells, and as many *styles; fruit*, a 3- to 5-celled berry; *seeds* numerous. A small Order, containing about thirty herbaceous plants with tuberous roots, whorled, netted leaves, and large, solitary, terminal flowers. They grow in the woods of the temperate climates, and, like the plants of the last Order, bear some resemblance to Dicotyledonous plants. The structure of the seed, however, and the fact that the leaves are not jointed to the stem, fix them in the class Endogenous or Monocotyledonous plants. Their properties are acrid and narcotic.

1. PARIS (Herb-Paris).—*Sepals* and *petals* 8, very narrow; *stamens* 8–10. (Name from the Latin, *par, paris*, equal, on account of the unvarying number of the leaves.)

1. PARIS (*Herb-Paris*)

1. *P. quadrifolia* (Four-leaved Herb-Paris, True Love-Knot).— The only British species. A singular plant, with a *stem* about a foot high, bearing near its summit four large pointed *leaves*, from the centre of which rises a solitary large green *flower*. Damp woods; local.—Fl. May. Perennial.

NATURAL ORDER LXXXV
LILIACEÆ.—LILY TRIBE

Perianth of 6 petal-like divisions, distinct or united into a tube; *stamens* 6; *ovary* superior, not united with the perianth, 3-celled, many-seeded; *style* 1; *stigma* simple or 3-lobed; *capsule* 3-celled, 3-valved. The parts of the flower are very rarely in fours or eights An extensive family of plants, of some 2500 species, of which the majority are herbaceous, with bulbous roots and showy flowers; some, however, attain the dimensions of shrubs, or even trees, in which case they resemble the Palms rather than exogenous trees, the trunk being destitute of true bark and pith, and the leaves being never jointed at the stem. Butcher's Broom (*Ruscus*) is the only British species which assumes a shrubby character; *Asparagus* is a branching, herbaceous plant, with creeping roots, scaly stems, and bristle-like leaves; *Convallaria* (Lily of the Valley) has also creeping roots. These three produce a berry-like fruit. Plants of the Lily tribe are most abundant in temperate climates, but attain their greatest magnitude in the tropics. A specimen of *Dracæna draco* (Dragon's Blood) in Teneriffe, which was blown down in 1867, and was known to have been an ancient tree in 1406, measured 70 feet high and some 48 feet in circumference. The leaves of many species contain a tough fibre, which is used as a substitute for hemp or flax. Among these the most remarkable is *Phormium tenax* (New Zealand Flax). The genus *Allium* (Onion, Garlic, and Leek) supplied food to the early inhabitants of Egypt, and had divine honours paid to it. In Kamtschatka, Tartary, and the Sandwich Islands, various species are cultivated for the same purpose. The bud and tender part of the stem of the Grass-tree, a native of Tasmania, is said to be nutritious, and of an agreeable flavour, and in our own country the young shoots of *Asparagus* rank among the most delicate of our esculent vegetables. In medicine many species are of great value, among which aloes, the condensed juice of *Aloe vulgaris*, etc., and squills, an extract of *Scilla maritima*, are well known. *Colchicum* (Meadow Saffron) is used as a specific for the gout, but it is considered a dangerous medicine. As ornamental plants the beauty of the Lily tribe has been for ages proverbial; *Lilium Chalcedonicum*, the scarlet Turk's-cap Lily, which covers the plains of Syria with its brilliant flowers, is said to have been the plant which was mentioned in the Sermon on the Mount under the title of " the lilies of the field." The innumerable varieties of *Hyacinth* are derived from an eastern plant, *Hyacinthus Orientalis ;* and the *Tulip* (*Tulipa*) was long the most highly prized among florist's flowers, and furnished in Holland a subject for the most absurd speculation.

1. ASPARAGUS.—*Corolla* deeply 6-cleft, bell-shaped ; *stamens* 6, distinct ; *stigmas* 3, bent back. (Name, the Greek name of the plant.)

2. RUSCUS (Butcher's Broom).—*Corolla* deeply 6-cleft ; *stamens* and *pistils* on different plants (*diœcious*) ; *stamens* connected at the base ; *style* surrounded by a *nectary*. (Name " anciently *bruscus*, from *bruskelen ;* in Celtic, box-holly."—Sir W. J. Hooker.)

3. CONVALLARIA (Lily of the Valley).—*Corolla* 6-cleft, bell-shaped, soon falling off, not jointed with the pedicle ; *stamens* 6, distinct ; *stigma* 1. (Name from the Latin, *convallis*, a valley, the usual locality of this family.)

4. POLYGONATUM (Solomon's Seal).—*Corolla* 6-cleft, elongated, persistent, jointed with the pedicle; *stamens* 6, distinct; *stigma* 1. (Name in Greek denoting "many angled," from the character of the stem.)

5. MAIANTHEMUM (May Lily).—*Stem* erect, with a few alternate *leaves; flowers* in a simple terminal raceme; *perianth* spreading, divided in four.

6. SCILLA.—*Flowers* blue, white, or pink; *perianth* 6-cleft, falling off. (Name, the Latin name of the plant.)

7. ORNITHOGALUM (Star of Bethlehem).—Like SCILLA, except that the *perianth* is white, and does not fall off. (Name from the Greek, *ornis*, a bird, and *gala*, milk. This plant is supposed by Linnæus to be the "dove's dung" mentioned in 2 Kings VI. 25.)

8. ALLIUM (Garlic).—*Corolla* of 6 spreading *petals; flowers* in an umbel, at the base of which is a *sheath* of 1 or 2 *leaves*. (Name, the Latin name of the plant.)

9. SIMETHIS.—*Roots* not bulbous; *flowers* panicled; *perianth* divided into 6 segments.

10. MUSCARI.—*Perianth* globular, with 6 minute, tooth-like, indications of division. (Name from its musky smell.)

11. FRITILLARIA (Fritillary).—*Flowers* solitary; *petals* 6, with a *nectary* at the base of each; *anthers* attached above their bases; *style* 3-cleft at the summit. (Name from the Latin, *fritillus*, a dice-box, the common accompaniment of a *chequer-board*, which the marking of the flower resembles.)

12. TULIPA (Tulip).—*Flowers* solitary, rarely 2 on a stem; *petals* and *anthers* as in GAGEA; *style* 0. (Name from *toliban*, the Persian name for a turban.)

13. GAGEA.—*Flowers* in an umbel or corymb; *petals* 6, without a *nectary; anthers* erect, attached to the *filaments* by their bases; *style* conspicuous. (Named in honour of *Sir Thomas Gage*.)

14. LLOYDIA.—*Flowers* mostly solitary, small; *perianth* 6-parted, spreading, not falling off. (Named after *Ed. Lloyd*, who discovered it.)

15. COLCHICUM (Meadow Saffron).—*Perianth* with a very long *tube*, rising from a *sheath*. (Name from *Colchis*, a country famous for medicinal herbs.)

16. TOFIELDIA (Scottish Asphodel).—*Perianth* 6-parted; *flowers* each from a small 3-lobed *sheath*, greenish yellow; *styles* 3. (Name in honour of *Mr. Tofield*, an English botanist.)

17. NARTHECIUM.—*Flowers* bright yellow; *perianth* 6-parted; *style* 1. (Name from the Greek, *narthex*, a rod.)

1. Asparagus

1. *A. officinalis* (Common Aparagus).—The only British species,
occurring sparingly on several parts of the sea-coast, especially near
the Lizard Point, Cornwall ; it differs only in size from the cultivated plant.—Fl. July, August. Perennial.

ASPARAGUS OFFICINALIS   RUSCUS ACULEATUS
(*Common Asparagus*)   (*Butcher's Broom*)

2. RUSCUS (*Butcher's Broom*)

1. *R. aculeatus* (Butcher's Broom, Knee Holly).—The only
British species, and the only British shrub of Endogenous growth.
A low shrub, 3–4 feet high, with erect green *stems*, which are
branched and plentifully furnished with very rigid *leaves*, terminating each in a sharp *spine*.   The *flowers* are minute, greenish white,
and grow singly from the centres of the leaves ; the *berries* are
two or three times as large as Holly berries, round, and of a brilliant
scarlet colour.   Waste and bushy places ; not uncommon, especially in the south of England.—Fl. April, May.   Shrub.

3. CONVALLARIA (*Lily of the Valley*)

1. *C. majalis* (Lily of the Valley).—*Leaves* all from the root ;
flowers drooping in a long, one-sided cluster. A common and
universally admired garden plant, equally prized for its globular,
pure white *flowers*, and for its delicious perfume. *Berries* scarlet.
Woods, in a light soil ; not common.—Fl. May.   Perennial.

PLATE LXXXIX.

Lily of the Valley
Round-headed Garlic

Herb-Paris

Bog Asphodel
Fritillary

POLYGONATUM MULTIFLORUM
(*Solomon's Seal*)

4. POLYGONATUM (*Solomon's Seal*)

1. *P. multiflorum* (Common Solomon's Seal). — A singular plant, 1–2 feet high, with roundish *stems*, which are rather arching than erect, and bearing numerous alternate, elliptical *leaves*, all turned one way, and opposite them are small clusters of whitish drooping *flowers*, tipped with green, which are all turned the other way; *filaments* hairy. Woods in several parts of England and Scotland, but not indigenous in the latter country, and not frequent.—Fl. June. Perennial.

2. *P. officinale* (Angular Solomon's Seal) differs from the last species in having an angular *stem* of lower stature, mostly solitary *flowers*, and smooth *filaments*. Rare.

3. *P. verticillatum* (Whorled Solomon's Seal).—Grows about 2 feet high, and bears its *leaves* in whorls of 3–5, from the axils of which hang several white, green-tipped *flowers*. Rare.

5. MAIANTHEMUM (*May Lily*)

1. *M. convallaria* (May Lily).—A pretty plant with a creeping *root stock*, and an erect *stem* 4–9 inches high. *Leaves* 2, alternate, acute, heart-shaped, stalked; *flowers* small and white, in a terminal raceme; *perianth* 4-cleft. A very rare plant, said to be truly wild not far from Scarborough, and planted elsewhere.— Fl. May, June. Perennial.

6. SCILLA (*Squill*)

1. *S. verna* (Vernal Squill).—*Flowers* in a corymb; *bracts* narrow; *leaves* lined, appearing with the *flowers*. A lovely little plant, 3–6 inches high, with corymbs, or flat clusters of blue, star-like flowers. The turfy slopes of the sea-coast of Cornwall are in many places as thickly studded with these pretty flowers as inland meadows are with Daisies. In a few weeks after flowering no part of the plant is visible but the

SCILLA VERNA
(*Vernal Squill*)

dry capsules, containing black, shining seeds. Sea-coast in the west and north of England.—Fl. May. Perennial.

S. autumnalis (Autumnal Squill). Flowers in an erect cluster; *bracts* o; *leaves* appearing after the flowers. *Bulb* somewhat larger than in the last, and *stems* rather taller; *flowers* of a purplish blue and less beautiful than in the last. Dry pastures, especially near the sea, in the south.—Fl. August to October. Perennial.

3. *S. nutans* (Wild Hyacinth, Blue-bell).—Too abundant and well known to need any description. The name Hyacinthus was originally given to some species of Lily into which the youth Hyacinthus was fabled to have been changed by Apollo. The petals are marked with dark spots, arranged so as to resemble the Greek word AI—*alas!* The present species, however, having no such characters on its petals, was named by Linnæus *non-scriptus* —not written. It is sometimes, though incorrectly, called Hair-bell, the true Hair-bell being *Campanula rotundifolia*, or Blue-bell of Scotland. Woods and hedges.—Fl. May, June. Perennial.

ORNITHOGALUM
PYRENAICUM
(*Spiked Star of Bethlehem*)

7. ORNITHOGALUM (*Star of Bethlehem*)

1. *O. Pyrenaicum* (Spiked Star of Bethlehem). —A bulbous plant, with long, narrow *leaves*, which wither very early in the season, and a leafless *stalk*, about 2 feet high, bearing a long, erect, spiked cluster of small, greenish-white *flowers*. Woods in the south; rare, but very abundant in the neighbourhood of Bath, where the spikes of unexpanded flowers are often exposed for sale as a pot-herb under the name of "French Asparagus."

2. *O. umbellatum* (Common Star of Bethlehem). —Grows about a foot high, with narrow limp *leaves*, and large, pure white *flowers*, which are green externally, and are borne in flattened *racemes*, or rather *corymbs*, opening only in sunny weather. A common garden plant, naturalized in occasional waste places.—Fl. April, May. Perennial.

3. *O. nutans* (Drooping Star of Bethlehem).— About a foot high, with a *raceme* of 5 or 6 large, drooping *flowers*, white, and partially green outside. Not indigenous, but rarely found naturalized.— Fl. April, May. Perennial.

8. ALLIUM (*Garlic*)

1. *A. ursinum* (Broad-leaved Garlic, Ramsons).—*Leaves* broad and flat; *flower-stalk* triangular; *flowers* in a flat umbel. The leaves of this plant are scarcely to be distinguished from those of the Lily of the Valley; the flowers are white and pretty, but the stench of the whole plant is intolerable. Woods and thickets; common.— Fl. May, June. Perennial.

Seven other species of *Garlic* are described by British botanists, but none of them are so common as the last, and many are difficult to distinguish. The student specially desirous of studying them should refer to a work of greater scope than the present.

ALLIUM URSINUM
(*Broad-leaved Garlic*)

A. Schœnoprasum (Chives) is a pretty plant, with dense heads of purplish flowers. In a wild state its foliage is scanty, but under cultivation becomes very abundant, in which state it is a favourite cottage pot-herb. Several other species are remarkable for bearing small bulbs among the flowers.

9. SIMETHIS (*Simethis*)

1. *S. bicolor* (Variegated Simethis).—A pretty plant, with narrow, radicle, grass-like *leaves*, and a slender *stem* about a foot high, bearing a terminal panicle of white, star-like *flowers*, tinged with purple on the outside. Very rare; found in Kerry and in fir woods at Branksome, near Bournemouth, where it was probably accidentally introduced.—Fl. May, June. Perenniai.

10. MUSCARI (*Grape Hyacinth*)

1. *M. racemosum* (Grape Hyacinth).—*Leaves* narrow, 6–18 inches long, prostrate; *stem* shorter, bearing a compact, cylindric head of small, deep blue, ovid *flowers*, bearing a faint resemblance to a bunch of grapes—the upper ones rudimentary. Eastern counties; rare.—Fl. April, May. Perennial. Several very pretty species with pale blue and white flowers are grown in gardens.

11. FRITILLARIA (*Fritillary*)

1. *F. meleagris* (Fritillary, Snake's Head).—The only British species. A bulbous plant, about a foot high, with very narrow *leaves* and a solitary drooping *flower*, shaped like a Tulip, and curiously chequered with pink and dull purple. Meadows and pastures

in the east and south of England ; rare.—Fl. April. Perennial. A white form is not uncommon.

Several species are cultivated in garden flower borders, perhaps the handsomest being the well-known Crown Imperial.

12. TULIPA (*Tulip*)

1. *T. sylvestris* (Wild Tulip).—The only British species. A bulbous plant, with very narrow *leaves ; stem* about a foot high ; *flower* solitary, yellow, fragrant, drooping in bud, becoming more erect with expansion. South and east ; rare.—Fl. April, May. Perennial.

13. GAGEA

1. *G. lutea* (Yellow Gagea).—The only British species. A bulbous plant, 6–8 inches high, with 1 or 2 long, narrow *leaves*, and umbels of yellow *flowers*. Woods and pastures ; rare.—Fl. March to May. Perennial.

14. LLOYDIA (*Lloydia*)

1. *L. serotina* (Mountain Lloydia).—A pretty plant, with several very slender *leaves*, and a slender *stem*, 2–6 inches high, bearing a solitary white *flower*, veined with red. Snowdon ; rare.—Fl. June, July. Perennial.

15. COLCHICUM (*Meadow Saffron*)

COLCHICUM AUTUMNALE
(*Meadow Saffron*)

1. *C. autumnale* (Meadow Saffron).—The only British species. A not unfrequent garden plant, with large broad *leaves*, which wither away in summer, and are succeeded by several light purple, or sometimes white *flowers*, resembling Crocuses in all respects except that they have 6 instead of 3 *stamens*. At the time of flowering the *seed-vessels* are concealed beneath the ground, where they remain until the following spring, when they rise above the surface and are ripened. Meadows ; not general.—Fl. September, October. Perennial.

16. TOFIELDIA (*Scottish Asphodel*)

1. *T. palustris* (Mountain Scottish Asphodel). — The only British species. A small plant, 4–6 inches high, with tufts of narrow, sword-shaped *leaves*, and egg-shaped, almost stalkless spikes of small, yellowish *flowers*. Boggy ground in the north.—Fl. July, August. Perennial.

17. NARTHECIUM (*Bog Asphodel*)

1. *N. ossifragum* (Bog Asphodel).—The only British species. An elegant little plant, 6–8 inches high, with tufts of narrow, sword-shaped *leaves*, like those of the Iris, and a tapering spike of star-like bright yellow *flowers*. The name *ossifragum*, bone-breaking, was given to this plant from its being supposed to soften the bones of cattle that fed on it. Other plants have had the same properties assigned to them, but there is little doubt that in every case the diseases in question are to be traced to the noxious exhalations from the bogs in which the plants grow, rather than to the plants themselves. Common in bogs.—Fl. July to September. Perennial.

NATURAL ORDER LXXXVI

JUNCACEÆ.—RUSH TRIBE

Calyx and *corolla* alike, of 6 usually chaffy pieces ; *stamens* 6, inserted into the base of the *petals* and *sepals,* or sometimes 3, inserted into the *sepals ; anthers* turned inwards ; *ovary* superior ; *style* 1 ; *stigmas* 3 ; *capsule* 3-valved, usually many-seeded. A tribe of marsh or bog plants, with cylindrical or flat *leaves*, sometimes filled with pith ; the flowers are usually small, and of a brownish-green hue. Scientifically they are near the Lily Tribe, but they bear a strong superficial resemblance to the Sedges and Grasses. This tribe, which is spread over all parts of the globe, is not a large one. The true rushes are for the most part social plants, and are often of considerable use in fixing the soil of marshes and bogs. The stems of the common species are used for making mats and the wicks of candles. The tall aquatic plant usually called the Bulrush, belongs to the Sedge Tribe, the Club-rush to the Order TYPHACEÆ, and the Flowering Rush to the Order BUTO-MACEÆ.

1. JUNCUS (Rush).—*Perianth* chaffy ; *filaments* smooth ; *stigmas* 3 ; *capsule* 3-celled, 3-valved ; *seeds* numerous. (Name, the Latin name of the plant, and that from *jungo,* to join, the stems having been woven into cordage.)

2. LUZULA (Wood-rush).—Like *Juncus,* except that the *capsule* is 1-celled and only 3-seeded. (Name supposed to have been altered from the Italian *lucciola,* a glow-worm, from the sparkling appearance of the heads of flowers when wet with rain or dew.)

U

1. Juncus (*Rush*)

Stems cylindrical, tapering to a point ; leaves none.

JUNCUS EFFUSUS
(Soft Rush)

1. *J. effusus* (Soft Rush).—*Stems* not furrowed; *panicle* below the summit of the stem, branched and spreading ; *capsule* blunt. This and the following species are well known as the rushes of which mats and the wicks of candles are made. Marshy ground ; common.—Fl. July. Perennial.

2. *J. conglomeratus* (Common Rush).—*Stems* not furrowed ; *panicle* below the summit of the stem, crowded ; *capsule* ending in a point. Only distinguished from the last by its dense panicle of flowers, and pointed capsule. Marshy places ; common.—Fl. July. Perennial.

3. *J. glaucous* (Hard Rush).—*Stems* deeply furrowed, rigid ; *panicle* below the summit of the stem, branched and spreading. Very distinct from the last two, from which it may be distinguished by its more slender, furrowed, glaucous stems, and its very loose panicle of slender flowers. Marshy places and roadsides ; common. — Fl. July. Perennial.

Several other species belong to this group, but none are common, except *J. maritimus* (Lesser Sea-Rush), which differs from those already described in having the portion of the *stem* which rises above the panicle dilated at the base, so as to resemble a bract ; it grows in salt marshes. *J. acutus* (Great Sea-Rush), the largest British species, grows on the sandy sea-shore in great abundance in a few places ; it is well marked by its stout, rigid habit, and by its large, polished *capsules*.

Stems leafless ; leaves all from the root.

4. *J. squarrosus* (Heath Rush).—*Leaves* rigid, grooved ; *panicle* terminal. Well marked by its rigid stems and leaves, of which the latter have mostly one direction. The *stems* are about 1 foot high ; the *flowers* larger than in the marsh species, and variegated with glossy brown and yellowish white. Moors and heaths ; abundant.—Fl. June, July. Perennial.

Stems leafy ; leaves cylindrical, or but slightly flattened, jointed internally.

The most common species in this group are—

J. acutiflorus (Sharp-flowered, jointed Rush).—A slender plant, 1–2 feet high, with slightly flattened *stems* and *leaves*, and terminal *panicles* of brown, sharp-pointed *flowers*.

J. lampocarpus (Shining-fruited jointed Rush).—Resembling the last, but distinguished by its large brown, glossy *capsule*.

J. obtusiflorus (Blunt-flowered jointed Rush). —Rather smaller than *J. acutiflorus*, and well distinguished by its blunt *flowers*.

J. uliginosus (Lesser Bog jointed Rush).—A small and very variable plant, 3–8 inches high, bearing a few *clusters* rather than *panicles* of *flowers*. All these are common in boggy ground.

Stems leafy ; leaves not cylindrical nor jointed.

In this group there are but two common species : *J. compressus* (Round-fruited Rush), a slender plant, about a foot high; the *leaves* are linear and grooved above; the *stem* is slightly flattened, and terminates in a panicle of greenish-brown *flowers ;* the *capsule* is nearly round, with a point : and *J. bufonius* (Toad Rush), a very

JUNCUS ULIGINOSUS
(*Lesser Bogjointed Rush*)

small species, 4–6 inches high, with repeatedly forked *stems*, and solitary green *flowers*, which grow mostly on one side of the stem. The above are the species of this dull tribe most likely to be met with by the beginner; for the few others, which are chiefly notable for their rarity, reference may be made to some such work as Bentham and Hooker's " British Flora."

2. LUZULA (*Wood-Rush*)

1. *L. sylvatica* (Great Wood-Rush).—*Leaves* hairy ; *panicle* spreading, much branched ; *flowers* in clusters of about 3. A common woodland plant, with more the habit of a Grass than a Rush. The *leaves* are flat, and clothed with long, scattered, white *hairs ;* the *stalk* rises to a height of about 2 feet, and bears a terminal loose cluster of brownish *flowers*, with large yellow *anthers*. Woods ; abundant.—Fl. May, June. Perennial.

2. *L. pilosa* (Hairy Wood Rush).—*Leaves* hairy ; *panicle* little branched ; *flowers* solitary. Smaller than the last, and well distinguished by its solitary flowers, the stalks of which are bent back when in fruit. Woods ; not unfrequent. — Fl. May, June. Perennial.

LUZULA CAMPESTRIS
(*Field Wood-rush*)

3. *L. campestris* (Field Wood-Rush).—*Leaves* hairy; *panicle* of 3 or 4 dense, many-flowered clusters. Much smaller than either of the preceding. This is one of the first grass-like plants to show flower in spring, when it may be distinguished from all other meadow herbs, by its close clusters or spikes of brownish-green flowers, each of which contains 6 large, light yellow anthers. Pastures; common.—Fl. March to May. Perennial.

Other British species of Wood-Rush are *L. Forsteri* (Forster's Wood-Rush), the *panicle* of which is slightly branched, and bears its *flowers* solitary; each *capsule* contains 3 *seeds*, having a straight *tail* at their summits; it resembles *L. pilosa* in habit, but is much smaller; the *seeds* of the latter plant are furnished with a long hooked tail: *L. spicata* (Spiked Mountain Wood-Rush) is about the same size as *L. campestris*; it has narrow *leaves*, bears its *flowers* in a compound, drooping *spike*, and grows only on high mountains: *L. arcuata* (Curved Mountain Wood-Rush) is a small and very rare species, found only on the summit of the Scottish mountains; it bears its *flowers* in *panicles*, 3–5 together, on drooping *stalks*.

Natural Order LXXXVII
BUTOMACEÆ.—Flowering Rush Tribe.

Sepals 3, green; *petals* 3, coloured; *stamens* varying in number; *ovaries* superior, 3, 6, or more, distinct, or united into a mass; *carpels* many-seeded. A small tribe of aquatic plants, with sword-shaped leaves and conspicuous flowers. The only British example is the Flowering Rush, described below.

1. Butomus (Flowering Rush).—*Stamens* 9; *carpels* 6. (Name from the Greek, *bous*, an ox, and *temno*, to cut, because cattle feeding on the leaves are liable to cut their mouths.)

1. Butomus (*Flowering Rush*)

1. *B. umbellatus* (Flowering Rush).—The only British species. A tall aquatic plant, growing in stagnant water and slow rivers; not uncommon. The *leaves* are sword-shaped, 2–4 feet long, and spring all from the root; the *flowers* are large, rose-coloured, and handsome, and grow in a simple *umbel* at the top of a round *stalk*, which rises several feet above the surface of the water.—Fl. June, July. Perennial.

Natural Order LXXXVIII
ALISMACEÆ.—Water Plantain Tribe

Sepals 3, green; *petals* 3, coloured; *stamens* varying in number; *ovaries* superior, numerous; *carpels* numerous, 1 or 2-seeded. A small tribe of aquatic plants, often floating, with long-stalked

PLATE XC.

Flowering Rush

leaves, and flowers which in some respects resemble the Crowfoot Tribe. Like the Crowfoots, too, they contain an acrid juice, though the roots of some species, deprived of their acridity by drying, are said to be used as food.

1. ALISMA (Water-Plantain).—*Flowers* containing both *stamens* and *pistils ; stamens* 6 ; *carpels* numerous, 1-seeded. (Name, the Greek name of the plant, and that said to be derived from the Celtic, *alis*, water.)

2. ACTINOCARPUS (Star-fruit).—Like *Alisma,* except that the *carpels* are 2-seeded, and spread in a radiate manner. (Name in Greek having the same meaning as the English name.)

3. SAGITTARIA (Arrow-head).—*Stamens* and *pistils* in separate flowers *(monœcious)* ; *stamens* numerous ; *carpels* numerous, 1-seeded. (Name from the Latin, *sagitta,* an arrow, from the shape of the leaves.)

1. ALISMA *(Water-Plantain)*

1. *A. plantago* (Great Water-Plantain).—*Leaves* all from the root, broad below, and tapering to a point ; *flowers* in a compound, whorled *panicle.* A stout, herbaceous plant, 2–3 feet high, with large, stalked leaves, ribbed like those of a Plantain, and a leafless whorled panicle of lilac flowers, the petals of which are very delicate and soon fall off. Margins of rivers, lakes, and ponds ; common.—Fl. June to August. Perennial.

2. *A. ranunculoides* (Lesser Water-Plantain).—*Leaves* narrow, and tapering at both ends ; *flowers* in umbels. Much smaller than the last, and well marked by the above characters, as well as by its larger flowers. Peaty bogs ; not uncommon.

3. *A. natans* (Floating Water-Plantain).—*Stems* leafy and floating ; *flowers* solitary, white, with a yellow spot. Found only in mountain lakes.

2. ACTINOCARPUS *(Star-fruit)*

1. *A. Damasonium* (Common Star-fruit).—The only British species. An aquatic plant, with the habits of a Water-Plantain. The *leaves* grow on long stalks and float on the surface of the water ; the *flowers,* which grow in whorls, are white, with a yellow spot at the base of each *petal ;* the *fruit* is composed of six pointed *carpels,* which are arranged in the form of a star. Ditches in the midland counties ; not common.—Fl. June, July. Perennial.

3. SAGITTARIA *(Arrow-head)*

1. *S. sagittifolia* (Common Arrow - head). — The only British species. A pretty plant, well distinguished by its large arrow-

shaped *leaves*, and whorled *panicles* of delicate,
flesh - coloured *flowers*, both of which rise 6 – 8
inches out of the water. Rivers and ditches; not
uncommon.—Fl. July to September. Perennial.

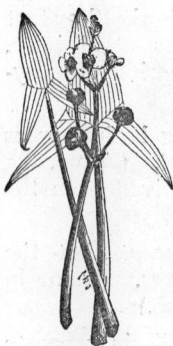

SAGITTARIA
SAGITTIFOLIA
(*Common Arrow-
head*)

NATURAL ORDER LXXXIX
JUNCAGINACEÆ.—ARROW-GRASS TRIBE

Flowers perfect; *sepals* and *petals* alike, green
and small; *stamens* 6; *ovaries* 3–6, superior, united
or distinct; *carpels* 3–6, 1 to 2-seeded. A small
Order of marsh plants, with linear leaves, all pro-
ceeding from the root, and spike-like clusters of
inconspicuous flowers. Found in many parts of
the world, and possessing no remarkable properties.

1. TRIGLOCHIN (Arrow-grass).—*Flowers* in a spike;
sepals and *petals* 6; *stamens* 6. (Name from the
Greek, *treis*, three, and *glochis*, a point, from the three points of
the capsule.)

1. TRIGLOCHIN (*Arrow-grass*)

1. *T. palustre* (Marsh Arrow-grass).—*Fruit*
linear, of 3 combined *carpels*. A plant with
something the habit of *Plantago maritima*,
from which it may easily be distinguished by
its fewer *flowers* and slenderer *spike*, as well as
by the different structure of the flowers. The
leaves are linear and fleshy. Marshy places;
frequent.—Fl. June to August. Perennial.

2. *T. maritimum* (Sea Arrow-grass).—*Fruit*
egg-shaped, of six combined *carpels*. Like the
last, but well marked by its rounded, not
linear *capsule*. Salt marshes; common.—
Fl. May to September. Perennial.

Scheuchzeria palustris, which belongs to this
Order, is a very rare plant, found only in the
north. It has a few sem-icylindrical, blunt
leaves, and a leafless *stalk* about a foot high,
terminating in a cluster of a few small green
flowers.

TRIGLOCHIN PALUSTRE
(*Marsh Arrow-grass*)

NATURAL ORDER XC
TYPHACEÆ.—REED-MACE TRIBE

Stamens and *pistils* separate, but on the same plant (*monœcious*);
flowers in dense spikes or heads, not enclosed in a sheath; *perianth*
composed of 3 *scales* or a tuft of *hairs*; *stamens* 3–6, distinct, or
united by their *filaments*; *anthers* long and wedge-shaped; *ovary*

PLATE XCI.

Great Water Plantain.

single, superior, 1-celled; *style* short; *stigma* linear, lateral; *fruit* 1-celled, 1-seeded, not opening, angular by mutual pressure. Herbaceous plants, growing in marshes and ditches, with jointless stems, sword-shaped leaves, and small flowers, which are only conspicuous from their compact mode of growth. The Order contains only two families, examples of both of which are of common occurrence in Great Britain.

1. TYPHA (Reed-mace).—*Flowers* in *spikes*. (Name from the Greek, *typhos*, a marsh, where these plants grow.)

2. SPARGANIUM (Bur-reed).—*Flowers* in globular *heads*. (Name in Greek denoting a *little band*, from the ribbon-like leaves.)

1. TYPHA (*Reed-mace*)

1. *T. latifolia* (Great Reed-mace, or Cat's Tail).— *Leaves* nearly flat; *barren* and *fertile spikes* continuous. Our largest herbaceous aquatic, often growing 6–8 feet high, with linear leaves, and stout, cylindrical stems, surmounted by a fertile club-like spike, the lower part of which contains fertile flowers only, the upper barren. It is often, but incorrectly, called Bulrush, the true Bulrush being *Scirpus palustris*, a plant which has more the habit of a gigantic rush. Ponds; common.—Fl. July, August. Perennial.

2. *T. angustifolia* (Lesser Reed-mace, or Cat's Tail). — *Leaves* grooved below; *barren* and *fertile spikes* slightly interrupted. Ponds; less frequent than the last, from which it differs by the above characters and by its smaller size.—Fl. July, August. Perennial.

TYPHA
LATIFOLIA
(*Great Reed-Mace, or Cat's Tail*)

2. SPARGANIUM (*Bur-reed*)

1. *S. ramosum* (Branched Bur-reed).— *Leaves* triangular at the base, with concave sides; *stem* branched. A large aquatic, which at a distance might be mistaken for a Flag (*Iris pseud-acorus*). The leaves are sword-shaped, and the flowers are collected into globular heads, of which the lower contain fertile flowers only, the upper barren. Ditches; common.—Fl. July, August. Perennial.

2. *S. simplex* (Unbranched upright Bur-reed). — *Leaves* triangular at the base, with flat sides; *stem* unbranched. Smaller than

SPARGANIUM RAMOSUM
(*Branched Bur-reed*)

the last, and at once distinguished by the above characters. Ditches ; common.

3. *S. natans* (Floating Bur-reed) is found only in the north. It has very long, pellucid, floating *leaves*, and *flowers* resembling those of the preceding species, except that the barren *head* is usually solitary.

Natural Order XCI
ARACEÆ.—The Cuckoo-pint Family

Stamens and *pistils* separate, but on the same plant (*monœcious*) ; *flowers* arranged on a *spadix*, or *central column*, and endorsed in a *sheath ; perianth* o ; *stamens* numerous, *sessile* on the *spadix ; ovaries* the same, below the stamens ; *stigma* sessile ; *fruit* a berry. A curious tribe of plants, all more or less resembling the British species, *Arum maculatum*, abounding in tropical countries, and possessing acrid, or even poisonous qualities, which, however, may be dissipated by heat. The most remarkable plant of the Order is the Dumb-Cane of the West Indies, a species growing as high as a man, and having the property, when chewed, of swelling the tongue and destroying the power of speech. The effects continue for several days, and are accompanied with much pain. Other species, which are scarcely less noxious in their fresh state, are extensively cultivated in tropical countries, and produce tuberous roots, which, when cooked, are important articles of food. Even the British example of this Order (*Arum maculatum*), though its juice is so intensely acrid that a single drop will cause a burning taste in the mouth and throat, which continues for hours, has roots which, when properly prepared, are wholesome and nutritious. This plant was formerly cultivated in the Isle of Portland, and the starch procured from its roots, under the name of Portland Sago, was used as a substitute for arrow-root. Several species have been observed to evolve a considerable quantity of heat from the spadix, at the time of the expansion of the sheath.

1. ARUM (Cuckoo-pint).—*Flowers* on a club-shaped *spadix*, which is naked above and enclosed in a convolute *sheath*. (Name, the Greek name of the plant.)

1. ARUM (*Cuckoo-pint*)

1. *A. maculatum* (Cuckoo-pint, Wake-Robin, Lords-and-Ladies). —The only British species. A succulent, herbaceous plant, with large, glossy, arrow-shaped *leaves*, which are often spotted with dark purple. The upper part of the *spadix* is club-shaped, and of a light pink, dull purple, or rich crimson colour, which is easily rubbed off ; about the middle of the spadix is a ring of *glands*, terminating in short *threads*, and below this is a ring of sessile

PLATE XCII.

Lords and Ladies

anthers ; and yet lower down, another ring of sessile *ovaries*. The upper part of the spadix soon falls off, leaving the ovaries, which finally become a cylindrical mass of scarlet *berries*, which are conspicuous objects when all the rest of the plant has withered and disappeared. The spadix with its sheath may be discerned wrapped up in the young *leaf-stalks*, even before the leaves have risen above the surface of the ground. Hedges and woods; common in most parts of England.—Fl. May, June. Perennial.

Natural Order XCII
ORONTIACEÆ.—Sweet Sedge Tribe

Flowers perfect, arranged on a central column or *spadix*, at first enclosed in a *sheath* ; *perianth* of 4–8 scales ; *stamens* equalling the *scales* in number ; *ovary* superior ; *fruit*, a berry. A tribe of plants nearly allied to the Araceæ, and resembling them in properties. *Calla Æthiopica*, the White Arum Lily so frequently seen in greenhouses, grows so plentifully in parts of Cape Colony that pigs are often turned into the swamps where it abounds, to fatten on its roots, whence it is commonly called " Pig Lily " in that country. *Acorus calamus*, or Sweet Sedge, supplied the " rushes " with which, before the use of carpets had been introduced into England, it was customary to strew the floors of the great. As it did not grow in the neighbourhood of London, but had to be fetched at considerable expense from Norfolk and Suffolk, one of the charges of extravagance brought against Cardinal Wolsey was that he caused his floors to be strewed with rushes too frequently.

1. Acorus (Sweet Sedge).—*Sheath* leaf-like, not convolute, overlapping the *spadix*. (Name in Greek denoting that the plant has the power of curing diseases of the eye.)

1. Acorus (*Sweet Sedge*)

1. *A. calamus* (Sweet Sedge).— The only British species. An aquatic plant, with somewhat of the habit of a sedge or large grass. It is easily distinguished from all other British plants by its peculiar *spadix*, and the fragrance of its roots, stems, and leaves. Watery places in Norfolk and Suffolk.—Fl. June. Perennial.

Acorus Calamus
(*Sweet Sedge*)

Natural Order XCIII

PISTIACEÆ.—Duck-weed Tribe

Minute floating plants, composed of simple or lobed *leaves*, and fibrous *roots*, which are not attached to the soil, propagating themselves principally by off-sets, but sometimes producing on the edge of the leaves 1–2 *stamens* and 1- to 4-seeded *ovaries*, enclosed in small sheaths. *Lemna* (Duck-weed) is the only British example, and the number of foreign species is but small.

1. Lemna (*Duck-weed*)

1. *L. minor* (Lesser Duck-weed).—A minute plant, but often so abundant as to cover the surface of stagnant water, where, with the insects which it harbours, it is greedily devoured by ducks. In this species the *leaves* are egg-shaped, and bear each a single *root*. Four other species have been found in Britain, for a description of which the student is referred to Bentham and Hooker's " British Flora."

Lemna Minor
(*Lesser Duck-weed*)

Natural Order XCIV

NAIADACEÆ.—Pond-weed Tribe

Submersed or floating aquatics, with very cellular *stems* and peculiar *leaves*, which are sometimes almost leathery, but more frequently thin and pellucid. The *flowers* are small, olive-green, resembling in structure the Arrow-grasses; sometimes solitary, but more frequently arranged in spikes. They inhabit ponds and slow streams, or rarely salt marshes. Our British species, *Zostera marina*, grows in the sea.

1. Potamogeton (Pond-weed). *Flowers* in a spike; *stamens* and *pistils* in the same flower; *perianth* of 4 sepals; *stamens* 4, sessile. (Name from the Greek, *potamos*, a river, and *geiton*, a neighbour.)

2. Ruppia.—*Flowers* about 2 on a stalk; *stamens* and *pistils* in the same flower; *perianth* 0; *stamens* 4; *carpels* 4, at first sessile, afterwards raised each on a long stalk. (Named in honour of *H. B. Ruppius*, a botanist of the eighteenth century.)

3. Zannichellia (Horned Pond-weed). — *Flowers* axillary; *stamens* and *pistils* separate (*monœcious*); *stamen* 1; *carpels* 4. (Named in honour of *J. J. Zannichelli*, a Venetian botanist.)

4. ZOSTERA (Grass-wrack).—*Flowers* composed of *stamens* and *pistils* alternately arranged in 2 rows in a long leaf-like sheath. (Name from the Greek, *zoster*, a girdle, which the leaves resemble in form.)

1. POTAMOGETON (*Pond-weed*)

1. *P. natans* (Floating Pond-weed). — *Upper leaves* elliptical, ribbed, and cellular ; *lower,* submersed, linear. An aquatic plant, with cord-like stems, propor-tioned to the depth of the water in which it grows ; smooth, floating leaves, on long stalks ; and cylindrical spikes of small green flowers, which rise above the surface of the water. The upper, or floating leaves, are 2–3 inches in length ; the lower, which are not always present, are very narrow, and a foot long or more. Ponds and ditches ; common.—Fl. June to August. Perennial.

POTAMOGETON NATANS
(*Floating Pond-weed*)

2. *P. perfoliatus* (Perfoliate Pond-weed).—*Leaves* alternate, all submersed, egg-shaped, embracing the *stem*, pellucid, 7-nerved. Remarkable for its brown, almost transparent leaves, 2–3 inches long, which when dry have the appearance of gold-beater's skin, and are so sensitive of moisture that they will curl when laid on the palm of the hand. Ponds and lakes ; common.—Fl. June to August. Perennial.

POTAMOGETON DENSUS
(*Opposite-leaved Pond-weed*)

3. *P. densus* (Opposite-leaved Pond-weed). —*Leaves* opposite, all submersed, embracing the *stem*, pellucid. Like the last in habit, but smaller. Ponds and rivers ; common. —Fl. June to August. Perennial.

4. *P. pusillus* (Small Pond-weed).—*Leaves* linear, very narrow ; *flowers* in a long-stalked, loose *spike*. A tangled mass of thread-like stems, and dull, olive-green leaves, with numerous spikes of brownish flowers, which are either submersed, or partially rise above the surface of the water. Ponds and lakes ; common.—Fl. June to August. Perennial.

From eighteen to twenty species of Pond-weed are described as natives of Britain ; they all, more or less, resemble the above in habit, and as they are by no means an interesting family of plants, easy to obtain, or pleasant to examine, it is not thought

RUPPIA MARITIMA
(*Sea Ruppia*)

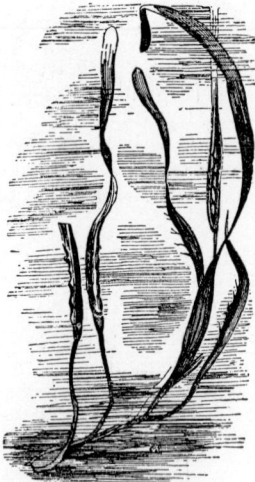

ZOSTERA MARINA
(*Grass-wrack*)

necessary to describe their characters in an elementary work like this.

2. RUPPIA

1. *R. maritima* (Sea Ruppia).—The only species, growing in salt-water ditches; distinguished from *Potamogeton pusillus* by its spiral *flower-stalks* and long-stalked *fruit*.—Fl. July, August.

3. ZANNICHELLIA (*Horned Pond-weed*)

1. *Z. palustris* (Horned Pond-weed). —The only British species. A submersed aquatic, with the habit of *Potamogeton pusillus*, from which it may be well distinguished by its small, almost sessile, axillary *flowers*, the *stigmas* of which are unevenly cup-shaped.—Fl. August, September. Perennial.

4. ZOSTERA (*Grass-wrack*)

1. *Z. marina* (Grass-wrack). — A submersed marine aquatic, with long, cord-like *stems*, and bright green, grass-like *leaves*, some of which serve as *sheaths* to the bead-like rows of small, simple *flowers*. The dried leaves and stems are used as beds, and are also employed in packing glass.—Fl. July, August. Perennial.

SUPPLEMENT

PIPE-WORTS, SEDGES AND GRASSES

CLASS II

MONOCOTYLEDONOUS PLANTS (p. 269)

SUB-CLASS II
GLUMACEÆ

Flowers without *petals,* usually arising in the axils of chaffy scales (*glumes*), which are often imbricate, sometimes (in *Eriocauleæ*) with a *perianth* of 4–6 segments.

NATURAL ORDER XCV
ERIOCAULEÆ.—PIPE-WORT TRIBE

Flowers unisexual ; *perianth* of 4 or 6 segments, the 2 or 3 inner ones in the male flowers united to near the summit ; *stamens* 2–6 ; *capsule* 2- or 3-lobed and 2- or 3-celled ; *style* single, with 2 or 3 stigmas ; *seeds* solitary in each cell and suspended from the top. Usually herbs with a rush-like habit, often growing in swampy places. The Order includes about 360 species which are dispersed through the warmer parts of the world, but are most numerous in Tropical America ; none is of economic importance.

1. ERIOCAULON (Pipe-wort).—*Leaves* tufted ; *peduncles* leafless, bearing a globose head of minute *flowers,* the central of which are chiefly males, the outer chiefly females, all intermixed with small bracts, and the whole surrounded by rather larger ones forming an involucre ; *perianth* very delicate, of 4 segments ; *stamens* 4 ; *stigmas* and *lobes* of the *ovary* 2. Aquatic or marsh herbs. (Name from the Greek *erion*, wool, and *kaulon*, a stem, from the fact that some species have woolly peduncles.)

1. ERIOCAULON· (*Pipe-wort*)

1. *E. septangulare* (Common Pipe-wort).—The only species found in the British Isles. It is a small herb with a slender, creeping rootstock ; *leaves* linear, very pointed, pellucid, 1–3 inches long ; *peduncles* 2–12 inches high ; *bracts* and *perianth* lead-coloured. Lakes in the Hebrides and west coast of Ireland.—Fl. August. Perennial.

Natural Order XCVI
CYPERACEÆ.—The Sedge Tribe

Herbs, often resembling Rushes or Grasses, but they are usually stiffer than the latter, with solid, often 3-angled stems, and leaves with closed sheaths, usually arranged in 3 rows ; *flowers* in small green-brown or sometimes blackish spikelets, which are either solitary and terminal or several together in a terminal, simple, or compound cluster, spike, umbel, or panicle ; each *spikelet* is placed in the axil of a scale-like or leafy outer bract, and consists of several scale-like, imbricate bracts (*glumes*), each containing in its axil a solitary sessile flower ; *perianth* none or represented by a few bristles or minute scales ; *stamens* 3 or rarely 2 ; *ovary* (in the same or in a distinct glume) 1-celled ; *style* more or less deeply divided into 2 or 3 branches ; *fruit* a small seed-like nut, flattened when the style is 2-branched, triangular when it is 3-branched ; *seed* solitary. The Order is a very large one, including upwards of 3300 species, which are widely distributed throughout the world, but are more numerous in the north temperate regions ; they usually grow in damp places, and many of the British species are found intermixed with Grasses. The Cyperaceæ contain very few important economic plants. Some possess a bitter principle in their rhizomes, and this has been used as a substitute for Sarsaparilla ; others, as *Cyperus esculentus*, which is common in the warmer parts of Africa and America, produce edible tubers. The long-creeping rhizomes of some species, particularly *Carex arenaria*, render the plants of great service in binding together the shifting sands in maritime regions. In France mattresses are made from the stems of *Scirpus lacustris*, and other Cyperaceæ are used in the making of mats and chairs. *Cyperus Papyrus*, or *Papyrus Antiquorum*, a native of swamps in Upper Egypt and other parts of Tropical Africa and in Sicily, is the well-known Papyrus of the ancients. The substance used as paper was obtained by pressing and joining together thin longitudinal slices of the long stems.

Spikelets many-flowered ; flowers 2-sexual ; perianth absent or consisting of scales or bristles.

1. Cyperus (Galingale).—Perennial or rarely annual herbs, rush- or grass-like ; *spikelets* linear, compressed, in lateral or terminal heads or in umbels or panicles ; *glumes* in 2 rows, deciduous, all or nearly all bearing a flower ; *bristles* 0 ; *stamens* 1–3 ; *stigmas* 2 or 3. (Name from the Greek *kupeiros*, a reed.)

2. Eleocharis (Spike-Rush).—Tufted, usually perennial herbs with slender stems ; *spikelets* terete, angular or compressed, solitary, terminal ; *glumes* many, imbricate, mostly containing perfect

flowers ; *bristles* 3–6 ; *stamens* 3 ; *style* deciduous, jointed with the top of the fruit ; *stigmas* 2 or 3. (Name from the Greek *helos*, a marsh, and *chairo*, I rejoice, because the species flourish in marshes.)

3. SCIRPUS (Club-Rush).—Perennial herbs, usually stiff and rush-like ; *spikelets* several, in terminal or lateral heads or clusters, or sometimes solitary ; *glumes* imbricate all round the axis, or in 2 rows, all but the 1 or 2 lowest bearing perfect flowers ; *bristles* 1–6 or none ; *stamens* 3 ; *style* deciduous, not swollen at the base ; *stigmas* 2 or 3. (*Scirpus* is the old Latin name.)

4. BLYSMUS (Blysmus).—Often included in *Scirpus* : it differs in having the spikelets sessile in 2 opposite rows, forming a short terminal spike. (Name from the Greek *bluso*, I gush out ; the species grow near springs or wet places.)

5. ERIOPHORUM (Cotton-Grass).—Similar to *Scirpus*, but as the flowering advances the bristles protrude a long way beyond the glumes, forming silky-cottony tufts ; *style* usually 3-branched. (Name from the Greek *erion*, wool, and *phero*, I bear.)

Spikelets 1- or few-flowered ; flowers usually 2-sexual ; perianth absent or consisting of bristles.

6. RHYNCHOSPORA (Beak-Sedge).—Tufted leafy herbs ; *spikelets* terete, in axillary and terminal corymbs or panicles ; *glumes* imbricate all round the axis, 1–3 of the upper or inner ones each containing a flower, the lower shorter and empty ; *stamens* 3, rarely 2 ; *bristles* 6 or sometimes more, shorter than the glumes ; *nut* tapering into a 2-branched style. (Name from the Greek *rhunchos*, a beak, and *spora*, a seed, in allusion to the beaked fruit.)

7. SCHŒNUS (Bog-Rush).—Usually stiff rush-like herbs ; *spikelets* in compact, compressed terminal heads ; *glumes* in 2 opposite rows, not more than 4 of the uppermost in each spikelet with flowers, the lower shorter and empty ; *bristles* none, or 3–6 and minute ; *nut* not beaked. Name from the Greek *schoinos*, cord ; some of the species have been used in making cordage.)

8. CLADIUM (Fen-Sedge).—Rush-like herbs, with a creeping rootstock ; *stem* 3–6 feet high, leafy ; *leaves* nearly erect, the lowest nearly as long as the stem, ending in a long, triangular point ; *spikelets* pale brown, in numerous small clusters placed in the upper axils, the whole forming a leafy panicle often a foot long or more, each spikelet 1–3 flowered ; *glumes* 5 or 6 in each spikelet, imbricate all round the axis ; *bristles* 0 ; *nut* tapering at the top, with a fleshy coat when fresh. (Name from the Greek *klados*, a twig.)

x

Spikelets 1- or 2-flowered ; flowers 1-sexual ; perianth none.

9. KOBRESIA (Kobresia).—Small herbs, with rigid, keeled, grass-like leaves ; *spikelets* sessile in a terminal, compressed, ovoid spike, with a glume-like bract under each spikelet ; *upper flower* in each spikelet male, the lower female ; *glumes* 2 or 3, imbricate all round the axis ; *stamens* 3 ; *stigmas* 3. (Named in compliment to Dr. Kobres, a German patron of Botany.)

Spikelets many-flowered ; flowers 1-sexual ; perianth of male flower none ; ovary enclosed in a persistent bottle-shaped sack or utricle.

10. CAREX (Sedge).—A large genus of herbs with grass-like leaves ; *spikelets* solitary, or several in a terminal spike, or the lower distant, sessile or stalked, the whole sometimes forming a dense compound spike or panicle ; *stamens* and *pistils* always in separate glumes, either in the same or distinct spikelets, sometimes confined to distinct plants (diœcious) ; *glumes* imbricated all round the axis ; *stamens* 3 or rarely 2 ; *style* 2- or 3-branched ; *nut* compressed or triangular, enclosed in a persistent sack or utricle. (Name from the Greek *keiro,* I cut, because the leaves usually have sharp edges.)

1. CYPERUS (*Galingale*)

1. *C. longus* (Sweet Galingale).—*Stem* stout, 1–4 feet high, with a few leaves at the base which are usually shorter than the stem and about 3, very unequal in length, around the large compound umbel ; *spikelets* very numerous, linear, about $\frac{1}{2}$ inch long ; *glumes* obtuse, bright chestnut, with a green keel ; *style* 3-branched. Wet meadows in the south of England ; rare.—Fl. August, September. Perennial.

2. *C. fuscus* (Brown Cyperus).—Much smaller than the preceding, often only a few inches high, with the clusters of spikelets more compact ; *spikelets* flattened, obtuse, not more than $\frac{1}{4}$ inch long. Wet meadows in the south of England and the Channel Islands ; rare.—Fl. August, September. Annual.

2. ELEOCHARIS (*Spike-Rush*)

1. *E. palustris* (Marsh Spike-Rush).—*Stems* rather stiff, often densely tufted, 3–12 inches high or more, all leafless and without leafy tips ; *spikelets* solitary, terminal, oblong, $\frac{1}{3}$–$\frac{1}{2}$ inch long ; *glumes* brown, green on the midrib ; *style* 2-branched. Edges of pools and wet ditches and in marshes ; frequent. Fl. June.—Perennial.

2. *E. uniglumis* (Link's Spike-Rush).—Differs chiefly from *E. palustris* in having the outermost bract broader, almost enclosing the base of the spike. Wet, sandy places, usually near the sea ; frequent.—Fl. June, July. Perennial.

PLATE XCIII

Meadow Fox-tail Grass   Sweet-Scented Vernal Grass   Fiorin or Marsh Bent-Grass

Common Quaking Grass   Common False Oat

3. *E. multicaulis* (Many-stemmed Spike-Rush).—Smaller than *E. palustris ; stems* more slender, often barren and leaf-like ; *spikelets* rather small ; *style* usually 3-branched. Marshy places ; frequent.—Fl. July, August. Perennial.

4. *E. acicularis* (Least or Slender Spike-Rush).—A slender little tufted plant scarcely 2 inches high ; *stems* needle-like, most of them bearing a single terminal oblong spikelet which is scarcely $\frac{1}{6}$ inch long and dark brown ; *style* 3-branched. Damp, sandy places ; rather common.—Fl. July, August. Perennial.

3. Scirpus (*Club-Rush*)
Spikelets 2 to many ; bristles 6

1. *S. maritimus* (Sea Club-Rush).—*Stems* sharply triangular, 2–5 feet high ; *leaves* flat, pointed, often longer than the stems ; *spikelets* about $\frac{3}{4}$ inch long, 2 or 3 in a sessile cluster, or 8–10, the inner sessile and the outer stalked ; *outer bract* long, leafy ; sometimes 1 or 2 other shorter leafy bracts are present. Salt marshes ; common.—Fl. July, August. Perennial.

2. *S. sylvaticus* (Wood Club-Rush).—*Stems* triangular, 2–3 feet high ; *leaves* long, grass-like ; *spikelets* very numerous, about $\frac{1}{6}$ inch long, in clusters of 2 or 3, forming a large terminal compound umbel or panicle, with 2 or 3 leafy bracts at the base. Moist woods and grassy banks of rivers ; frequent.—Fl. July, August. Perennial.

3. *S. triqueter* (Three-edged Bulrush).—*Stems* sharply triangular, 2–3 feet high, leafless, but the few loose sheaths at the base have a short blade ; *spikelets* 8–10 or more, the central ones sessile, the outer stalked, the whole forming a lateral umbel or cluster, the stiff triangular outer bract often projecting 1 or 2 inches beyond ; *style* 2-branched. Muddy banks of tidal rivers ; rare.—Fl. August, September. Perennial.

4. *S. pungens* (Sharp Club-Rush).—Rather smaller than *S. triqueter*, and 1 or 2 of the sheaths bear narrow keeled leaves 1–3 inches long ; *spikelets* few, all sessile, forming a close cluster. Bogs and margins of ponds in Jersey.—Fl. June, July. Perennial.

5. *S. lacustris* (Common Bulrush).—*Stems* stout, 2–8 feet high, cylindrical at the base, tapering upwards, sometimes obtusely triangular near the top, bearing 1 short leaf near the base ; *spikelets* rather numerous, $\frac{1}{4}-\frac{1}{2}$ inch long, in a lateral cluster, the outer bract continuing the stem ; *style* 2- or 3-branched. Margins of ponds and rivers ; common.—Fl. June, July. Perennial.

6. *S. Tabernæmontani* (Glaucous Bulrush).—Differs from *S. lacustris* in having glaucous stems and the glumes are furnished with

raised dots. Rivers and ponds, usually near the sea.—Fl. June, July. Perennial.

7. *S. carinatus* (Trigonous-stemmed Bulrush).—Similar to the preceding, but the stems are a bright deep green, obtusely tri-angular near the top, and the glumes are smooth. Near rivers in the southern counties ; rare.—Fl. June, July. Perennial.

Spikelets solitary, terminal ; bristles 4–6.

8. *S. pauciflorus* (Chocolate-headed Club-Rush).—*Stems* tufted, slender, not 6 inches high, many of them barren ; *spikelet* small, with not more than 5 or 6 flowers ; *bristles* 6 ; *style* 3-branched. Wet heaths ; frequent.—Fl. July, August. Perennial.

9. *S. cæspitosus* (Deer's-hair or Scaly-stemmed Club-Rush).— *Stems* densely tufted, 6–12 inches high, covered for some distance from the base with more prominent sheaths than in *S. pauciflorus*, and these bear leafy tips $\frac{1}{12}-\frac{1}{6}$ inch long ; *bract* about as long as the spikelet, with a somewhat leafy tip ; *flowers* usually 6–8 ; *bristles* 6 ; *style* 3-branched. Marshy places ; frequent.—Fl. June to August. Perennial.

10. *S. parvulus* (Least Club-Rush).—A very small plant with grooved stems only 1–2 inches high ; *sheaths* transparent ; *leaves* similar to the stems ; *spikelets* about $\frac{1}{10}$ inch long, pale ; *bris les* 4–6. Sandy places near the sea in the south ; rare.—Fl. July. Annual.

Spikelets 1–3 ; bristles none

11. *S. fluitans* (Floating Club-Rush).—*Stems* long, slender, branching, floating on the water or forming soft, dense masses on its margin ; *leaves* linear, $\frac{1}{2}$–2 inches long ; *spikelets* solitary, ter-minal, not $\frac{1}{6}$ inch long ; *outer bract* without a leafy point ; *style* 2-branched. Pools and ditches ; common.—Fl. June, July. Perennial.

12. *S. setaceus* (Bristle-like Club-Rush).—A little plant only 2 or 3 inches high, forming dense tufts ; *stems* slender, with 1 or 2 awl-shaped leaves sheathing each at the base ; *spikelets* solitary or 2 or 3 together in a little cluster which appears to be lateral, ovoid, seldom $\frac{1}{6}$ inch long ; *glumes* broad, dark brown with a green mid-rib ; *style* 3-branched. Wet, sandy places ; common.—Fl. July, August. Perennial.

13. *S. cernuus* (Savi's Club-Rush).—Very similar to *S. setaceus*, but often still more slender and the outer bract is scarcely longer than the spikelet. Marshes and edges of pools, usually near the coast ; rare.—Fl. July. Annual or perennial.

Spikelets many, clustered ; bristles none

14. *S. Holoschœnus* (Round-headed Club-Rush).—A stiff, rush-like plant ; *stems* cylindrical, 1–2 feet high or more, with 1 or 2 stiff leaves sheathing the base ; *spikelets* clustered, in one or more round heads about ⅓ inch across, which form a lateral cluster or umbel ; *style* usually 2-cleft. Moist places near the sea in North Devon, Somerset, and the Channel Islands ; rare.—Fl. September. Perennial.

4. BLYSMUS (*Blysmus*)

1. *B. compressus* (Broad-leaved Blysmus).—*Stems* 6–8 inches high, with a creeping rootstock ; *leaves* shorter than the stems, flat or keeled, $\frac{1}{12}$–$\frac{1}{8}$ inch broad ; *spike* terminal, about 1 inch long, consisting of 10 or 12 oblong chestnut-brown spikelets each about ¼ inch long ; *bract* glume-like, shorter than the mature spikelets. Boggy pastures ; rather frequent.—Fl. June, July. Perennial.

2. *B. rufus* (Narrow-leaved Blysmus).—*Leaves* narrower than in the preceding, erect, channelled or rarely cylindrical ; *spike* rather shorter, consisting of about 6 dark brown spikelets. Marshy places near the sea ; not uncommon, especially in the north.—Fl. June, July. Perennial.

5. ERIOPHORUM (*Cotton-Grass*)

Spikelets solitary on each stem

1. *E. alpinum* (Alpine Cotton-Grass).—*Stems* densely tufted, 6–10 inches high, with sheaths at the base bearing very short, leafy tips ; *spikelet* small, terminal, brown ; *bristles* about 6 to each flower, growing out after the flowering stage, and forming a white cotton-like tuft often an inch long. Mountain bogs in Forfar ; now extinct.—Fl. June. Perennial.

2. *E. vaginatum* (Hare's-tail Cotton-Grass).—*Stems* tufted, 1 foot high or more, some of the sheaths at the base bearing linear leaves about as long as the stems ; *spikelet* ½–⅔ inch long, the numerous bristles forming a white cotton-like tuft about 1 inch across. Bogs and wet moors ; common.—Fl. May. Perennial.

Spikelets several on each stem

3. *E. polystachion* (Common Cotton-Grass).—About 1 foot high ; *leaves* linear, channelled, triangular in the upper half ; *stems* nearly round ; *peduncles* smooth ; cotton-like tufts smaller than in the preceding. Bogs and wet moors ; common.—Fl. May, June. Perennial.

4. *E. latifolium* (Broad-leaved Cotton-Grass).—Slender, 12–18 inches high ; *leaves* flattened the greater part of their length, about

⅙ inch broad ; *stems* 3-angled in the upper half ; *peduncles* rough. Bogs ; rather rare.—Fl. May, June. Perennial.

5. *E. gracile* (Slender Cotton-Grass).—Tall and slender ; *leaves* very narrow, 3-angled ; *stem* almost 3-angled ; *peduncles* downy ; *spikelets* about 4, almost erect. Bogs in the south ; very rare.— Fl. June, July. Perennial.

6. RHYNCHOSPORA (*Beak-Sedge*)

1. *R. fusca* (Brown Beak-Sedge).—A very slender, rush-like plant ; *stem* 6–10 inches high, with a few short, erect, subulate leaves, the uppermost (bracts) projecting an inch or more beyond the spikelets ; *spikelets* brown, less than ¼ inch long, usually in 2 rather loose clusters ; *flowers* usually 2 to each spikelet ; *bristles* about 6, very unequal. Bogs in the south-west of England and in Ireland ; rare.—Fl. July, August. Perennial.

2. *R. alba* (White Beak-Sedge).—Differs from *R. fusca* in having whitish spikelets, and the uppermost leaves (bracts) are shorter or scarcely longer than the spikelets. Bogs ; frequent.—Fl. June, July. Perennial.

7. SCHŒNUS (*Bog-Rush*)

1. *S. nigricans* (Black Bog-Rush).—A rush-like plant with stiff stems about 1 foot high ; *leaves* short, stiff, arising from the base of the stems, with dark brown sheaths ; *spikelets* several, dark shining brown, in compact terminal heads about ½ inch across, surrounded by 2 or 3 brown bracts, 1 at least with a point ½–2 inches long. Bogs ; frequent, especially in the west.—Fl. June, July. Perennial.

2. *S. ferrugineus* (Brown Bog-Rush).—Smaller than the preceding, and the leaf-sheaths are reddish brown with usually very short blades ; *spikelets* reddish brown, only 2 or 3 in a head. Open peat moors in Perthshire ; very rare.—Fl. June, July. Perennial.

8. CLADIUM (*Fen-Sedge*)

1. *C. Mariscus* (Prickly Fen-Sedge).—The only British species, sometimes called *C. jamaicense*. It is a tall, rush-like plant, with leafy stems 3–6 feet high ; *leaves* nearly erect, the lowest nearly as long as the stems, rough on keel and edges ; *spikelets* pale brown, ⅙–¼ inch long, very numerous, arranged in small clusters which form a leafy, oblong, terminal panicle often a foot long or more ; *stamens* usually 2. Bogs ; very local. It was formerly abundant in the fen country of Cambridge and Suffolk, but has been destroyed to a great extent by the draining of the fens.—Fl. July. Perennial.

9. KOBRESIA (*Kobresia*)

1. *K. caricina* (Sedge-like Kobresia).—A small tufted plant, closely resembling a Sedge ; *stems* seldom above 6 inches high ; *leaves* spreading from the base, shorter than the stems ; *spikelets* 4 or 5, brown, sessile, in a short, terminal spike. Wet moors in the north ; rare.—Fl. July. Perennial.

10. CAREX (*Sedge*)
§ 1.   *Spikelet solitary, terminal, unbranched*
* *Style 2-branched*

1. *C. dioica* (Diœcious Sedge).—*Rootstock* usually creeping ; *stems* slender, usually not more than 6 or 8 inches high ; *leaves* narrow, often shorter than the stems ; *spikelets* brown, about ½ inch long, male and female on distinct plants (diœcious). Bogs ; common.—Fl. May, June. Perennial.

2. *C. Davalliana* (Davall's Sedge).—Like the preceding, but differs in having the fruits deflexed instead of ascending. It is now extinct in Britain ; it used to grow on Lansdown, near Bath.

3. *C. pulicaris* (Flea-Sedge).—*Stems* tufted, 3–6 inches high ; *leaves* very slender, shorter than the stems ; *spikelets* about ¾ inch long, male in the upper half, female in the lower ; *fruits* spreading. Bogs ; frequent.—Fl. May, June. Perennial.

** *Style 3-branched*

4. *C. rupestris* (Rock-Sedge).—*Rootstock* creeping ; *leaves* broader and flatter than in *C. pulicaris ; spikelet* similar ; *fruit* shorter, not pointed and not so spreading. Wet rocks on the higher Scottish mountains ; rare.—Fl. July to September. Perennial.

5. *C. pauciflora* (Few-flowered Sedge).—A slender plant with long, creeping runners ; *stem* branched, often about 6 inches high or less ; *leaves* very narrow, the upper often nearly as long as the stem ; *spikelet* very short, few-flowered, male at the top ; *fruit* long, narrow, spreading or reflexed. Bogs ; frequent in the north. —Fl. June, July. Perennial.

§ 2.   *Spikelets several in a compound spike or panicle, each spikelet containing both male and female flowers, or sometimes nearly unisexual ; style 2-branched*
* *Spikelets nearly entirely either male or female*

6. *C. arenaria* (Sand-Sedge).—*Rootstock* creeping, often several feet long ; *stems* a few inches to 1½ feet high, leafy at the base ;

spikelets rather large, sessile, 8–10 crowded together in a terminal spike 1–2 inches long ; *fruits* much flattened, beaked and winged. Sandy seashores ; common.—Fl. June, July. Perennial.

7. *C. disticha* (Soft Brown Sedge).—Usually taller and more slender and leafy than *C. arenaria*, with usually longer and less winged fruits. Marshy places.—Fl. May to July. Perennial.

** *Spikelets male at the top only*

8. *C. incurva* (Curved Sedge).—*Stems* 2–3 inches high, often curved as well as the rush-like leaves, which are about the same length ; *spikelets* 3 or 4, crowded in a broadly ovoid brown head, each spikelet with a few male flowers at the top ; *fruits* broad, rather inflated, shortly beaked. Sandy seashores in the north-east of Scotland ; rare.—Fl. June, July. Perennial.

9. *C. chordorrhiza.*—Much taller than *C. incurva*, the stems being 6–12 inches high, straight or only slightly curved. Very wet peat-bogs in Sutherlandshire.—Fl. July, August. Perennial.

10. *C. divisa* (Bracteated Marsh-Sedge).—*Stems* slender, often 1 foot high ; *spikelets* few, short, crowded into an oblong or ovoid spike or head, seldom more than $\frac{1}{2}$ inch long, the lowermost bract sometimes longer than the spike ; *fruits* not winged, more or less beaked. Meadows and marshy places near the sea in the south and east ; not uncommon.—Fl. May to July. Perennial.

11. *C. vulpina* (Fox-Sedge).—A stout plant, 2–4 feet high ; *stems* sharply triangular ; *leaves* rather broad, but not very long ; *spikelets* many, green or pale brown, densely crowded in a terminal spike 1–2 inches long ; *fruits* much flattened, broadly beaked. Wet places ; common.—Fl. June, July. Perennial.

12. *C. muricata* (Prickly Sedge).—*Stems* usually less than 1 foot high ; *leaves* narrow, shorter than the stems ; *spikelets* about 6, brown or shining green, crowded in a terminal spike, or the lower somewhat distant and slightly compound ; *fruit* broadly beaked, spreading. Marshy and gravelly pastures ; common.—Fl. May, June. Perennial.

13. *C. divulsa* (Grey Sedge).—Differs from *C. muricata* in having longer stems and leaves, and paler, more distant spikelets. Moist, shady places ; not uncommon.—Fl. June. Perennial.

14. *C. paniculata* (Greater Panicled Sedge).—A stout, tufted plant ; *stems* 1–3 or even 4 feet high ; *leaves* $\frac{1}{4}$–$\frac{1}{3}$ inch broad, usually longer than the stems ; *spikelets* many, brown, sessile, crowded in a compound spike or panicle which is sometimes 4 or 5 inches long, with the lower branches spreading, 1 inch long ; *fruits* beaked. Bogs ; common.—Fl. June, July. Perennial.

15. *C. teretiuscula* (Lesser Panicled Sedge).—Smaller than *C. paniculata*, and the panicle is contracted into a spike about 1 inch long. Boggy meadows ; rare.—Fl. June. Perennial.

16. *C. paradoxa* (Paradoxical Sedge).—Intermediate between the two preceding ; it is much more slender than *C. paniculata*, and differs from *C. teretiuscula* in being more densely tufted, with the base of each stem furnished with more numerous black sheaths, while the spikes are longer and branched. Bogs ; very local (Ireland, Yorkshire, Norfolk).—Fl. June, July. Perennial.

*** *Spikelets male at the base only or sometimes at both ends*

† *Bracts leaf-like, the lower as long as or longer than the spike*

17. *C. remota* (Distant-spiked Sedge).—Very slender, 1–2 feet high ; *spikelets* small, pale, placed very far apart, the lower ones having a long leaf-like bract ; *male flowers* at the base of each spikelet. Woods and moist, shady places ; common.—Fl. June. Perennial.

18. *C. axillaris* (Axillary Sedge).—*Stems* often 2 feet high, leafy ; *spikelets* not so widely separated as in *C. remota*, and the lowest is branched, or there are 2 or 3 together, either sessile or very shortly stalked. Hedge-banks and damp meadows ; rare.—Fl. June, July. Perennial.

19. *C. Boenninghauseniana* (Bönninghausen's Sedge).—Similar to the preceding, but it grows in denser tufts, the stems are more slender and rigid, and the leaves are darker green. It is supposed to be a hybrid between *C. paniculata* and *C. remota*. Woods and margins of ponds ; rare.—Fl. June, July. Perennial.

†† *Bracts none or very short, not leaf-like*

20. *C. echinata* (Star-headed or Little Prickly Sedge).—Often called *C. stellulata*. *Stems* slender, rarely above 6 or 8 inches high ; *leaves* mostly shorter than the stems ; *spikelets* 3 or 4, rather distant from one another, especially the lower ; *fruits* beaked, spreading. Boggy places ; common.—Fl. May, June. Perennial.

21. *C. canescens* (White Sedge).—Also known as *C. curta*. *Stems* about 1 foot high, with rather long leaves ; *spikelets* 4–6, rather far apart or the uppermost closer, $\frac{1}{4}$–$\frac{1}{2}$ inch long, pale green, with male flowers at the base of most of them ; *fruit* rounded at the top, whitish. Bogs ; rather common.—Fl. June, July. Perennial.

22. *C. vitilis* is probably an Alpine form of the preceding, with smaller spikelets.—Fl. July, August. Perennial.

23. *C. leporina* (Oval-spiked Sedge).—Often called *C. ovalis*. *Stems* tufted, 1 foot high or more ; *leaves* usually much shorter

than the stems ; *spikelets* 4–6, sessile, very close together, ovoid, brownish green, about ⅓ inch long, chiefly female, with a few male flowers at the base ; *fruits* flat, winged, shortly beaked. Moist meadows ; common.—Fl. June, July. Perennial.

24. *C. lagopina* (Hare's-foot Sedge).—Similar to *C. leporina*, but smaller, and there are usually only 3 or 4 spikelets ; *fruits* flat, but not winged. Damp rocks and grassy places on mountains in Aberdeenshire and Inverness-shire ; very rare.—Fl. July, August. Perennial.

25. *C. elongata* (Elongated Sedge).—Much taller than the two preceding species, often 2 feet high ; *spikelets* longer, narrower, and not so close together as in *C. leporina*, and the fruits are not winged. Marshes ; rare.—Fl. July, August. Perennial.

§ 3. *Spikelets several, the terminal one or more usually wholly male, the others wholly female, or sometimes male and female*

* *Fruit with a short beak*

† *Style 2-branched ; fruit plano-convex*

26. *C. elata* (Tufted Sedge).—Densely tufted ; *stems* 1½–2 feet high, surrounded at the base by the brown sheaths of the leaves, the outer of which are split into ragged fibres ; *leaves* ⅛–¼ inch broad ; *spikelets* 3–6, ½–2 inches long, the terminal one and the upper portion or whole of the next male, the others female ; *lowest spikelet* usually shortly stalked ; *glumes* dark brown or black, often with a green midrib ; *fruit* almost flat, with a short point. Marshes ; common.—Fl. June. Perennial.

27. *C. acuta* (Slender-spiked Sedge).—More luxuriant than *C. elata*, with long, flaccid leaves and leafy bracts ; *female spikelets* often 3 inches long or more ; *glumes* narrow and acute ; *fruits* ribbed. Wet places ; not uncommon.—Fl. June. Perennial.

28. *C. rigida* (Stiff Mountain-Sedge).—Appears to be a dwarf Alpine form of *C. elata ;* it is about 6 inches high, with short, flat, rigid leaves, short spikelets, and ribless fruits. Stony and wet places on mountains ; rather common.—Fl. June, July. Perennial.

29. *C. aquatilis* (Water-Sedge).—A very tall leafy plant with slender spikelets ; it resembles *C. acuta*, but it has ribless fruits, as in *C. rigida*. Alpine bogs and river-sides ; rare.—Fl. July. Perennial.

30. *C. salina* is a very variable species, a form of which has been found in Caithness ; it is allied to *C. aquatilis*, but the glumes of the lower part of the female spikelets have a long, rigid point, and the fruits have many veins.—Fl. July, August. Perennial.

31. *C. Goodenovii* (Common Tufted Sedge).—*Stems* about 1 foot high, tufted ; *leaves* slender ; *bracts* without sheaths ; *spikelets* 4–6, erect, short, close together, subsessile, 1 or 2 male ; *glumes* blunt, purple, shorter than the fruit, which is broader than long. Marshes ; common.—Fl. May to July. Perennial.

32. *C. trinervis.*—A short, stout plant ; *leaves* usually longer than the stems, narrow, rigid, with involute margins ; *bracts* with strongly ribbed sheaths ; *spikelets* 4–9, erect, very stout, close to-gether ; *glumes* narrower than in the preceding ; *fruit* longer than broad. Wet sands on the Norfolk coast ; very rare.—Fl. June. Perennial.

†† *Style usually 3-branched ; fruit triangular*
‡ *Fruit glabrous*

33. *C. alpina* (Alpine Sedge).—A rather slender tufted or shortly creeping plant, 6–12 inches high ; *leaves* short ; *spikelets* about 3, ovoid, rather close together, black or dark brown, the terminal one containing male and female flowers, the others female ; *fruits* green. Clova Mountains, Forfarshire ; rare.—Fl. July, August. Perennial.

34. *C. fusca* (Dark or Buxbaum's Sedge).—Also known as *C. Buxbaumii.* *Rootstock* shortly creeping ; *stems* tufted, 1–2 feet high ; *leaves* rather long ; *spikelets* usually 4, in a loose spike, the terminal one male at the base, the others female and sessile, or the lowest shortly stalked ; *glumes* dark brown, usually pointed ; *fruits* pale, rather obtusely angled, not beaked. Inverness-shire and island in Lough Neagh, Ireland.—Fl. June. Perennial.

35. *C. atrata* (Black Sedge).—*Stems* loosely tufted, 6–18 inches high ; *leaves* broad, flaccid, with loose sheaths ; *spikelets* 3 or 4, black or dark brown, $\frac{2}{3}$–$\frac{3}{4}$ inch long, the terminal one with a few male flowers at the base or irregularly mixed, the other female, stalked ; *outer bract* leafy ; *glumes* pointed ; *fruits* dark and shining. Rocks on mountains in the north and in North Wales ; rather frequent.—Fl. June, July. Perennial.

36. *C. pallescens* (Pale Sedge).—*Stems* tufted, seldom more than 1 foot high, leafy at the base ; *spikelets* 3 or rarely 4, the terminal one entirely male, about $\frac{1}{2}$ inch long, light brown, the others female, shorter, pale yellowish green in fruit, shortly stalked ; *bracts* leafy ; *fruits* obtuse. Marshy places ; frequent.—Fl. June. Perennial.

37. *C. panicea* (Pink-leaved Sedge or Carnation-Grass).—*Stems* tufted, 1–1$\frac{1}{2}$ feet high, with runners at the base ; *leaves* rather short, erect, flat, rather glaucous ; *spikelets* usually 3, the terminal one male, the others female and distant, $\frac{1}{2}$–1 inch long, stalked ;

flowers often at a little distance from one another ; *bracts* with short leafy tips ; *glumes* brown. Marshy places and wet meadows ; common.—Fl. June. Perennial.

38. *C. vaginata* (Short Brown - spiked Sedge). — Similar to *C. panicea*, of which it is probably an Alpine form. It has the sheaths of the bracts looser, the spikelets darker and few-flowered, and the fruits more distinctly tapering into a beak. Mountains of Scotland.—Fl. July. Perennial.

39. *C. limosa* (Narrow-leaved Mud-Sedge).—*Rootstock* creeping ; *stems* slender, 3–12 inches high ; *leaves* narrow ; *spikelets* 2 or 3, the terminal one male, $\frac{1}{2}$–1 inch long, the others female, $\frac{1}{2}$–$\frac{2}{3}$ inch long, on slender stalks, drooping, rather loose ; *bracts* leafy ; *glumes* rather dark brown ; *fruits* scarcely pointed, not distinctly beaked. Bogs ; rare.—Fl. June. Perennial.

40. *C. irrigua* (Broad-leaved Mud-Sedge).—Closely related to the last, but it is not so slender ; the leaves are much broader, the bracts longer, and the male spikelet is less erect. Bogs in the north ; rare.—Fl. June. Perennial.

41. *C. rariflora* (Loose-flowered Mud-Sedge).—Similar to *C. limosa*, but the glumes are almost black and are more obtuse, and there are only 5 or 6 fruits in each spikelet. Bogs on mountains in Scotland.—Fl. June. Perennial.

42. *C. capillaris* (Capillary Sedge).—*Stems* slender, densely tufted, without runners, 3–9 inches high ; *leaves* narrow, rigid ; *terminal spikelets* male, small ; *female spikelets* 2 or 3, on long thread-like stalks, rather pale, loose-flowered, seldom $\frac{1}{2}$ inch long ; *bracts* shortly leafy ; *glumes* very membranous on the edge ; *fruits* 10 or 12 in each spikelet, beaked. Alpine meadows and moist rocks in the north ; not uncommon.—Fl. June. Perennial.

43. *C. strigosa* (Loose-spiked Wood-Sedge).—This resembles *C. sylvatica* (No. 65), but the female spikelets are much longer and more slender, usually about 2 inches long, their stalks are much shorter, the flowers are placed at some distance from one another, and the fruits have not the long beak of *C. sylvatica*. Woods and thickets ; rare.—Fl. May, June. Perennial.

44. *C. pendula* (Great Pendulous Sedge).—A robust plant with triangular leafy stems 3–5 feet high ; *leaves* long, often nearly $\frac{1}{2}$ inch broad ; *spikelets* 4–6 inches long, more or less drooping, the terminal one male, and the 3 or 4 others female, placed at some distance below, their stalks almost hidden in the sheaths of the long leafy bracts ; *glumes* brown with a green centre. Woods and shady places ; rather common.—Fl. May. Perennial.

‡‡ *Fruit downy, hairy or scabrous*

45. *C. humilis* (Dwarf Silvery Sedge).—A densely tufted plant ; *stems* 3–5 inches high ; *leaves* very narrow, much longer than the stems ; *spikelets* 4 or 5, the terminal one male, about ¾ inch long, the others female and much smaller, placed far apart almost to the base of the stems, their stalks enveloped in the white membranous sheaths of the bracts ; *fruits* obtuse, more or less ribbed, slightly downy. Dry hills in some of the southern and south-western counties, and in Herefordshire.—Fl. June. Perennial.

46. *C. digitata* (Fingered Sedge).—Densely tufted, 6–12 inches high ; *leaves* short ; *male spikelet* about ½ inch long ; *female spikelets* 3 or 4, all shortly stalked, more or less spreading ; *flowers* rather distant ; *bracts* brown, sheathing, without leafy tips or only very short ones ; *fruits* minutely downy. Woods on limestone hills ; rare.—Fl. April, May. Perennial.

47. *C. ornithopoda* (Bird's-foot Sedge).—Very similar to the last, but the female spikelets are more distant and the fruits are longer than the glumes. Derbyshire and Yorkshire.—Fl. April to July. Perennial.

48. *C. ericetorum* (Heath Sedge).—Differs from *C. digitata* in having keeled leaves and smaller, shorter, crowded spikelets. Chalk hills in some of the eastern counties ; rare.—Fl. April, May. Perennial.

49. *C. pilulifera* (Round-headed or Pill-headed Sedge).—*Stems* 6–12 inches high, in broad tufts ; *leaves* shorter than the stems, weak ; *female spikelets* 2 or 3, short and compact, close to the terminal male one ; *bracts* leafy, usually short, sheathless ; *glumes* brown ; *fruits* small, obovoid or nearly globose, scarcely beaked, very shortly downy. Hilly pastures and moors ; common.—Fl. May. Perennial.

50. *C. verna* (Spring or Vernal Sedge).—Similar to *C. pilulifera*, but the leaves are shorter and stiffer, the spikelets are not so close together, and the lowest bract has a short sheath with a small leafy point. Dry pastures and heaths ; uncommon.—Fl. April, May. Perennial.

51. *C. montana* (Mountain-Sedge).—This is distinguished from *C. pilulifera* by the bracts having scarcely any leafy points, the shorter female spikelets with much darker glumes, and by the much longer hairy rather than downy fruits with acute angles. Pastures and heaths in Sussex, Monmouth, Hereford, and Worcester ; rare.—Fl. April, May. Perennial.

52. *C. tomentosa* (Downy-fruited Sedge).—*Rootstock* creeping ; *stems* slender, 1 foot high or more ; *leaves* narrow, erect, much

shorter than the stems ; *spikelets* 2 or 3, the terminal one male, about 1 inch long, the others female, about ½ inch long, erect, nearly sessile ; *lower bract* leafy, sheathless ; *fruits* downy, not beaked.   Moist meadows in Wiltshire and E. Gloucester ; very rare.—Fl. June. Perennial.

53. *C. glauca* (Glaucous Sedge).—Sometimes called *C. flacca. Rootstock* creeping ;   *stems* 6–18 inches high ;   *leaves* glaucous ; *male spikelets* usually 2 or 3 ; *female* 2 or 3 ;   all on rather long stalks, the female ½–1 inch long, often drooping when ripe ; *glumes* dark brown ; *fruits* not beaked.   Marshes and wet meadows ; common.—Fl. June. Perennial.

** *Fruit usually with a long beak*
† *Male spikelet* 1, *rarely* 2 *or more*
‡ *Style* 3-*branched*

54. *C. atrofusca* (Dusky Sedge).—*Rootstock* shortly creeping ; *stems* erect, 6–12 inches high, leafy only at the base ; *leaves* short, broad ; *male spikelet* ⅜–½ inch long ; *female spikelets* 2–4, often slightly longer, pendulous on rather long stalks ; *bracts* slightly sheathing, the lowest with a short leafy tip ; *glumes* dark purple with a pale midrib. Ben Lawers ; probably now extinct.—Fl. July. Perennial.

55. *C. Sadleri* (Cold Sedge).—Also called *C. frigida. Stems* 3–12 inches high, with broad leaves ; *male spikelet* solitary, terminal ; *female spikelets* 3–6, spindle-shaped, the upper sessile, the lower finally pendulous on long stalks ; *bracts* sheathing, leaf-like ; *glumes* dark brown. Wet turf in Aberdeenshire ; very rare.—Fl. August. Perennial.

56. *C. flava* (Yellow Sedge).—Usually densely tufted, seldom reaching 1 foot high, leafy, becoming yellowish, especially the fruiting spikelets ; *leaves* flat ; *male spikelet* terminal, ½–¾ inch long ; *female spikelets* 1–3, sessile or shortly stalked, nearly globose when ripe ; *bracts* all leafy and sheathing ; *fruits* distinctly nerved and beaked, very spreading or reflexed. Boggy places ; common.— Fl. May, June. Perennial.

57. *C. Oederi* (Oeder's Sedge).—Distinguished from *C. flava* by its smaller, more numerous fruits, which have a shorter beak, narrow at the base. Bogs ; rather rare.—Fl. June, July. Perennial.

58. *C. extensa* (Long-bracteated Sedge).—Similar to *C. flava* and *C. distans*, but distinguished from both by the longer and narrower leafy bracts, the lowest of which are usually much longer than the stems ; *spikelets* brown-green ; *fruits* triangular, strongly nerved. Marshes, usually near the sea ; rather common.—Fl. June. Perennial.

PLATE XCIV

Crested Dog's-tail Grass	Cock's Foot Grass	Sheep's Fescue
Barren Brome		Yorkshire Fog

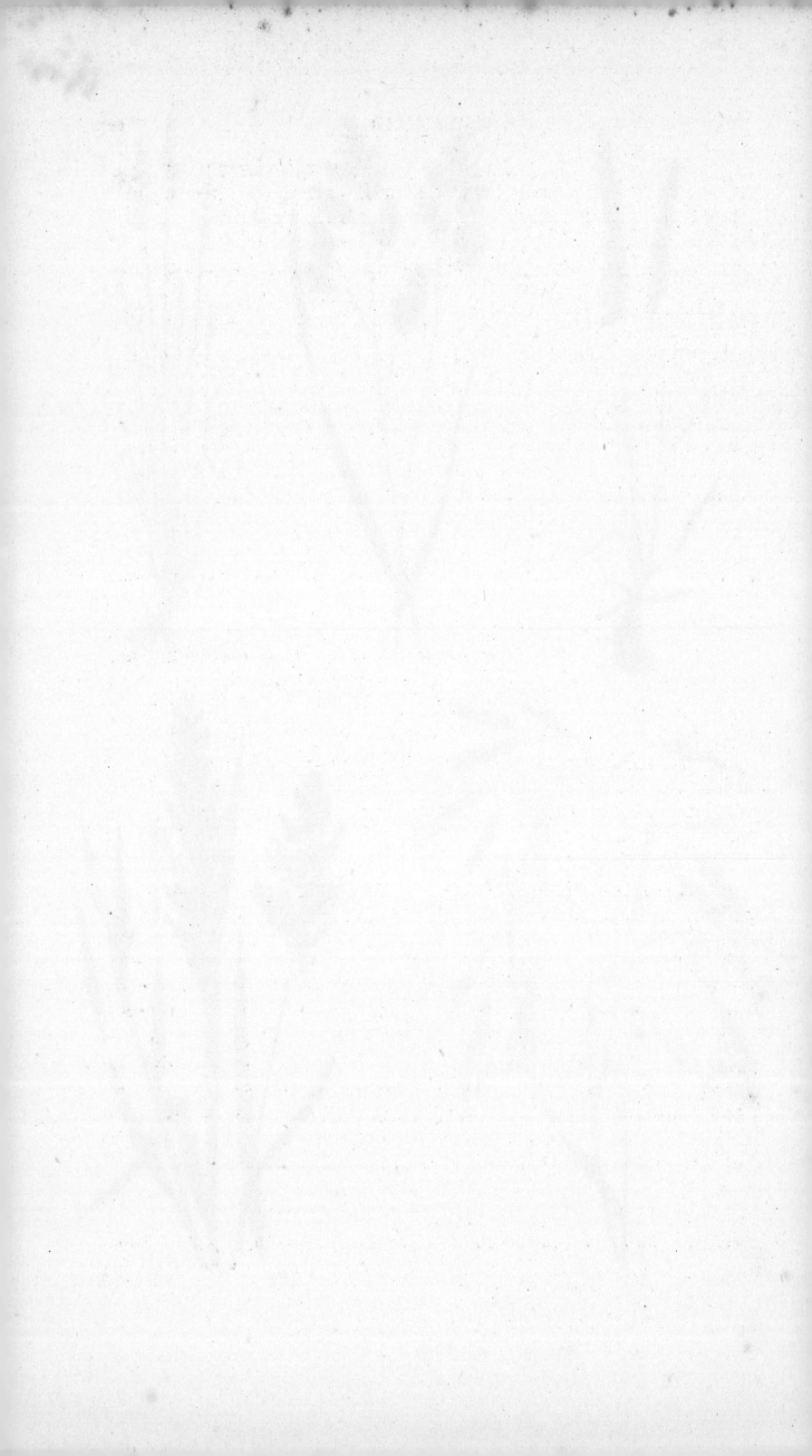

59. *C. fulva* (Tawny Sedge).—Regarded by some authors as a variety of the last, from which it mainly differs in having short pale-coloured spikelets and a rather longer beak to the fruit. Bogs and wet pastures.—Fl. June. Perennial.

60. *C. distans* (Distant-spiked Sedge).—*Stems* tufted, slender, 1–2 feet high ; *leaves* flat, narrow, much shorter than the stems ; *spikelets* few, distant, $\frac{1}{2}$–1 inch long, stalked, the stalks enclosed in the long sheaths of the leafy bracts ; *glumes* brown ; *fruits* erect, nerved or ribbed. Marshy places, especially near the sea ; common. —Fl. May. Perennial.

61. *C. punctata* (Dotted-fruited Sedge).—Very much like *C. distans*, but it has looser spikelets and the fruits are much more spreading, apparently without longitudinal ribs except the 3 slightly prominent angles. Marshy places near the sea ; very rare.—Fl. June. Perennial.

62. *C. binervis* (Green-ribbed Sedge).—Differs from *C. distans* in having the spikelets darker in colour and the fruits more angular, with 2 prominent green ribs on the back. Heaths and moors ; common.—Fl. June, July. Perennial.

63. *C. lævigata* (Smooth-stalked Sedge).—Resembles the last, but the slender green spikelets are often 1–1$\frac{1}{2}$ inches long, much like those of *C. sylvatica*, differing in being erect instead of drooping. Marshes and damp woods ; rather rare.—Fl. June. Perennial.

64. *C. depauperata* (Starved Wood-Sedge).—Perhaps only a variety of *C. distans*, from which it may be distinguished by the spikelets having only 4 or 5 fruits each ; these are larger and somewhat inflated, and have a very long beak. Dry woods ; very rare.—Fl. June. Perennial.

65. *C. sylvatica* (Wood-Sedge).—*Stems* weak, tufted, leafy, 1–2 feet high ; *leaves* thin ; *bracts* with long sheaths ; terminal *spikelet* male, about 1 inch long ; other *spikelets* 2–4 or rarely more, entirely female or partly male, loose-flowered, on long slender stalks, finally more or less drooping ; *glumes* narrow, very pointed, green ; *fruits* glabrous, ribbed. Woods ; common.—Fl. May. Perennial.

66. *C. Pseudo-cyperus* (Cyperus-like Sedge).—*Stems* tall, stout ; *leaves* broad ; *spikelets* about 4, 1–3 inches long, the terminal one wholly male or with some female flowers at the top, on slender stalks, drooping when in fruit ; *glumes* green, very narrow and pointed ; *fruits* spreading, with a long, slender beak. Marshes and wet ditches ; rather rare.—Fl. June. Perennial.

‡‡ *Style 2-branched*

67. *C. pulla* (Russet Sedge).—*Stems* 4–12 inches high ; *leaves* narrow ; *male spikelets* 1, rarely 2, $\frac{1}{2}$–$\frac{3}{4}$ inch long ; *female spikelets*

1 or 2, very rarely 3, roundish ovoid, the lowest about $\frac{1}{2}$ inch long ; *glumes* dark purple tipped with white ; *fruit* roundish, abruptly beaked. Wet places on the higher Scottish mountains ; rare.—Fl. July. Perennial.

68. *C. Grahami* (Graham's Sedge).—Larger in every way than *C. pulla*, with more spikelets and longer fruits. Wet places on Scottish mountains ; very rare.—Fl. July. Perennial.

†† *Male spikelets 2 or many*

69. *C. filiformis* (Slender-leaved Sedge).—*Rootstock* creeping ; *stems* 1–3 feet high ; *leaves* and *bracts* long and narrow, the latter without or almost without sheaths ; *male spikelets* 2 or 3, the terminal one 1$\frac{1}{2}$ inches long ; *female spikelets* 1 or 2, distant, $\frac{1}{2}$–$\frac{3}{4}$ inch long, almost sessile ; *fruits* shortly beaked, very downy. Wet ditches and marshes ; rare.—Fl. May. Perennial.

70. *C. hirta* (Hairy or Hammer-Sedge).—*Rootstock* creeping ; *stems* weak, 1–2 feet high, leafy, hairy like the leaves ; *lower bracts* long and leafy, with long sheaths ; *male spikelets* 2 or 3 ; *female spikelets* very distant, rather loose, 1 inch long or more ; *fruits* covered with short hairs, long-beaked. Wet places ; rather common.—Fl. April. Perennial.

71. *C. rostrata* (Bottle-Sedge).—Also called *C. ampullacea*. A stout tufted species, 1–3 feet high, with scarcely angled stems and long leaves ; *bracts* leafy, sheathless ; *spikelets* 1–2 inches long or more, 2 or 3 male and 2 or 3 female, the latter erect, compact ; *fruits* spreading, inflated, with a rather long beak. Boggy places ; common.—Fl. June. Perennial.

72. *C. rhynchophysa*.—Closely related to the last, but it is taller, with more glaucous leaves, and the spikelets are very much stouter. In the British Isles this species is known only from Mullaghmore Lough, in Co. Armagh.—Fl. July, August. Perennial.

73. *C. vesicaria* (Bladder-Sedge).—Similar to *C. rostrata*, but the stem is more angular, the spikelets rather shorter, and the fruits, though inflated as in that species, are more conical. Bogs ; not uncommon.—Fl. May. Perennial.

74. *C. acutiformis* (Lesser Pond-Sedge).—A stout plant, 2–3 feet high ; *rootstock* creeping ; *leaves* long ; *bracts* leafy, sheathless ; *male spikelets* 2 or 3, about 1 inch long, sessile ; *female spikelets* 2 or 3, often 2 inches long, sessile or the lowest shortly stalked ; *fruits* slightly 3-angled, much flattened, with a short, spreading beak. Also known as *C. paludosa*. Wet places ; not uncommon.— Fl. May. Perennial.

75. *C. riparia* (Greater Pond-Sedge).—Taller and stouter than the preceding, with broader leaves, longer female spikelets on longer stalks, and with more distinctly beaked fruits. Wet places ; rather common.—Fl. May. Perennial.

Natural Order XCVII

GRAMINEÆ.—The Grass Tribe

Herbs usually easily distinguished from the Sedges by having their stems hollow except at the nodes, often round or somewhat compressed, not angular, and the sheaths of the leaves are split down on the side opposite to the blade ; *flowers* usually enclosed in 2 or more bracts (*glumes*) instead of 1. The *leaves* are narrow, parallel-veined and entire, clasping the stem with long sheaths, and bear at the point where the blade joins the sheath a membranous appendage called a *ligule ; flowers* 1 or more, in *spikelets* which are arranged in terminal spikes, heads, panicles or racemes ; the main axis of the spike or other inflorescence is often termed the *rachis ;* each *spikelet* consists of a slender short axis (*rachilla*), usually bearing 3 or more chaff-like bracts or glumes ; the 2 lowest glumes (often called the *outer* or *empty glumes*) are usually empty ; the next glume is known as the *flowering glume*, and this usually encloses another, the *pale*, which is often smaller and thinner ; inside the pale, between it and the flowering glume, may be present 2 minute scales (*lodicules*), which are supposed to represent the perianth, 3 (rarely 2 or 6) *stamens*, and a 1-celled, 1-ovuled *ovary* which usually bears 2 more or less feathery *styles* or *stigmas ; fruit* 1-seeded, seed-like ; it is free or adheres to the persistent pale, and is sometimes enclosed in the other glumes as well. The glumes vary considerably in shape and size ; they may be obtuse or pointed, or may bear at their tips, on their back or at their base, a needle-like appendage (*awn*). The number of flowers in the spikelet, the arrangement of the spikelets, and the shape of the glumes mainly furnish the characters by which the genera of this difficult family are distinguished.

The Gramineæ includes about 330 genera and upwards of 3500 species. The fifth Order amongst flowering plants in number of species, it is easily first in economic importance. Included in it are the cereals and fodders which provide the staple foods of man and beast. The wheat (*Triticum sativum*), barley (*Hordeum vulgare*), oat (*Avena sativa*), rye (*Secale cereale*), rice (*Oryza sativa*), maize (*Zea Mays*) are a few of the grain-producing Gramineæ which are familiar to all.

Though all the British species are herbs, many of the tribe Bambuseæ, mostly natives of tropical and subtropical regions, and

Y

especially of India, have woody stems which in one species, *Den-drocalamus giganteus*, attain a height of 80–100 feet and a thickness of from 8–10 inches.

Grasses are present in all regions where flowering plants can exist. In temperate countries they are the dominating constituents of meadows and pastures and of the herbage that clothes the country road-sides.

The fruit of grasses, commonly called the grain, is usually rather small, as canary seed, wheat, maize, etc., but in an Indian bamboo, *Melocanna bambusoides*, the globose or ovoid fruit is 3–5 inches long and 2–3 inches thick.

Amongst the grasses which are cultivated for decorative purposes *Stipa pennata* and the species of *Cortaderia* (Pampas-grass), more familiar under the name of *Gynerium*, may be mentioned. Their feathery or plume-like inflorescences are commonly dried and coloured.

Esparto-grass, which is employed for making baskets, hats, mats, paper, etc., is botanically known as *Stipa* (or *Macrochloa*) *tenacissima*. It is a native of Spain, Italy, and North Africa.

Cane-sugar is the product of a woody-stemmed grass (*Saccharum officinarum*), which grows from 8–12 feet high, a native of tropical and subtropical Asia, and now largely cultivated in most of the warmer countries ; and various fragrant oils are obtained from other grasses, especially from species of *Andropogon*.

For binding the loose maritime sands, an important factor in checking coast erosion, the Marram-grass (*Ammophila arenaria*), with its far-creeping rootstock and sand-loving nature, is peculiarly well fitted ; while recently special attention has been directed to the species of *Spartina*, which appear to be serving the purpose of mud-binders along the Hampshire coast, where they flourish.

SUB-ORDER I. CLISANTHEÆ.—*Flowers closed ; styles long, pro-truded at or near the top of the flower.*

A. *Rachis of inflorescence without lateral hollows*

TRIBE i. PANICEÆ.—*Spikelets dorsally compressed, 1-flowered, sometimes with a rudimentary flower as well ; lowest glume much the smaller.*

1. PANICUM (Panic).—*Spikelets* in a loose or close and spike-like panicle or along one side of the simple branches of a panicle, usually small, 1-flowered, rarely awned ; *pedicels* of spikelets naked or hairy. (*Panicum* is the Latin name for a kind of millet.)

2. SETARIA (Bristle-Grass).—*Spikelets* in a compound cylindrical spike, usually small, 1-flowered, similar to those of *Panicum*, but their pedicels bear a number of bristles. (Name from the Latin *seta*, a bristle.)

TRIBE ii.   CHLORIDEÆ.—*Spikelets laterally compressed, 1-flowered, sometimes with a rudimentary flower as well, arranged in 2 rows on 1 side of a flattened rachis, or alternate and all turned to 1 side.*

3.   SPARTINA (Cord-Grass).—*Spikelets* awnless, sessile along 1 side of the 2–7 branches of a panicle ; *glumes* long and narrow, strongly keeled ; *pale* as long as or longer than the flowering glume. (Name from the Greek *spartion*, rope or cord, the leaves having been used for making cord.)

4.   CYNODON (Dog's-tooth-Grass).—*Spikelets* awnless, sessile, arranged singly along 1 side of the slender branches which arise, 3–5 together, at the top of the stem ; *rachilla* continued beyond the pale as a small bristle, which sometimes bears a minute glume. (Name from the Greek *kuon*, a dog, and *odous*, a tooth.)

5.   MIBORA (Sand-Grass).—*Inflorescence* a simple 1-sided spike or raceme ; *spikelets* awnless ; *glumes* blunt, not keeled ; *flowering glume* membranous, very hairy, blunt.   (Derivation of the name unknown.)

TRIBE iii.   PHALARIDEÆ.—*Inflorescence a panicle, sometimes compact and spike-like ; spikelets laterally compressed, 1-flowered, with 1 or 2 rudimentary or male flowers as well ; outer glumes equal, covering the flowers ; styles long.*

6.   PHALARIS (Reed-Grass).—*Spikelets* broad and very flat, in a compact panicle or in an ovoid or cylindrical, spike-like panicle ; *outer glumes* nearly equal, keeled, the keel sometimes winged ; there are usually 1 or more minute scales between the empty outer glumes and the flowering one.   (Name from the Greek *phalos*, white or splendid, on account of the white, shining fruits.)

7.   ANTHOXANTHUM (Vernal Grass).—*Spikelets* narrow, crowded into a spike-like panicle ; *outer 2 glumes* unequal, keeled, pointed, but not awned ; *next 2 glumes* also empty, shorter than the outer pair, hairy, one with a short awn on the back, the other with a longer awn arising from the base ; *flowering glume* and *pale* membranous, awnless ; *stamens 2.* (Name from the Greek *anthos*, a flower, and *xanthos*, yellow.)

8.   HIEROCHLOE (Holy Grass).—*Spikelets* with 1 perfect flower and 2 male flowers, in a spreading panicle ; *glumes* all membranous, boat-shaped, keeled, pointed, the empty ones as long as the flowers ; *perfect flower* with 2 stamens, the male with 3.   (Name from the Greek *hieros*, holy, and *chloe*, a grass ; it was formerly strewn about Catholic churches on festival days.)

TRIBE iv. PHLEINEÆ.—*Inflorescence dense, spike-like; spikelets laterally compressed, 1-flowered, sometimes with a rudimentary flower as well; outer glumes nearly equal, covering the flowers; styles long.*

9. PHLEUM (Timothy or Cat's-tail-Grass).—*Outer glumes* boat-shaped, their keels projecting into a point or very short awn; *flowering glume* shorter, very thin, awnless or with a very short awn on its back; *pale* very thin, sometimes with a minute bristle at its base outside. (Name from the Greek *phleos*, a reed-like plant.)

10. ALOPECURUS (Fox-tail-Grass).—*Outer glumes* boat-shaped, prominently keeled, awnless; *flowering glume* shorter, with a very slender awn on the back; *pale* wanting. (Name from the Greek *alopex*, a fox, and *oura*, a tail.)

TRIBE v. SESLERIEÆ.—*Inflorescence a spike-like panicle; spikelets laterally compressed, 2-flowered or more; style none; stigmas very long.*

11. SESLERIA (Moor-Grass).—*Spikelets* in nearly sessile clusters, crowded into an ovoid or cylindrical, spike-like panicle, the lower with a glume-like bract at the base; *outer glumes* nearly equal, pointed; *flowering glumes* 3- or 5-toothed at the top, the middle tooth prolonged into a point. (Named in compliment to Leonard Sesler, an Italian botanist.)

B. *Spikelets sessile in hollows of the rachis*

TRIBE vi. NARDEÆ.—*Spikelets 1-flowered, each consisting of 1 glume enclosing a pale, 3 stamens, and an unbranched style.*

12. NARDUS (Mat-Grass).—*Spikelets* arranged alternately in 2 rows on 1 side of an erect, slender, simple spike. (Etymology of the name obscure.)

SUB-ORDER II. EURYANTHEÆ.—*Flowers open; style short; stigmas protruded near to the bottom of the flower.*

A. *Inflorescence a panicle or raceme; rachis without lateral hollows*

TRIBE vii. ORYZEÆ.—*Spikelets laterally compressed, 1-flowered; outer glumes wanting; stigmas feathery.*

13. LEERSIA (Cut-Grass).—*Spikelets* loosely panicled, consisting of only 2 keeled glumes, the first rather broad, with 2 nerves on each side, the second much narrower, with only 1 faint nerve on each side. (Named in compliment to J. D. Leers, a German pharmacist and botanist, who died in 1774.)

TRIBE viii. STIPACEÆ.—*Spikelets cylindric, 1-flowered, without any rudiment ; outer glumes unequal, membranous, enclosing the flowers.*

14. MILIUM (Millet-Grass).—*Spikelets* loosely panicled, awnless ; *outer glumes* 2, concave ; *flowering glume* concave, hard and shining when in fruit. (Name from the Latin for millet.)

TRIBE ix. AGROSTIDEÆ.—*Spikelets laterally compressed, 1-flowered, sometimes with a rudiment as well, or many-flowered ; all the glumes and the pale membranous.*

* *Outer glumes shorter than the flowering glume ; style long ; stigmas often protruded near the middle of the flower*

15. PHRAGMITES (Reed).—*Panicle* very spreading ; *spikelets* several-flowered, with long silky hairs on the axis enveloping the flowers, awnless ; *outer glumes* unequal, the lower much the smaller. (Name from the Greek *phragma*, a hedge or enclosure.)

** *Outer glumes longer than the flowers ; style short or none*

16. AMMOPHILA (Marram-Grass).—*Panicle* spike-like ; *spikelets* 1-flowered, with hairs on the axis ; *flowering glume* very shortly awned. (Name from the Greek *ammos*, sand, and *philo*, I love ; the plant flourishes in sand.)

17. CALAMAGROSTIS (Small Reed-Grass).—*Panicle* very spreading ; *spikelets* 1-flowered, with silky hairs on the axis ; *outer glumes* nearly equal, keeled, pointed ; *flowering glume* much smaller, very thin, bearing a hair-like, short, straight awn on its back. (Name from the Greek *kalamos*, reed, and *agrostis*, a kind of grass.)

18. APERA (Wind-Grass).—Similar to *Agrostis*, but the lower glume is smaller than the upper ; *flowering glume* entire, with an awn inserted a little below the apex, more than 3·times as long as the glume. (Name from the Greek *aperos*, undivided, having reference to the entire flowering glume.)

19. AGROSTIS (Bent-Grass).—*Spikelets* small, numerous, in an elegant spreading or narrow panicle ; *outer glumes* narrow, boat-shaped, pointed, awnless, equal or the second smaller ; *flowering glume* shorter, often with a fine straight awn on the back below the middle ; *pale* much smaller or wanting. (Name from the Greek *agrostis*, which is applied to a kind of grass.)

20. LAGURUS (Hare's-tail-Grass). — *Spikelets* crowded in an ovoid or oblong, softly hairy head ; *outer glumes* subulate ; *flowering glume* much shorter, thin, cleft into 2 awn-like points about as long as the outer glumes, bearing on its back a hair-like bent awn

usually about twice as long as the spikelet. (Name from the Greek *lagos*, a hare, and *oura*, a tail.)

21. POLYPOGON (Beard-Grass).—*Spikelets* densely crowded in a spike-like or slightly branched panicle ; *outer glumes* ending in a fine awn, a character which distinguishes the genus from *Agrostis*. (Name from the Greek *polus*, many, and *pogon*, a beard, in reference to the many long awns.)

22. GASTRIDIUM (Nit-Grass).—Distinguished from *Agrostis* by the shining, enlarged base of the outer glumes. (Name from the Greek *gastridion*, a little belly, in allusion to the base of the outer glumes.)

TRIBE X. AVENEÆ.—*Spikelets with 2 or more flowers, the upper often barren ; outer glumes as long as or longer than the flowers ; flowering glume awned ; style short or none.*

23. HOLCUS (Soft Grass).—*Spikelets* 2-flowered, numerous, in a rather loose panicle ; *outer glumes* keeled, compressed ; *lower flower* hermaphrodite, its glume usually awnless ; *upper flower* male, its glume with a short awn ; *axis* of the spikelet without hairs. (Name from the Greek *holkos*, drawing ; the ancients believed the plant had the power of drawing thorns from the flesh.)

24. WEINGAERTNERIA (Grey Hair-Grass).—Similar to *Aira*. *Spikelets* 2-flowered, awned ; *awn* straight, jointed in the middle, slenderly club-shaped above, with a minute tuft of hairs at the joint. (Named in compliment to Weingärtner, a German who was interested in the flora of Erfurt.)

25. AIRA (Hair-Grass).—Differs from *Avena* in having much smaller spikelets with usually only 2 flowers or rarely 1, the flowering glumes are more membranous and do not project beyond the outer, and the hair-like awn is shorter ; *panicle* loose. (Name from the Greek *aira*, a kind of grass.)

26. TRISETUM (Yellow Oat).—*Spikelets* numerous, small, in a loose panicle. Differs chiefly from *Avena* in having a glabrous ovary, while the fruit is not crested or furrowed. (Name from the Latin *tri*, three, and *seta*, a bristle.)

27. AVENA (Oat).—*Spikelets* rather large, 2–5 flowered, in a loose panicle ; *glumes* membranous, at least at the top, the outer lanceolate and tapering to a point, the flowering ones smaller, 2-cleft at the top and bearing a long twisted and bent awn on the back ; *axis* of the spikelet hairy ; *ovary* hairy at the top ; *fruit* crested and furrowed. (*Avena* is the old Latin name.)

28. ARRHENATHERUM (False Oat.)—Very much like *Avena*, but differs in the lower of the 2 flowers of the spikelet containing

stamens only ; its glume has a long bent and twisted awn arising from below the middle, while the glume of the upper flower has a short, straight awn near the top ; *fruit* downy, not furrowed. (Name from the Greek *arrhen*, male, and *ather*, an awn.)

Tribe xi. Festuceæ.—*Spikelets with 2 or more flowers, the upper often barren ; outer glumes shorter than the lowest flower ; style short or none.*

* *Flowering glume with nearly parallel veins which do not join to form an awn ; awn none ; styles terminal*

† *Flowering glume 2- or 3-fid*

29. Sieglingia (Heath-Grass).—*Spikelets* few-flowered, rather large, few, in a panicle or simple raceme ; *outer glumes* pointed, nearly equal ; *flowering glume* rather leathery, rounded on the back, 3-fid at the top. (Named in compliment to Professor Siegling of Erfurt.)

†† *Flowering glume nearly or quite entire*

30. Koeleria (Crested Hair-Grass).—*Spikelets* few-flowered, in nearly sessile clusters, crowded in an oblong or nearly cylindrical, spike-like panicle ; *outer glumes* unequal, keeled, membranous on the edges ; *flowering glume* keeled, pointed or with a straight, nearly terminal awn. (Named in compliment to G. L. Koeler, a German botanist who died in 1807.)

31. Melica (Melic-Grass).—*Panicle* slender, of a few rather large awnless spikelets each containing 1 or 2 flowers and a terminal wedge-shaped glume enclosing 1 or 2 minute ones ; *glumes* broad, several-nerved, not keeled. (Name from the Latin *mel*, honey, because of the sweetness of the stem.)

32. Molinia (Purple Melic-Grass).—Differs from *Poa* in having much-pointed glumes, and from *Festuca* in the smaller, rather less flattened spikelets ; *pale* of the uppermost flower with a small bristle-like appendage at the base. (Named in compliment to J. I. Molina, an Italian botanist.)

33. Poa (Meadow-Grass).—*Spikelets* several-flowered, rarely only 2-flowered, awnless, numerous, in a spreading or compact panicle ; *outer glumes* rather unequal, usually keeled ; *flowering glume* obtuse or pointed, membranous at the top, keeled from the base ; *fruit* elliptic, 3-angled. (Name from the Greek *poa*, fodder or grass.)

34. Glyceria (Manna-Grass).—Similar to *Poa*, but the spikelets are not so much flattened, and the flowering glumes are rounded on the back or keeled only at the top, with 5–7 prominent or faint veins ; *fruit* oblong, convex on the back. (Name from the Greek *glukeros*, sweet, in allusion to the sweetness of the grain.)

35. BRIZA (Quaking Grass).—*Spikelets* several-flowered, flat, broad, short, hanging from the very slender branches of a loose panicle ; *glumes* broad, concave, not keeled, imbricate, obtuse, membranous on the edges. (Name from the Greek *britho*, I balance, because of the suspended spikelets.)

††† *Flowering glume truncate and slightly jagged at the top*

36. CATABROSA (Whorl-Grass).—Closely allied to *Poa*, but the spikelets have only 2 flowers, and the glumes are broad truncate and slightly jagged at the top. (Name from the Greek *katabrosis*, an eating out, referring to the jagged glumes.)

** *Flowering glume with converging veins all or* 1–3 *of which combine in the awn*

37. CYNOSURUS (Dog's-tail-Grass).—*Spikelets* in sessile clusters which form a 1-sided spike or head ; *outer spikelets* of each cluster consisting of several empty glumes, the others with 2–5 flowers ; *glumes* pointed or awned, as in *Festuca*. (Name from the Greek *kuon*, a dog, and *oura*, a tail.)

38. DACTYLIS (Cock's-foot-Grass).—Differs from *Festuca* in having the spikelets densely crowded in thick 1-sided clusters, which are arranged in an irregular short spike or slightly branched panicle. (Name from the Greek *daktulos*, a finger, in allusion to the arrangement of the spikelets.)

39. FESTUCA (Fescue).—*Spikelets* usually numerous, several-flowered, in a compact or spreading panicle ; *outer glumes* unequal, keeled ; *flowering glumes* lanceolate, convex on the back, pointed or awned, scarcely membranous on the edges ; *fruit* furrowed ; *style* terminal. (*Festuca* is the old Latin name.)

40. BROMUS (Brome).—*Spikelets* several-flowered, rather large, erect or drooping, in a branched loose or compact panicle ; *outer glumes* unequal, usually keeled and awnless ; *flowering glumes* longer, rounded on the back, membranous on the edges, with a usually long awn inserted below the notched or cleft apex ; *ovary* often hairy, with the style inserted below the apex. (Name from the Greek *bromos*, oats.)

B. *Inflorescence spike-like ; spikelets borne in hollows of the rachis*

TRIBE xii. HORDEIEÆ.—*Spikelets solitary or 2 or 3 together, sessile or shortly stalked on opposite sides of a channelled and toothed, jointed rachis ; uppermost flowers often barren.*

41. BRACHYPODIUM (False Brome).—*Spikelets* many-flowered, long, in a single spike, as in *Agropyron*, but they are not so much

flattened as is usual in that genus and not so closely sessile ; *outer glumes* opposite, unequal, their edges towards the rachis. (Name from the Greek *brachus*, short, and *podion*, a footstalk.)

42. AGROPYRON (Couch-Grass). — *Spikelets* several-flowered, closely sessile, 1 in each notch of a simple spike ; *outer glumes* opposite, nearly equal, their edges towards the rachis. (Name from the Greek *agros*, a field, and *puron*, wheat. Some writers place this genus with *Triticum*, which includes the cultivated wheats.)

43. ELYMUS (Lyme-Grass).—*Spikelets* 2–4 flowered, awnless, sessile in pairs in the notches of a simple spike ; *outer glumes* both on the same side of the spikelet. (Name said to be from Elyma, a town in Macedonia, or from the Greek *eluo*, to roll up, the fruit being rolled up in the pale.)

44. HORDEUM (Barley).—*Spikelets* 3 together in alternate notches of a simple spike, 1 or 2 of them consisting each of 2 glumes, either empty or with male or rudimentary flowers, the others containing 1 perfect flower ; *empty glumes* often reduced to mere awns, which form a kind of involucre round the flowering glume. (*Hordeum* is the old Latin name.)

45. LEPTURUS (Sea Hard Grass).—*Spikelets* 1-flowered, awnless, inserted singly in notches on alternate sides of a simple, jointed spike ; *outer glumes* 2, hard, ribbed, both on the same side of the spikelet. (Name from the Greek *leptos*, slender, and *oura*, a tail.)

46. LOLIUM (Rye-Grass).—*Spikelets* several-flowered, closely sessile in each notch of a simple spike, the edge of the spikelet, not the side as in *Agropyron*, being turned towards the rachis ; *outer glumes* 1 or 2 ; if 2, that next the rachis is very small. (*Lolium* is the old Latin name.)

1. PANICUM (*Panic*)

1. *P. sanguinale* (Fingered Panic).—*Stems* 1–2 feet high ; *leaves* flat, hairy ; *panicle* of 2–6 (rarely more) slender branches 2–4 inches long, arising together at the top of the stem ; *spikelets* 2 together, along 1 side of the branches, each about $\frac{1}{12}$ inch long. A weed occasionally met with on cultivated ground ; not native.—Fl. August. Annual.

2. *P. lineare* (Red Millet or Glabrous Finger-Grass).—Much smaller than the preceding, and the *panicle* has only 2 or 3 spike-like branches scarcely more than 1 inch long. Sandy places and cultivated ground ; rare.—Fl. July, August. Annual.

3. *P. Crus-galli* (Loose or Cockspur-Panic).—A robust, broad-leaved species with an irregularly pyramidal *panicle* 4–6 inches long ; *spikelets* crowded along the spike-like branches, larger than

in the other species ; the third *glume* ends in a short point or a long, coarse awn. Cultivated ground and waste places ; not native. —Fl. July. Annual.

2. Setaria (*Bristle-Grass*)

1. *S. glauca* (Glaucous Bristle-Grass).—Erect, 1–2 feet high ; *leaves* rather broad, flat ; *spike* compact, regularly cylindrical, 1–1½ inches long, with many projecting bristles ; *flowering glume* with transverse wrinkles which are conspicuous in the fruiting stage. Cornfields ; rare ; not native.—Fl. September. Annual.

2. *S. viridis* (Green Bristle-Grass).—Distinguished from *S. glauca* by having the second and third *glumes* about the same length, and the *flowering glume* is destitute of the conspicuous transverse wrinkles. Sandy and cultivated places ; uncommon ; not really native.—Fl. July, August. Annual.

3. *S. verticillata* (Rough Bristle-Grass).—*Spike* less regularly cylindrical, the *bristles* are fewer and have short, stiff reflexed hairs ; in the other species the *hairs* are less prominent and are directed upwards. Cultivated places near London and Norwich ; not native.—Fl. July, August. Annual.

3. Spartina (*Cord-Grass*)

1. *S. stricta* (Twin-spiked or Common Cord-Grass).—Grows in small tufts ; *rootstock* wiry ; *stems* 1–1½ feet high ; *leaves* rather short, erect, flat except at the ends ; *spikes* usually 2 together, rigid, erect, 3 or 4 inches long ; *spikelets* about ½ inch long. Salt marshes on the south and east coasts of England.—Fl. August. Perennial.

2. *S. alterniflora* (Many-spiked Cord-Grass).—Grows in large clumps or beds ; *rootstocks* soft ; *stems* 2–3 feet high, with 8 or 9 soft, very smooth *sheaths ;* *spikes* usually 5–7 together ; *spikelets* ½–⅔ inch long. Mud-flats near Southampton.—Fl. August. Perennial.

3. *S. Townsendii* (Townsend's Cord-Grass).—Similar to the last ; *stems* 2–4 feet high, with sometimes as many as 10 or 12 rather soft *sheaths ;* *spikes* usually 3–5 together ; *spikelets* nearly ¾ inch long. Mud-flats on the coast of Hampshire, Sussex, and the Isle of Wight.—Fl. August. Perennial.

4. Cynodon (*Dog's-tooth-Grass*)

1. *C. Dactylon* (Creeping Dog's-tooth-Grass).—A low, far-creeping grass ; *leaves* short, narrow, pointed, bluish green ; *spikes* 3–5 together, 1–1½ inches long ; *spikelets* scarcely 1/12 inch long. Sandy places in the south-west, especially near the sea ; rare.— Fl. August. Perennial.

PLATE XCV

Rye Grass

Annual Meadow Grass

Wall Barley

Smooth Meadow-Grass

Common Timothy

5. MIBORA (*Sand-Grass*)

1. *M. verna* (Early Sand-Grass).—A tufted plant, seldom 3 inches high ; *leaves* short and narrow ; *spikelets* small, purplish, almost sessile in a simple slender spike about ½ inch long ; *flowering glume* hairy outside, jagged at the top, awnless. Sandy pastures in Anglesea and the Channel Islands ; rare.—Fl. April. Annual.

6. PHALARIS (*Reed-Grass*)

1. *P. canariensis* (Canary-Grass).—Erect, leafy, 2–3 feet high ; *spikelets* in a dense ovoid spike 1–1½ inches long, glabrous, variegated with green and white ; *outer glumes* ¼–⅓ inch long, acute, not awned, winged on the back. Occasionally as a weed ; not native. From this is obtained the well-known canary-seed.—Fl. July. Annual.

2. *P. minor* (Smaller Canary-Grass).—Smaller than the last, with a longer and narrower spike ; *glumes* narrower, toothed on the keel. Channel Islands ; rare ; doubtfully native.—Fl. July. Annual.

3. *P. paradoxa* is like *P. minor*, but the *spikelet* contains besides the perfect flower several rudimentary ones. A casual near Swanage.—Fl. July. Annual.

4. *P. arundinacea* (Reed-Grass).—A large, densely tufted plant with broad, long *leaves ;* *spikelets* in a rather compact *panicle* 6–8 inches long ; *outer glumes* about ⅙ inch long, pointed, not awned, keeled but not winged, pale green or whitish with green nerves. A variety with variegated leaves is commonly grown in gardens under the name of Striped Grass or Ribbon-Grass. River banks and marshes ; common.—Fl. June, July. Perennial.

7. ANTHOXANTHUM (*Vernal Grass*)

1. *A. odoratum* (Sweet-scented Vernal Grass).—Slender, 1–2 feet high ; spike-like *panicle* 1–2 inches long ; *flowering glumes* quite included in the outer glumes or rarely with the longer awn slightly protruding. This is the grass that imparts the characteristic odour to hay. Pastures ; common.—Fl. May, June. Perennial. (Pl. xciii.)

2. *A. Puelii* is smaller, less fragrant, the *spikelets* glabrous and narrower with longer *awns*. A weed in pastures ; rare ; not native. —Fl. July. Annual.

8. HIEROCHLOE (*Holy Grass*)

1. *H. odorata* (Northern Holy Grass).—Also known as *H. borealis*. A slender, fragrant grass, ¾–1½ feet high ; *rootstock* creeping ; *leaves* usually short and flat ; *panicle* about 2 inches long ; *spikelets*

ovate, shining brown ; *outer glumes* nearly ¼ inch long, very pointed, glabrous. Damp places in Caithness and Kirkcudbright.—Fl. May, June. Perennial.

9. PHLEUM (*Timothy or Cat's-tail-Grass*)

1. *P. pratense* (Common Timothy or Meadow Cat's-tail-Grass).— *Stems* 1–3 feet high ; *spike* cylindrical, very dense, 1–4 inches long ; *outer glumes* about $\frac{1}{12}$ inch long, with broad membranous edges, truncate at the top ; *keel* green, slightly ciliate, shortly pointed. Meadows and pastures ; very common.—Fl. June. Perennial. (Pl. xcv.)

2. *P. alpinum* (Alpine Timothy-Grass).—Usually much smaller than the preceding ; *spike* ovoid or oblong, seldom 1 inch long, usually becoming purplish ; *keel* of outer glumes continued into an awn $\frac{1}{12}$–$\frac{1}{16}$ inch long. Marshy places on the higher Scottish mountains.—Fl. July. Perennial.

3. *P. Boehmeri* (Purple-stalked Timothy-Grass).—*Stems* often purplish ; *spike* cylindrical, 1–3 inches long ; *outer glumes* narrow-lanceolate, tapering into a minute point, not truncate and membranous as in *P. pratense*. Dry, chalky places in the eastern counties of England ; rare.—Fl. July. Perennial.

4. *P. arenarium* (Sand Timothy-Grass).—Usually only 6–8 inches high ; *spikes* nearly cylindrical, $\frac{3}{4}$–1¼ inch long ; *outer glumes* as in the last, but their keels are ciliate with stiff hairs. Sandy places, usually near the sea ; rather common.—Fl. May to July. Annual.

10. ALOPECURUS (*Fox-tail-Grass*)

1. *A. pratensis* (Meadow Fox-tail-Grass).—The largest and commonest species in Britain ; *spikes* 2–3 inches long, very dense, rather blunt ; *outer glumes* free or only slightly united at the base, shortly hairy on the keel ; *awns* projecting $\frac{1}{6}$–$\frac{1}{3}$ inch beyond the outer glumes. Meadows, etc. ; abundant.—Fl. April to June. Perennial. (Pl. xciii.)

2. *A. myosuroides* (Slender Fox-tail-Grass).—Commonly known as *A. agrestis*. Differs from the other British species by being annual ; *spike* 2–3 inches long, thinner and more pointed than in the last ; *outer glumes* united to about the middle. Cultivated fields and waste places ; not uncommon in the south of England.— Fl. April to November. Annual.

3. *A. geniculatus* (Marsh or Bent-stemmed Fox-tail-Grass).— *Stems* usually procumbent at the base, then bent upwards at the nodes ; *spikes* 1–2 inches long, more slender than those of *A. pratensis*, with much smaller spikelets ; *awns* projecting about $\frac{1}{12}$ inch ; *anthers* finally violet-yellow. *A. pronus* is a prostrate form. Moist places ; common.—Fl. June, July. Perennial.

4. *A. æqualis* (Orange-anthered Fox-tail-Grass).—Very much like the preceding, but the *awns* are still shorter and the *anthers* are at first white, afterwards orange-scarlet or yellowish white. Moist places in some of the southern and midland counties ; rare.—Fl. June to September. Perennial.

5. *A. bulbosus* (Tuberous Fox-tail-Grass).—Differs from *A. geniculatus* in having the *stem* at the base swollen into a kind of bulb. Salt marshes, chiefly in the south ; rare.—Fl. May, June. Perennial.

6. *A. alpinus* (Alpine Fox-tail-Grass).—Known amongst the British species by the ovoid or shortly cylindrical *spike*, which is often less than 1 inch long. Higher mountains of Scotland.—Fl. July. Perennial.

11. Sesleria (*Moor-Grass*)

1. *S. cærulea* (Blue Moor-Grass).—Densely tufted, 6–12 inches high ; *leaves* basal, short, rather stiff ; *spikelets* not many, in a spike-like head $\frac{1}{2}$–$\frac{3}{4}$ inch long, often bluish grey ; *glumes* about $\frac{1}{6}$ inch long. Mountain pastures, especially on limestone, in the north and in Ireland.—Fl. April, May. Perennial.

12. Nardus (*Mat-Grass*)

1. *N. stricta* (Mat-Grass).—A densely tufted, wiry grass, 6–12 inches high, with fine stiff leaves ; *spikelets* often purplish, sessile. Moors and heaths ; common.—Fl. July. Perennial. (Pl. xcvi.)

13. Leersia (*Cut-Grass*)

1. *L. oryzoides* (European Cut-Grass).—*Stems* about 3 feet high ; *leaves* and *sheaths* very rough ; *panicle* 6–8 inches long ; *spikelets* numerous, $\frac{1}{6}$ inch long or more, all turned to one side. Wet places in the south.—Fl. August, September. Perennial.

14. Milium (*Millet-Grass*)

1. *M. effusum* (Wood Millet-Grass).—Tall and slender, often 4 or 5 feet high ; *leaves* rather short, flat ; *spikelets* pale green or purple ; *outer glumes* $1\frac{1}{2}$–$\frac{1}{8}$ inch long ; *flowering glume* about as long ; *pale* rather smaller, faintly 2-nerved, notched at the top. Moist woods ; common.—Fl. June. Perennial.

2. *M. scabrum* (Scabrous Millet-Grass).—Much smaller than the last, slightly scabrous ; *panicle* much closer and smaller, being almost spike-like and usually only about 2 inches long or less. Cliffs in Guernsey.—Fl. April. Annual.

15. PHRAGMITES (*Reed*)

1. *P. communis* (Common Reed).—A stout plant, usually 5–6 feet high or taller ; *leaves* often 1 inch broad ; *panicle* up to 1 foot long, more or less drooping, often purplish brown ; *spikelets* about ½ inch long, narrow, with the white silky hairs on the axis conspicuous in the fruiting stage. Wet ditches and marshes ; common. —Fl. August. Perennial.

16. AMMOPHILA (*Marram-Grass*)

1. *A. arenaria* (Sea Marram-Grass, Murram- or Mat-Grass).— Commonly known as *Psamma arenaria. Rootstock* far-creeping ; *stems* stiff, 2–3 feet high ; *leaves* narrow, stiff, erect ; *panicle* 5–6 inches long ; *spikelets* crowded, nearly ½ inch long ; *hairs* on the axis ⅓ as long as the *pale.* Maritime sands ; frequent. An important sand-binding plant.—Fl. July. Perennial.

2. *A. baltica* has a longer and less compact *panicle*, the *glumes* are more pointed, and the hairs on the axis of the *spikelet* are ½ as long as the *pale.* Northumberland and Norfolk ; rare.—Fl. July. Perennial.

17. CALAMAGROSTIS (*Small Reed-Grass*)

1. *C. epigeios* (Wood Small Reed-Grass).—*Rootstock* creeping ; *stems* 3 or 4 feet high ; *leaves* long, narrow, somewhat glaucous ; *panicle* narrow, a few inches to 1 foot long ; *spikelets* nearly ¼ inch long ; *outer glumes* almost subulate ; *hairs* at the base of the flowering glume longer than the glume. Damp, shady places, frequent.—Fl. July. Perennial.

2. *C. lanceolata* (Purple Small Reed-Grass).—Usually more slender than *C. epigeios ; panicle* much looser, 5–6 inches long, often shining purple ; *outer glumes* rather broader, about ⅙ inch long ; *hairs* longer than the flowering glume. Wet places ; rare.— Fl. July. Perennial.

3. *C. neglecta* (Narrow Small Reed-Grass).—*Leaves* stiffer than in the last ; *panicle* very narrow, 4–6 inches long ; *spikelets* smaller ; *hairs* much shorter than the flowering glume. Bogs in Cheshire, near Loch Tay, and in Antrim ; rare.—Fl. June, July. Perennial.

4. *C. strigosa.*—In Britain known only from Caithness. It is more slender than *C. neglecta,* and the glumes are distinctly longer. —Fl. July. Perennial.

18. APERA (*Wind-Grass*)

1. *A. Spica-venti* (Silky Wind-Grass).—A rather tall and very elegant grass ; *leaves* rather narrow, flat ; *panicle* often 6–8 inches long or more, usually spreading ; *spikelets* very small, shining ; *awn* 3 or 4 times as long as the spikelet. Sandy fields ; rare.—Fl. June, July. Annual.

2. *A. interrupta* differs very slightly from the preceding ; it has the *spikelets* more crowded in a narrow *panicle* with erect branches. Sandy fields in the eastern counties ; rare.—Fl. June, July. Perennial.

19. AGROSTIS (*Bent-Grass*)

1. *A. setacea* (Bristle-leaved Bent-Grass).—*Leaves* in a dense tuft, very slender ; *stems* 1–2 feet high, erect ; *panicle* slender, always contracted except when the flowers are expanded ; *lowest glume* longer than the second ; *flowering glume* with a fine awn at the base which slightly protrudes from the outer glumes. Dry heaths in the south.—Fl. July. Perennial.

2. *A. alba* (Fiorin or Marsh Bent-Grass).—*Stems* creeping and rooting in the lower part, then erect ; *leaves* flat, rather broad, roughish on the sheaths ; *panicle* spreading when in flower, afterwards compact ; *glumes* nearly equal ; *flowering glume* awnless or with a minute awn at the base. Fields and waste places ; common. —Fl. July. Perennial. (Pl. xciii.)

3. *A. canina* (Brown Bent-Grass).—Very similar to *A. alba ; leaves* rather narrower ; *panicle* less spreading ; *outer glumes* longer and more pointed ; *flowering glume* with a slightly protruding awn borne on the back below the middle. Wet heaths, pastures, and damp woods ; common.—Fl. July, August. Perennial.

4. *A. vulgaris* (Common Bent-Grass).—Usually grows in denser tufts than *A. alba,* and the *stems* are not creeping at the base or only very shortly ; *panicle* spreading when in flower and after. *A. nigra* is similar, but more robust, the *panicle* rougher, with more rigid branches and larger *spikelets.* Dry heaths, pastures, and waste places ; common.—Fl. July. Perennial.

20. LAGURUS (*Hare's-tail-Grass*)

1. *L. ovatus* (Ovate Hare's-tail-Grass).—Erect, up to 1 foot high ; *leaves* hoary with a soft down ; *sheaths* rather swollen. Often cultivated in gardens. Sandy places near the sea in Guernsey.— Fl. June, July. Annual.

21. POLYPOGON (*Beard-Grass*)

1. *P. monspeliensis* (Annual Beard-Grass).—*Stems* 1–1½ feet high ; *leaves* flat, rather flaccid ; *panicle* 2–3 inches long, contracted into a cylindrical or slightly branched spike, yellowish shining green, beard-like from the numerous long, straight *awns,* which are 3 or 4 times as long as the *glumes.* Marshes and waste places near the sea and tidal rivers in the south-eastern counties.— Fl. June, July. Annual.

2. *P. littoralis* (Perennial Beard-Grass).—*Stems* procumbent ; *panicle* more branched ; *awns* scarcely longer than the glumes. Salt marshes on the south-east coast ; rare.—Fl. June, July. Perennial.

22. GASTRIDIUM (*Nit-Grass*)

1. *G. lendigerum* (Awned Nit-Grass).—An elegant grass, 6–8 inches high ; *leaves* flat ; *panicle* contracted into a loose, tapering spike 2–3 inches long ; *outer glumes* about $\frac{1}{6}$ inch long. Damp places, especially near the sea ; rare.—Fl. June to September. Annual.

23. HOLCUS (*Soft Grass*)

1. *H. lanatus* (Meadow Soft Grass, Yorkshire Fog).—*Rootstock* creeping ; *stems* 1–2 feet high, very softly grey-hairy like the leaves ; *panicle* 2–3 inches long, pale or reddish ; *awn* scarcely protruding. Meadows, etc. ; very common.—Fl. July. Perennial. (Pl. xciv.)

2. *H. mollis* (Creeping Soft Grass).—Usually not so downy as the last ; *spikelets* rather larger ; *awn* usually protruding. Meadows, etc. ; less common.—Fl. July. Perennial.

24. WEINGAERTNERIA (*Grey Hair-Grass*)

1. *W. canescens* (Grey Hair-Grass).—A small tufted plant, seldom above 6 inches high, bluish green or purplish ; *leaves* very narrow, rolled inwards along the margin ; *panicle* dense and narrow, 1–2 inches long ; *spikelets* about $\frac{1}{6}$ inch long. Sandy coasts of Norfolk, Suffolk, and Jersey.—Fl. June, July. Perennial.

25. AIRA (*Hair-Grass*)

1. *A. cæspitosa* (Tufted Hair-Grass).—A tall plant growing in large, dense tufts ; *leaves* rather stiff, flat, very rough on the upper surface ; *panicle* spreading, 6–12 inches long ; *spikelets* about $\frac{1}{8}$ inch long ; *awns* not projecting beyond the outer glumes. Moist, shady places ; common.—Fl. July. Perennial.

2. *A. alpina* (Alpine Hair-Grass).—Sometimes regarded as a variety of the last ; it is dwarfer (4–15 inches high), with shorter *leaves* and more or less enlarged *glumes*. The *panicle* sometimes becomes viviparous, when the *spikelets* resemble tiny tufts of leaves. Scottish mountains.—Fl. July. Perennial.

3. *A. flexuosa* (Heath or Wavy Hair-Grass).—Tufted ; *stems* 1–1$\frac{1}{2}$ feet high ; *leaves* very narrow, rolled inwards along the margins ; *panicle* spreading, 2–3 inches long ; *spikelets* $\frac{1}{6}$–$\frac{1}{4}$ inch long, very shining ; *awns* projecting beyond the outer glumes. Heaths and hilly pastures ; common.—Fl. July. Perennial. (xcvi.)

4. *A. setacea* (Bog Hair-Grass).—Similar to *A. flexuosa*, but the basal leaves are longer, slenderer, and are folded, not rolled inwards

along the margins ; *panicles* sometimes 5–6 inches long ; *spikelets* more numerous. Bogs ; rather rare.—Fl. July, August. Perennial.

5. *A. caryophyllea* (Silvery Hair-Grass).—An elegant little tufted grass 4–6 inches high, with fine short leaves ; *panicle* loose and spreading, with very slender branches usually in threes ; *spikelets* rather more than $1\frac{1}{2}$ inch long ; *awns* slightly protruding. Dry, sandy places ; common.—Fl. May. Annual.

6. *A. præcox* (Early Hair-Grass).—Tufted, 3–6 inches high ; *leaves* very fine, short ; *panicle* contracted, $\frac{1}{2}$–1 inch long ; *spikelets* as in the last. Dry, sandy places ; common.—Fl. April, May. Annual.

26. TRISETUM (*Yellow Oat*)

1. *T. pratense* (Yellow Oat).—Often called *T. flavescens*. Erect, 1–2 feet high ; *panicle* oblong, 3–5 inches long ; *spikelets* erect, often yellowish, less than $\frac{1}{4}$ inch long ; *flowering glume* cleft into 2 awn-like points and with a fine bent, twisted awn on its back. Rather dry meadows, etc. ; frequent.—Fl. July. Perennial.

27. AVENA (*Oat*)

1. *A. pratensis* (Perennial or Glabrous Oat).—Erect, 1–3 feet high ; *leaves* usually narrow ; *sheaths* much flattened ; *panicle* slightly compound or reduced to a simple raceme ; *spikelets* erect, glabrous, shining, nearly 1 inch long without the awns. Meadows and pastures, especially in dry, hilly districts ; common.—Fl. June. Perennial.

2. *A. pubescens* (Downy Oat).—Differs from the last in having the *leaf-sheaths* more or less hairy, and rather smaller *spikelets* with much longer hairs on their axis. Limestone districts ; common.— Fl. June. Perennial.

3. *A. fatua* (Wild Oat).—A rather robust, erect, glabrous grass 2–3 feet high ; *leaves* long and broad ; *panicle* large, very loose ; *spikelets* large, hanging from very slender stalks ; *outer glumes* nearly $\frac{3}{4}$ inch long ; *awn* about twice as long as the spikelet, rather stout, abruptly bent. The cultivated Oat (*A. sativa*) is closely related to this and by some is considered a variety of it. Cornfields ; common.—Fl. July. Annual.

4. *A. strigosa* (Bristle Oat or Black Oat).—Resembles *A. fatua*, but the *flowering glumes* are larger, and instead of being covered outside with hairs are hairy only below the middle. Cornfields ; rare.—Fl. July. Annual.

28. ARRHENATHERUM (*False Oat*)

1. *A. avenaceum* (Common False Oat).—Erect, 2–3 feet high ; *leaves* few, flaccid ; *panicle* narrow, loose, 6–8 inches long ; *spikelets*

z

$\frac{1}{4}$–$\frac{1}{3}$ inch long ; *glume* of lower flower with a long bent awn. Meadows, hedges, and thickets ; common.—Fl. June. Perennial. (Pl. xciii.)

29. SIEGLINGIA (*Heath-Grass*)

1. *S. decumbens* (Decumbent Heath-Grass).—Commonly called *Triodia decumbens*. Tufted, 6–12 inches high ; *leaves* long, narrow, with a few long hairs on their sheaths and edges and a tuft in place of the ligule ; *spikelets* seldom more than 5 or 6, $\frac{1}{4}$–$\frac{1}{3}$ inch long. Dry heaths and pastures ; rather common.—Fl. July. Perennial. (Pl. xcvi.)

30. KOELERIA (*Crested Hair-Grass*)

1. *K. cristata* (Crested Hair-Grass).—Usually about 6 inches high, with a basal tuft of short *leaves*, but sometimes *stems* and *leaves* are as much as 1 foot long ; *spike* 1–2 inches long or more, rather irregular, the lower clusters of spikelets being more or less distant, shining silvery grey ; *spikelets* 2- or 3-flowered ; *glumes* $\frac{1}{8}$–$\frac{1}{6}$ inch long, very pointed. Dry pastures ; common.—Fl. June, July. Perennial.

31. MELICA (*Melic-Grass*)

1. *M. montana* (Mountain Melic-Grass).—Slender, erect, 1–2 feet high ; *leaves* erect, flat ; *panicle* 1-sided, 2–3 inches long ; *spikelets* about 10–15, drooping, $\frac{1}{4}$–$\frac{1}{3}$ inch long, each 2-flowered. Woods and shady banks in hilly districts ; rather scarce.—Fl. May, June. Perennial.

2. *M. nutans* (Wood Melic-Grass).—More slender than *M. montana ;* *panicle* sometimes reduced to a simple raceme with only 3 or 4 spikelets ; *spikelets* $\frac{1}{4}$ inch long, erect, 1-flowered. Woods and shady places ; frequent.—Fl. May, June. Perennial.

32. MOLINIA (*Purple Molinia or Purple Melic-Grass*)

1. *M. varia* (Purple Molinia or Purple Melic-Grass).—Also known as *M. cœrulea*. A rather stiff, coarse grass, often 3 feet high, forming large tufts ; *panicle* narrow, loose, 6–12 inches long, green or purplish ; *spikelets* erect, narrow, pointed, $\frac{1}{6}$–$\frac{1}{3}$ inch long, usually about 3-flowered. Heaths and moist woods ; common.—Fl. July, August. Perennial.

33. POA (*Meadow-Grass*)
* Annual

1. *P. annua* (Annual Meadow-Grass).—Tufted, up to about 6 inches high ; *leaves* flat, flaccid, bright green ; *panicle* loose, spreading, 1$\frac{1}{2}$–3 inches long ; *spikelets* all stalked, oblong or linear, each usually 3–6-flowered, without woolly hairs on the axis ; *flowering glumes* membranous at the top, keeled from the base. Cultivated and waste places ; very common.—Fl. nearly all the year. Annual. (Pl. xcv.)

* *Perennial ; rootstock not or only slightly creeping*

† *Lower branches of the panicle solitary or in pairs*

2. *P. bulbosa* (Bulbous Meadow-Grass).—Remarkable for the bulb-like swellings at the base of the stems and leaf-sheaths ; *leaves* short, the upper with prominent ligules ; *panicle* rather compact, only about 1 inch long ; *spikelets* 3- or 4-flowered, with a few woolly hairs on the axis at the base of the pointed, keeled flowering glumes. Sandy places, chiefly near the sea in the south and east.—Fl. April, May. Perennial.

3. *P. alpina* (Alpine Meadow-Grass).—Much like the last, but the *stems* are scarcely bulbous at the base, and the *panicle* is rather larger and looser ; *spikelets* often viviparous, resembling tiny tufts of leaves. Common on the higher mountains in the north and in Ireland.—Fl. June, July. Perennial.

4. *P. laxa* (Wavy Meadow-Grass).—Tufted or slightly creeping, more slender than *P. alpina ; panicle* loose, with few spreading branches ; *spikelets* 1–3 on each branch, each 3- or 4-flowered, often viviparous ; *glumes* about $\frac{1}{6}$ inch long, more pointed than is usual for a *Poa*. Higher Scottish mountains ; very rare.—Fl. July, August. Perennial.

5. *P. minor* is only slightly different from the last ; *leaves* folded, not flat, the ligules of the upper long and acute ; *spikelets* rarely viviparous ; *flowering glumes* with 5 instead of 3 veins. Higher Scottish mountains ; very rare.—Fl. July, August. Perennial.

6. *P. glauca* (Glaucous Meadow-Grass).—*Rootstock* slightly creeping ; *leaves* slightly incurved, tapering at the tip ; *ligule* blunt ; *panicle* erect, slender ; *spikelets* 2- or 3-flowered ; *flowering glumes* with 5 veins, 3 of them hairy as in *P. minor*. Scottish and Welsh mountains ; rare.—Fl. July. Perennial.

†† *Lower branches of the panicle usually 3 or 5 together*

7. *P. nemoralis* (Wood Meadow-Grass).—Tufted or slightly creeping, slender ; *leaves* narrow, flaccid, with very short ligules ; *panicle* loose, with slender branches ; *spikelets* compressed, 2–5-flowered, with scarcely any woolly hairs on the axis ; *flowering glumes* more pointed than in *P. pratensis* or *P. trivialis*, each with 5 veins of which 3 are hairy. Woods and shady places ; frequent.—Fl. June, July. Perennial. [*P. Balfourii* and *P. Parnellii* are probably only mountain forms of *P. nemoralis ;* the former has more prominent ligules, and in the latter the upper sheaths are usually longer than the leaves. In *P. nemoralis* the sheaths are not longer than the leaves.]

8. *P. Chaixii.*—Tufted ; *stems* 2–3 feet high, 2-edged ; *leaves* and their sheaths rough ; *panicle* loose, often more than 6 inches long ; *spikelets* 3-, rarely 5-flowered ; *flowering glumes* with 5 glabrous veins. Very shady places near Kelso and a few other places in Scotland and England ; naturalised.—Fl. June, July. Perennial.

9. *P. palustris* (Marsh Meadow-Grass).—Tufted ; *stems* glabrous ; *leaves* rather narrow, scabrid ; *ligules* oblong, acute ; *panicle* large ; *spikelets* acute, 2–5-flowered ; *flowering glumes* obscurely 5-veined, hairy on the keel and margins near the base. Marshes ; very local ; probably introduced.—Fl. June, July. Perennial.

10. *P. trivialis* (Rough Meadow-Grass).—Very much like *P. pratensis*, but the *rootstock* is not creeping, the *sheaths* of the *leaves* are usually slightly rough, and the *ligules* are much longer and pointed ; *spikelets* usually 2-flowered. Meadows, etc. ; very common.—Fl. June, July. Perennial.

*** *Perennial ; rootstock far-creeping*

11. *P. pratensis* (Smooth Meadow-Grass).—*Leaves* rather narrow, with smooth sheaths ; *ligules* short, obtuse ; *panicle* 2–3 inches long, loose ; *spikelets* mostly stalked, each about 4-flowered ; *flowering glumes* rather obtuse, with very faint lateral nerves, minutely hairy on the keel. Meadows, etc. ; very common.—Fl. June, July. Perennial. (Pl. xcv.)

12. *P. compressa* (Flat-stemmed Meadow-Grass).—Similar to the last, but the *panicle* is rather crowded, and it is distinguished from all the allied species by having much flattened *leaf-sheaths*. Dry places ; frequent.—Fl. July. Perennial.

34. GLYCERIA (*Manna-Grass*)

* *Flowering glumes with 5–7 prominent ribs*

1. *G. fluitans* (Floating Manna-Grass or Flote-Grass).—*Stems* rather thick, but weak, 2–3 feet high, creeping at the base ; *leaves* often floating on the water ; *panicle* erect, slender, 1 foot long or more, with few usually erect branches ; *spikelets* few, ½ inch long. Wet places ; common.—Fl. June to September. Perennial.

2. *G. plicata* (Plaited-leaved Manna-Grass).—Very near the last, but it has a compound *panicle* with more numerous *spikelets* which are widely spreading when in fruit ; *flowering glumes* broader. Wet places ; frequent.—Fl. June to August. Perennial.

3. *G. declinata* is probably only a dwarf form of *G. plicata*, with smooth *leaf-sheaths*, few-flowered *spikelets*, and the *pales* longer than the 3-toothed flowering glumes. Wet places ; Hants and Scilly Isles.—Fl. June to August. Perennial.

4. *G. aquatica* (Reed Manna-Grass).—A stout, reed-like grass, 4–6 feet high ; *panicle* much branched, about 1 foot long ; *spikelets* $\frac{1}{4}$ to nearly $\frac{1}{2}$ inch long, 8–10-flowered. Easily distinguished from *G. fluitans* by the more numerous, shorter spikelets. Wet places ; frequent.—Fl. April to August. Perennial.

** *Flowering glumes with 5 faint veins*

† *Outer glumes with 3 veins ; panicle 1-sided*

5. *G. maritima* (Sea Manna-Grass).—*Rootstock* creeping ; *stems* up to 1 foot high ; *leaves* rather short, usually convolute ; *panicle* erect, rather stiff, usually about 3–4 inches long ; *branches* erect or the lower spreading ; *spikelets* about $\frac{1}{2}$ inch long, 6- or 8-flowered ; *glumes* about $\frac{1}{8}$ inch long. Maritime sands ; frequent.—Fl. June, July. Perennial.

6. *G. Borreri* (Borrer's Manna-Grass).—*Rootstock* not creeping ; *leaves* flat ; *panicle* contracted, 3–6 inches long, with very short, finally spreading branches ; *spikelets* smaller than in the last, 4–7-flowered ; *flowering glumes* ending in a very small rigid point. Salt marshes on the east and south coasts ; rare.—Fl. June to August. Perennial.

7. *G. procumbens* (Procumbent Manna-Grass).—*Stems* only 3–6 inches high, stout, rigid ; *leaves* flat, short, glaucous ; *panicle* 1–2 inches long, with short, rigid, ascending branches ; *spikelets* rather crowded, nearly sessile, about 4-flowered. Muddy sea-shores ; not common.—Fl. June, July. Annual.

†† *Outer glumes with 3 veins ; panicle regular*

8. *G. distans* (Reflexed Manna-Grass).—Very similar to *G. maritima*, but the *rootstock* is scarcely creeping, the *leaves* are flatter, the *panicle* much more spreading, not 1-sided, with long slender branches, and the *spikelets* are smaller ; *glumes* not more than $\frac{1}{12}$ inch long. Sandy pastures and waste places, chiefly near the sea ; rare.—Fl. July, August. Perennial.

††† *Outer glumes with 1 (rarely 3) veins ; panicle 1-sided*

9. *G. rigida* (Hard Manna-Grass).—Tufted, usually about 6 'nches high ; *stems* stiff ; *panicle* lanceolate, about 2 inches long, 1-sided, rather crowded ; *branches* slightly spreading ; *spikelets* on short, stiff stalks, linear, about $\frac{1}{4}$ inch long, each about 6- or 8-flowered. Dry places ; common.—Fl. June. Annual.

10. *G. loliacea* (Dwarf Darnel-like Manna-Grass).—Usually smaller than the last, and the *panicle* is reduced to almost a simple spike ; *spikelets* almost sessile, alternate in 2 rows, but turning to

1 side, about ¼ inch long. Sandy sea-shores ; not common.—Fl.
June, July. Annual.

35. BRIZA (*Quaking Grass*)

1. *B. media* (Common Quaking Grass).—Erect, rather stiff, 1–1½
feet high ; *leaves* flat, narrow ; *panicle* 2–4 inches long ; *spikelets*
at first circular, then ovate, ⅙–¼ inch long, green and purple,
about 6-flowered. Meadows, etc. ; common.—Fl. June. Perennial.
(Pl. xciii.)

2. *B. minor* (Lesser Quaking Grass).—Smaller than *B. media*,
the *ligules* much longer, *panicle* more branched and more slender,
and *spikelets* smaller. Dry fields and waste places in the south-
west.—Fl. July. Annual.

3. *B. maxima* (Greatest Quaking Grass).—Known by its very
large *spikelets*, which are few and are about ½ inch long. Not
native, but often cultivated ; naturalised in Guernsey.—Fl. June,
July. Annual.

36. CATABROSA (*Whorl-Grass*)

1. *C. aquatica* (Water Whorl-Grass).—Glabrous, pale green, the
young leaves and stem sweet to the taste ; *stems* creeping or floating at the base, rooting at the joints, sometimes 2–3 feet long ;
leaves short, flat, broad, obtuse ; *panicle* spreading, 4–6 inches long ;
spikelets about ⅛ inch long. Shallow pools and wet ditches ; frequent.—Fl. June, July. Perennial.

37. CYNOSURUS (*Dog's-tail-Grass*)

1. *C. cristatus* (Crested Dog's-tail-Grass).—Slightly tufted ;
stems slender, ¾–2 feet high ; *leaves* narrow ; *spike* 1-sided, narrow,
1–3 inches long. Rather dry pastures, etc. ; very common.—Fl.
August. Perennial. (Pl. xciv.)

2. *C. echinatus* (Rough Dog's-tail-Grass).—Easily distinguished
from the last by the ovoid, much less regular *spike* and the distinct
awns to the *glumes*. Sandy pastures in the Channel Islands ; very
rare ; occasionally in England as a weed.—Fl. July. Perennial.

38. DACTYLIS (*Cock's-foot-Grass*)

1. *D. glomerata* (Cock's-foot-Grass).—Coarse, 1–2 feet high, forming dense tufts ; *leaves* very rough ; *spikelets* ovate, much flattened,
3–5-flowered, in dense ovoid clusters which sometimes form a
solitary thick spike 1–2 inches long, or there may be several such
spikes arranged in a panicle several inches long ; *flowering glumes*
often shortly awned. Meadows and waste ground ; common.—Fl.
June, July. Perennial. (Pl. xciv.)

PLATE XCVI

Couch Grass   Decumbent Heath-Grass   Slender False Brome

Mat-Grass   Heath Hair-Grass

39. FESTUCA (*Fescue*)

* *Basal leaves very narrow ; ligule with auricles*

† *Awn longer than the flowering glume*

1. *F. uniglumis* (Single-glumed Fescue).—Tufted, rarely above 6 inches high ; *leaves* convolute, with loose sheaths ; *panicle* 1-sided, spike-like, about 2 inches long ; *spikelets* much crowded on short, erect stalks thickened at the top ; *lowest glume* reduced to a minute scale ; *second glume* $\frac{1}{3}-\frac{1}{2}$ inch long, with an awn-like point ; *flowering glumes* 3 or 4, rather shorter. Sandy seashores ; rare.—Fl. June. Annual.

2. *F. Myuros* (Rat's-tail-Fescue).—Similar to the last in habit and leaves ; *panicle* 1-sided, sometimes reduced to a simple spike, 2–6 inches long ; *spikelets* smaller than in *F. uniglumis ;* *lowest glume* $\frac{1}{12}-\frac{1}{6}$ inch long ; *second glume* $\frac{1}{6}-\frac{1}{4}$ inch long. Walls and sandy places ; rather uncommon.—Fl. June, July. Annual.

3. *F. sciuroides* (Squirrel's-tail-Fescue or Barren Fescue).— Probably only a variety of *F. Myuros* with a longer, more slender *panicle,* smaller *flowering glumes* with shorter *awns,* and the *lowest glume* not $\frac{1}{12}$ inch long. Walls and sandy places ; rather uncommon.—Fl. June, July. Annual.

4. *F. ambigua* (Doubtful Fescue).—Dwarfer than *F. Myuros,* the *second glume* is 3–6 times as long as the lowest, and each *flower* has only 1 *stamen.* Sandy places in the Isle of Wight, Kent, Dorset, and Suffolk ; very rare.—Fl. May, June. Annual.

†† *Awn shorter than the flowering glume*

5. *F. ovina* (Sheep's Fescue).—Densely tufted, 6 inches to nearly 2 feet high ; *leaves* chiefly basal, almost cylindrical ; *panicle* rather compact, slightly 1-sided, $1\frac{1}{2}$–4 inches long ; *spikelets* usually $\frac{1}{4}-\frac{1}{3}$ inch long ; *glumes* very faintly nerved, almost always with a fine point or awn about $\frac{1}{12}$ inch long. A very variable grass. Several varieties have received names, one of them, *duriuscula,* is sometimes regarded as a distinct species. It is taller, with cylindrical basal leaves and 1 or 2 stem-leaves which are usually flattened. Dry, open places ; abundant.—Fl. June. Perennial. (Pl. xciv.)

6. *F. rubra* (Creeping Fescue).—Also a very variable species. It may be distinguished from *F. ovina* by the more or less creeping *rootstock ;* all the *leaves* are subulate. Usually dry, sandy places ; common.—Fl. June. Perennial.

7. *F. heterophylla* (Various-leaved Fescue).—Close to *F. rubra,* but the *rootstock* is not creeping ; the *stems* are taller ; *basal leaves* subulate ; *stem-leaves* flat. Shady places ; rare ; probably not native.—Fl. June, July. Perennial.

8. *F. oraria* has a far-creeping *rootstock*, subulate *leaves*, the lowest with hairy *sheaths*, and a 1-sided *panicle*. Sandy sea-shores ; rare.—Fl. June. Perennial.

** *Basal leaves broad and flat ; ligule without auricles*

9. *F. sylvatica* (Wood- or Reed-Fescue).—Tall and reed-like ; *leaves* broad ; *panicle* rather compact, 4–6 inches long ; *spikelets* usually 4- or 5-flowered ; *outer glumes* very narrow ; *flowering glumes* about ⅙ inch long, finely pointed, but not distinctly awned. Woods in hilly districts ; not common.—Fl. July, August. Perennial.

10. *F. elatior* (Tall Fescue).—Tufted or *rootstock* shortly creeping ; *stems* 2–4 feet high ; *leaves* flat ; *panicle* always erect, 5 to nearly 12 inches long ; *spikelets* ½ to nearly 1 inch long ; *flowering glumes* scarcely pointed or sometimes shortly awned, 5-ribbed. Damp meadows ; common.—Fl. June, July. Perennial.

11. *F. arundinacea* (Sea-Fescue).—Taller than the last, with broader *leaves* and a more branched, spreading *panicle*. Banks of rivers and wet places, especially near the sea.—Fl. June, July. Perennial.

12. *F. pratensis* (Meadow-Fescue).—Smaller than *F. elatior ;* *rootstock* less creeping ; *panicle* much narrower, sometimes 10 inches long, with the branches shorter and in pairs, 1 branch with 1 *spikelet*, the other with 2 or more. Wet meadows and river banks ; common.—Fl. June, July. Perennial. [*F. loliacea*, in which the inflorescence is reduced to a 2-sided, spike-like raceme, much resembling *Lolium perenne*, is regarded as a hybrid between *Festuca pratense* and *Lolium perenne ;* it is not rare.]

40. BROMUS (*Brome*)

* *Lowest glume 1-veined ; second 3–5-veined ; flowering
glume usually with a long awn*

† *Ovary glabrous*

1. *B. giganteus* (Tall or Giant Brome).—Erect, glabrous, 3 or 4 feet high ; *panicle* loose, long, more or less drooping ; *spikelets* about ⅔ inch long without the awns, 3–6-flowered. Much like *B. ramosus*, but distinguished by the smaller *spikelets*, slender *awns*, and glabrous *ovary*. Hedges and woods ; common.—Fl. July. Perennial.

‡ *Ovary hairy*

2. *B. ramosus* (Rough Brome).—Also known as *B. asper*. Similar to *B. giganteus* in habit, but the *sheaths* of the broad, flat *leaves* have long, reflexed hairs, the *flowering glumes* are longer (nearly

¼ inch long), and the *awns* are shorter or not longer than the glumes. Damp woods and thickets; common.—Fl. July. Annual or perennial.

3. *B. erectus* (Upright Brome).—Erect, 2 feet high or more; *rootstock* slightly creeping; *leaves* narrower than is usual in the genus, with a few long hairs on the sheaths; *panicle* 3–5 inches long, much more compact than in *B. sterilis*, with nearly erect branches; *spikelets* ½–1½ inches long; *flowering glumes* lanceolate, with a straight awn scarcely half as long. Sandy or chalky fields and waste places; common.—Fl. June, July. Perennial.

4. *B. sterilis* (Barren Brome).—Erect, 1–2 feet high or more; *leaves* softly downy; *panicle* 6 inches long or more, with numerous drooping branches, many of them as long as the spikelets or longer; *spikelets* linear-lanceolate, about 6–8-flowered, up to 2 inches long or more, including the awn, which is longer than the glume. Waste places and roadsides; abundant.—Fl. June. Annual. (Pl. xciv.)

5. *B. madritensis* (Compact Brome).—Smaller than the last, rarely more than 1 foot high, less downy; *leaves* narrower; *panicle* erect or nearly so, compact, often purplish; *spikelets*, including the awns, rarely more than 2 inches long. Dry places in the south; rare.—Fl. June, July. Annual.

6. *B. tectorum* is an introduced species met with occasionally as a weed. It is much like *B. madritensis*, but it has a drooping, 1-sided *panicle*.

7. *B. maximus* (Great Brome).—More erect and compact than *B. sterilis*, the branches are much shorter, few of them as long as the spikelets without the awns; *flowering glumes* larger and broader, with very long, stouter *awns;* the whole spikelet, with the awns, is often 3½ inches long. Sandy places in the Channel Islands.—Fl. August. Annual.

** *Lowest glume 3–5-veined ; second 7–9-veined ; flowering glume with a short awn*

8. *B. secalinus* (Rye-Brome).—A more or less softly downy grass, 2–3 feet high; *panicle* rather small, usually more or less drooping; *spikelets* narrowly ovoid-oblong, usually ⅔–¾ inch long, excluding the rather short, slender awns; *flowers* at first loosely imbricate, afterwards distinct and spreading. Cornfields; common. —Fl. June, July. Annual.

9. *B. racemosus* (Smooth Brome).—Much more slender and usually taller than the last, and easily distinguished from it by the flowers being closely imbricate in the fruiting stage. Similar to *B. mollis*, but much less hairy. Cultivated and waste places, meadows, etc.; common.—Fl. June. Biennial.

10. *B. commutatus* (Meadow-Brome).—Differs from *B. racemosus* in having more or less drooping instead of erect *panicle* and *spikelets*, and the *flowering glumes* are uniformly rounded at the side instead of being bluntly angled about the middle. Roadsides, cultivated ground, and dry pastures ; common.—Fl. June, July. Biennial.

11. *B. mollis* (Soft Brome, Lop-Grass).—Very variable, some-times only a few inches high, sometimes 2 feet or more, the whole plant softly hairy ; *panicle* more erect than in the allied species, 1–6 inches long. It differs from the 2 preceding by having the sides of the *flowering glumes* strongly angled. Roadsides and waste places ; common.—Fl. May to July. Annual.

12. *B. interruptus* is a recently described species which has hitherto been regarded as a variety of *B. mollis ;* it is remarkable for its narrow, compact, interrupted *panicle*, the branches being very short and stiff. Fields in some of the south-eastern counties ; rare.—Fl. May, June. Annual, biennial, or perennial.

13. *B. arvensis* (Field-Brome).—Slender, 1–3 feet high, softly hairy ; *panicle* spreading, up to 8 inches long, with very slender, finally horizontal branches ; *spikelets* linear-lanceolate, green or somewhat violet, about ¾ inch long with the awns, which are about ⅓ inch long ; *flowering glume* 7-ribbed. Naturalised in many places.—Fl. July, August. Annual.

41. BRACHYPODIUM (*False Brome*)

1. *B. sylvaticum* (Slender False Brome).—Slender, erect, 2–3 feet high ; *rootstock* slightly creeping ; *leaves* tufted, flat, rather long ; *spikelets* usually 6 or 7, 1 inch long or more, more or less drooping, 8–12-flowered or more, arranged in a loose spike ; *outer glumes* pointed ; *flowering glumes* with an awn as long as or longer than themselves. Woods and hedges ; common.—Fl. July. Perennial. (Pl. xcvi.)

2. *B. pinnatum* (Heath False Brome).—*Rootstock* more creeping than in the last ; the *spikelets* are more erect, and the *awns* are scarcely as long as the flowering glumes. Pastures and stony, waste places on dry limestone soil ; rather uncommon ; absent from Scotland.—Fl. July. Perennial.

42. AGROPYRON (*Couch-Grass*)

1. *A. caninum* (Bearded or Wood Couch-Grass).—Distinguished from *A. repens* by the absence of a creeping *rootstock ;* the plant is more leafy and not so glaucous ; *flowering glumes* prominently 5-ribbed, ending in a rather long awn ; *outer glumes* usually smaller, with shorter awns and often only 3 ribs. Woods and shady places ; not common.—Fl. June, July. Perennial.

2. *A. Donianum* closely resembles the last and *A. repens*, but differs from both in the *flowering glumes*, which are bluntly pointed, are densely covered with little asperities, and have a well-marked midrib towards the apex, the 2 lateral ribs ending in teeth. Rocks on Ben Lawers.—Fl. August. Perennial.

3. *A. repens* (Quitch, Couch-Grass).—*Rootstock* far-creeping ; *spikelets* 2–3 inches up to 6 inches long, with 8–10 or more spikelets at regular distances on alternate sides ; *glumes* all similar, narrow, stiff, 5-nerved or more, pointed or ending in an awn which is short or as long as the glume. Fields and waste places ; abundant ; a very troublesome weed.—Fl. June. Perennial. (Pl. xcvi.)

4. *A. pungens* (Stiff-leaved Couch-Grass).—Differs from *A. repens* by the *leaves*, which are more or less rolled inwards along the margins, awl-like and rigid in the upper part, with many thick, slightly rough ribs. Sea-shores.—Fl. July. Perennial.

5. *A. junceum* (Rush-like or Sand Couch-Grass).—*Rootstock* creeping as in *A. repens*, which it closely resembles ; it is much stiffer and more glaucous ; the *leaves* are rolled inwards along the margins and are rather sharp at the tips ; *spike* rather loose ; *glumes* often obtuse, with 9–11 slender, raised ribs. Sandy sea-shores ; common.—Fl. July, August. Perennial.

6. *A. acutum* (Acute or Decumbent Sea Couch-Grass).—Intermediate between *A. junceum* and *A. repens ; stems* rather loosely tufted, more or less prostrate at the base ; *leaves* with the margins rolled inwards, but not so regularly as in *A. junceum*, the ribs covered all over with minute asperities. Sandy sea-shores ; frequent.—Fl. July, August. Perennial.

43. ELYMUS (*Lyme-Grass*)

1. *E. arenarius* (Sand Lyme-Grass).—Stiff, glaucous, 2–4 feet high ; *rootstock* far-creeping ; *leaves* stiff, rolled inwards along the margins, sharp-pointed ; *spikes* 3–4 or sometimes 8–9 inches long ; *spikelets* in rather distant pairs ; *glumes* stiff, the outer ones about $\frac{3}{4}$ inch long, very sharp-pointed. Sandy seashores, especially in the north.—Fl. July. Perennial.

44. HORDEUM (*Barley*)

1. *H. sylvaticum* (Wood-Barley).—Erect, about 2 feet high ; *leaves* flat, usually hairy on the sheaths ; *spike* cylindrical, not very dense, about 3 inches long ; *flowers* of the 2 lateral spikelets perfect, of the central one male or rudimentary or none. Woods on chalky soil ; rare.—Fl. July, August. Perennial.

2. *H. nodosum* (Meadow-Barley).—Often known as *H. pratense.* Erect or decumbent, often 2 feet high, tufted or bulbous at the base ; *leaves* glabrous, rather narrow ; *spike* 1½–2 inches long, close, cylindrical ; *flowers* of the central spikelet perfect, of the lateral ones male or rudimentary or none ; *outer glumes* all awn-like from the base. Moist meadows and pastures ; common.—Fl. July. Perennial.

3. *H. murinum* (Wall-Barley).—Tufted, rather coarse ; *stems* decumbent at the base, 1–2 feet long ; *leaves* often hairy ; *spikes* dense, cylindrical, 3–4 inches long ; *spikelets* differing from those of the last in having the *glumes* of the central one lanceolate and ciliate at the base. Waste places and roadsides ; common.—Fl. June, July. Biennial. (Pl. xcv.)

4. *H. marinum* (Sea-Barley).—Also called *H. maritimum.* Similar to the preceding, but smaller and somewhat glaucous ; *spikes* smaller, with shorter awns ; *outer glumes* all lanceolate at the base, but not ciliate. Common on some parts of the coast in England.—Fl. June, July. Annual.

45. Lepturus (*Sea Hard Grass*)

1. *L. filiformis* (Sea Hard Grass).—Usually small, decumbent and much branched at the base ; *leaves* short, almost needle-like ; *spike* 2–4 inches long, very slender, usually curved ; *outer glumes* about ⅙ inch long, stiff and pointed. Gravelly places near the sea ; not generally common.—Fl. July. Annual.

46. Lolium (*Rye-Grass*)

1. *L. perenne* (Rye-Grass, Way-Bent).—Slender, 1–2 feet high, leafy only at the base ; *spike* 6–12 inches long ; *spikelets* more or less distant ; *outer glumes* stiff, strongly nerved, seldom ½ inch long, never so long as the whole spikelet ; *flowering glumes* 8–16 or more, obtuse or pointed or shortly awned. Very variable in the shape of the glumes. Luxuriant specimens with branched spikes are occasionally found. Meadows, pastures, and waste places ; abundant. —Fl. June. Usually perennial. (Pl. xcv.)

2. *L. linicola.*—Unlike the last, this has no barren shoots, the *outer glumes* are shorter and less acute, and the *flowering glumes* have a somewhat swollen appearance when in fruit. Cultivated places.—Fl. June, July. Perennial.

3. *L. italicum* (Italian Rye-Grass).—Sometimes considered as a cultivated variety of *L. perenne ;* it has leafy barren shoots, as in that species, but the whole plant is paler green, the *spikelets* are longer, and the *flowering glumes* have long awns. Cultivated fields. —Fl. June. Perennial.

4. *L. temulentum* (Darnel).—Always annual ; *rootstock* not creep-ing ; *outer glumes* usually as long as the spikelets ; *flowering glumes* shorter and broader than in *L. perenne*, and some of them have an awn longer than themselves. The grain of this grass is poisonous, causing, when eaten repeatedly in small quantities, a disease called dry gangrene, similar to that produced by the ergot of rye. Culti-vated fields, sometimes growing with wheat ; not common.—Fl. June to August. Annual.

GLOSSARY OF SOME BOTANICAL TERMS

Abrupt, blunt, as if broken off.

Acuminate, tapering to a sharp point.

Acute, sharp pointed.

Æstivation, the state of flowers in bud.

Alternate, the arrangement of leaves on a stem when they alternate from side to side.

Angular, leaves or stems when angled.

Annual, lasting one year.

Anther, the top of a stamen which contains the pollen.

Apetalous, without petals.

Aquatic, growing in water.

Arillus, a dry covering of some seeds, as Mace.

Ascending, applied to stems which first lie prostrate on the ground and then rise perpendicularly.

Awn, a stiff bristle, as in barley.

Axil, the angle between a leaf and the stem.

Axillary, growing in an axil.

Barren, bearing stamens, but no pistils.

Biennial, lasting two years.

Bifid, two-cleft.

Bipinnate, twice pinnate.

Bipinnatifid, twice cut in a pinnate manner.

Border, the expanded part of the corolla.

Bracts, small leaves at the base of a flower-stalk.

Caducous, falling off very early, as the sepals of the Poppy.

Calyx, the outer case or sepals of a flower.

Capillary, hair-like.

Capitate, round like a head.

Capsule, a dry seed-vessel.

Carpels, ovaries with their styles and stigmas.

Cell, a vesicle, or little bladder, the simplest form of vegetable structure.

Cellular, composed of cells.

Cernuous, nodding.

Ciliated, fringed.

Circinate, curled, like the young frond of a fern.

Claw, the base of a petal.

Club-shaped, cylindrical, but becoming larger from the base upwards.

Coloured, not green.

Column, a name given to the united pistil and stamens in the Orchis Tribe.

Cone, the fruit of the Fir Tribe.

Conical, cone-shaped.

Connate, growing together.

Convolute, rolled together.

Corculum, the same as embryo.

Cordate, heart-shaped.

Corm, a solid bulbous root, as Crocus.

Corolla, the inner leaves or petals of a flower.

Cotyledon, a seed-lobe.

Crenate, scolloped at the edge.

Cruciform, placed crosswise.

Cryptogamous, or *Cryptogamic*; plants are so called which are reproduced without the aid of stamens or pistils.

Culm, the stalk of grasses.

Cuticle, the thin outer skin of a plant.

Deciduous, soon falling off.

Decurrent, running down the stem.

Dichlamydeous, having a double perianth.

Dicotyledonous, composed of two seed-lobes.

Didynamous, having four stamens, two long and two short.

Diœcious plants, are those which have the stamens and pistils in separate flowers and on different plants.

Disk, the central part of a compound flower ; a flat space surrounding the ovary.

Drupe, a nut enclosed in pulp.

Duct, an imperfectly spiral vessel.

Egg-shaped, oval, with the base broader than the extremity.

Elliptical, egg-shaped, with both ends alike.

Emarginate, notched.

Embryo, the bud contained in a seed.

Ensiform, sword-shaped.

Entire, not cut at the edge.

Epidermis, the cuticle or skin of a plant.

Erect, growing perpendicularly.

Exserted, protruded beyond the other parts.

Farinaceous, abounding in flour.

Fascicled, growing in a dense tuft.

Fertile, bearing pistils and producing seeds.

Floret, one of the small flowers composing a composite flower. Natural Order, Compositæ.

Free, not united.

Frond, the leaf of a fern.

Fructification, the parts composing the fruit.

Fruit, the seed with its covering.

Furcate, forked.

Fusiform, spindle-shaped.

Gaping, having an open mouth.

Germen, or ovary, the lowest part of the pistil.

Gibbous, swollen at the base, as in the flowers of Snapdragon.

Glabrous, perfectly smooth.

Gland, a cell containing some secretion.

Glaucous, covered with a pale green bloom.

Glume, the chaff of the grasses.

Habitat, the locality in which a plant grows.

Halbert-shaped, arrow-shaped,with the barbs turned outwards.

Hastate, halbert-shaped.

Herbaceous, having a succulent stem.

Hispid, bristly.

Hybrid, intermediate between two distinct species, and partaking the characters of both.

Imbricated, overlapping, like the tiles of a house.

Indehiscent, not opening with joints.

Indigenous, native, or growing wild.

Inflorescence, mode of flowering.

Interruptedly pinnate, pinnate,with smaller leaflets between.

Inversely egg-shaped or heart-shaped oval or heart-shaped, with the base narrower than the extremity.

Involucre, a whorl.

Irregular, unequally divided.

Labiate, lipped.

Laciniated, jagged.

Lamina, a plate, the broad part of a leaf.

Leaflet, a single portion of a compound leaf.

Legume, a long pod without a partition.

Ligulate, strap-shaped.

*Limb,*the expanded part of a petal.

Linear, very narrow, with the edges parallel.

Lyrate leaf, a pinnatifid leaf with a rounded terminal lobe, and smaller divisions near the base.

Marcescent, withering.

Membranous, membranaceous, having the texture of a membrane, or parchment.

Midrib, the principal vein of a leaf.
Moniliform, having the appearance of a necklace.
Monochlamydeous, having a single perianth.
Monœcious plants, are those which have the stamens and pistils in separate flowers, but on the same plant.

Nectary, any distinct organ in a flower containing honey.
Nut, a seed contained in a hard, dry shell.

Obcordate, inversely heart-shaped.
Obovate, inversely egg-shaped.
Orbicular, round.
Ovary, or germen, the lower part of the pistil containing ovules.
Ovule, the embryo seed.

Paleaceous, chaffy.
Palmate, divided into five or more narrow lobes.
Papilionaceous, butterfly-shaped.
Pappus, a feathery appendage of the seed.
Parasitic, growing on another living vegetable.
Parenchyma, cellular tissue.
Parted, deeply divided.
Patent, spreading.
Pectinate, divided like the teeth of a comb.
Pedate, palmate, with the outer lobes divided.
Pedicle, the stalk of a flower in a compound inflorescence.
Peduncle, a flower-stalk.
Peltate, circular, with the stalk in the middle ; applied to leaves.
Perennial, lasting many years.
Perfoliate, having a stem passing through a pair of leaves.
Perianth, a name sometimes given to the calyx or corolla.
Pericarp, or fruit, the seed with its covering.
Persistent, not falling off ; opposed to caducous.
Petaloid, petal-like.

Petals, the inner leaves of a flower.
Petiole, a leaf-stalk.
Petiolate, having a leaf-stalk.
Phænogamous, furnished with evident stamens and pistils.
Pinnate, divided like a feather.
Pinnatifid, lobed in a pinnate manner.
Pistil, fertile organs of a flower.
Pistiliferous, bearing pistils.
Plumule, the bud contained in a seed.
Pollen, the fertilizing powder contained in the anthers.
Poly, many, as polypetalous, etc.
Pome, an apple.
Pore, a small hole.
Pouch, a small pod with a partition.
Premorse, bitten off.
Prickle, a sharp point, not having a woody centre.
Pseudo, false.
Pubescent, downy.

Quinate, growing in fives.

Radiate, a term applied to those compound flowers the outer florets of which are larger than those of the disk.
Radical, springing from the root.
Radicle, the embryo root.
Ray, the outer florets of a compound flower.
Reflexed, bent back.
Regular, equally divided.
Ringent, gaping.
Rostrate, beaked.
Rotate, the same as wheel-shaped.
Runcinate, pinnatifid, with the lobes pointing backwards.

Sagittate, arrow-shaped.
Saline, abounding in salt.
Samara, the winged seed of the Ash, Sycamore, etc.
Scabrous, rough to the touch.
Scandent, climbing.
Scape, a flower-stalk springing direct from the root and bearing no leaves.
Scion, a creeping shoot.

2 A

Secund, all arranged on one side.
Seminal, relating to the seed.
Sepals, calyx-leaves.
Serrate, saw-edged.
Sessile, sitting, destitute of a stalk.
Setaceous, bristly.
Silicle, a short pod with a partition.
Silique, a long pod with a partition.
Sinuous, wavy, like the edge of an oak leaf.
Spathulate, oblong, but widening towards the end.
Spindle-shaped, cylindrical, but tapering to a point like a carrot.
Spores, the seeds of ferns, mosses, etc.
Spur, a sharp horn-shaped swelling
Squarrose, at right angles with the stem.
Stamen, one of the male organs of a flower which produce the pollen.
Stellate, star-like.
Sterile, barren, having stamens, but no pistils.
Stigma, the summit of the pistil.
Stipitate, stalked.
Stipules, wings at the base of a leaf-stalk.
Stolon, a rooting scion.
Style, the middle part of the pistil.
Subulate, awl-shaped.
Suture, a seam or joint.
Syngenesious, united with the anthers.

Tap-root, the main verticle root.

Tendril, a twisted stalk, bearing neither leaf nor flower.
Terete, long and cylindrical.
Ternate, growing in threes.
Testa, the outer shell of a seed.
Tetradynamous, having six stamens, four long and two short.
Thalamus, the receptacle.
Thorn, a sharp point having a woody centre.
Throat, the upper part of a tube.
Tormentose, covered with thick cotton.
Trifid, three-cleft.
Truncate, ending abruptly, as if cut off.

Uncinate, hooked.
Unilateral, one-sided.
Urceolate, pitcher-shaped.
Valvate, opening with valves.
Vascular, containing vessels.
Vermicular, worm-like.
Vernation, the state of leaves in bud.

Verrucose, warty.
Verticillate, whorled.
Vesicle, a bladder.
Villous, shaggy.
Viscous, clammy.
Viviparous, producing young plants instead of seeds.

Whorl, three or more leaves springing from the same point on a stem.
Whorled, growing in a whorl.
Wings, the name often given to any leaf-like expansion.

ENGLISH INDEX

355

Common Hemp - agri-
mony, 166
Common Hemp-nettle,
227
Common Henbane, 207
Common Hop, 263
Common Horn-wort, 97
Common Hound's-
tongue, 204
Common House-leek,105
Common Ivy; 131
Common Juniper, 268
Common Knot-grass,248
Common Lady's Fin-
gers, 72
Common Lady's Mantle,
87
Common Larkspur, 9
Common Lime, 52
Common Lungwort, 200
Common Mallow, 50
Common Maple, 55
Corn Marigold, 174
Common Marjoram, 225
Common Marsh Mallow,
51
Common Medlar, 91
Common Milkwort, 35
Common Mistletoe, 134
Common Monk's Hood,9
Common Moschatell,131
Common Motherwort,
227
Common Mouse-tail, 7
Common Mud-wort, 214
Common Nipple - wort,
160
Common Orache, 245
Common Parsnip, 126
Common Pellitory - of -
the-wall, 262
Common Rag-wort, 171
Common Red Poppy, 13
Common Rest-harrow,
66
Common Rock-Rose, 32
Common Rœmeria, 14
Common Romulea, 277
Common Rush, 290
Common Saint-foin, 76
Common Saw-wort, 161
Common Scurvy Grass,
21
Common Shepherd's
Purse, 19
Common Soap-wort, 40
Common Solomon's Seal,
285

Common Sorrel, 251
Common Sow - thistle,
157
Common Speedwell, 217
Common Spindle Tree,
61
Common Spurrey, 45
Common Star of Bethle-
hem, 286
Common Star-fruit, 293
Common Star - thistle,
165
Common Tamarisk, 99
Common Tansy, 166
Common Thorow-wax,
122
Common Tutsan, 53
Common Vervain, 233
Common Vetch, 74
Common Viper's Bu-
gloss, 199
Common Water-cress,27
Common White-rot, 116
Common Wild Navew,
29
Common Winter Cress,
26
Common Winter-green,
186
Common Wood Sorrel,
59
Common Wormwood,
166
Common Yellow Cow-
wheat, 214
Common Yellow Melilot,
68
Common Yellow Milfoil,
175
Common Yellow Water
Lily, 11
Common Yew, 268
Compound Flowers,146–
176
Copse Buck-wheat, 249
Coral-root, 25, 275
Coriander, Common, 130
Corn Bedstraw, 141
Corn Blue-bottle, 164
Corn Campanula, 178
Corn Catchfly, Striated,
41
Corn Chamomile, 175
Corn Cockle, 42
Corn Crowfoot, 6
Corn Feverfew, 174
Corn Gromwell, 200
Corn Mint, 224

Corn Parsley, 119
Corn Salad, 143 ; Com-
mon, 144 ; Toothed,
144.
Corn Wound-wort, 229
Cornel, 132 ; Dwarf,
133 ; Wild, 132
Cornish Bladder - seed,
129
Cornish Heath, 183
Cornish Money-wort,
211, 216
Corydalis, Climbing, 15 ;
Yellow, 15
Cotton-thistle, 151, 163
Cotton-weed, 152 ; Sea-
side, 166
Cotoneaster, 81 ; Com-
mon, 92
Cow Parsnip, 115, 126
Cowbane, 118
Cowberry, 180
Cowslip, 236
Cow-wheat, 210 ; Com-
mon Yellow, 214 ;
Crested, 214 ; Small,
214
Crab Apple, 90
Crake-berry, 255
Crambe, 23
Cranberry, 180, 181
Crane's-bill, 56; Bloody,
57 ; Dove's-foot, 58 ;
Dusky, 57 ; Jagged-
leaved, 58 ; Long-
stalked, 58 ; Meadow,
57 ; Mountain, 57 ;
Round - leaved, 58 ;
Shining, 58 ; Small-
flowered, 58 ; Wood,
57
Creeping Bell-flower,178
Creeping Buttercup, 6
Creeping Cinquefoil, 84
Creeping Goodyera, 275
Creeping Jenny, 238
Creeping Plume-thistle,
163
Creeping Water Scor-
pion-grass, 202
Creeping Yellow Cress,
27
Cress, 18 ; Alpine Penny,
19 ; Alpine Rock, 26 ;
American, 26 ; Bitter,
17, 24 ; Bristol Rock,
26 ; Bulbiferous Bit-
ter; 25; Common Win-

ter, 26; Creeping Yellow, 27; Fringed Rock, 26; Glabrous Rock, 25; Hairy Bitter, 24; Hairy Rock, 25; Large - flowered Bitter, 24; Lesser Wart, 24; Marsh Yellow, 27; Narrow - leaved Bitter, 24; Northern Rock, 26; Penny, 16, 18; Perfoliate Penny, 19; Rock, 17; Swine, 24; Thale Rock, 26; Tower, 25; Wart, 17, 24; Winter, 18.

Crested Cow-wheat, 214

Crimson Clover, 68

Crimson Vetchling, 74

Crocus, 276; Saffron, 277

Cross-leaved Bedstraw, 140

Cross-leaved Heath, 182

Crosswort, 139

Crow-berry, Black, 255

Crowfoot, 2; Celery-leaved, 6; Corn, 6; Ivy-leaved, 5; Meadow, 6; Small-flowered, 7; Water, 5; Wood, 6

Cuckoo-flower, 24

Cuckoo-pint, 296

Cudweed, 152; Dwarf, 168; Jersey, 168; Marsh, 167; Mountain, 167; Narrow-leaved, 168; Wood, 168

Cup, King, 7

Curled Dock, 250

Currant, Black, 107; Red, 107; Tasteless Mountain, 108

Cut-leaved Germander, 226

Cut-leaved Saxifrage, 109

Cyphel, 46

Dabeoc's Heath, St., 184

Daffodil, Common, 279

Daisy, 153; Common, 173

Dandelion, 150; Common, 160

Danewort, 136

Danish Scurvy Grass, 21

Dark Mullein, 220

Dead-nettle, 222; Red, 228; Spotted, 228; White, 228; Yellow, 228

Deadly Nightshade, 206

Deptford Pink, 39

Devil's-bit Scabious, 146

Dewberry, 86

Dittander, 20

Dock, 248; Bloody-veined, 250; Broad-leaved, 250; Curled, 250

Dodder, 196; Clover, 197; Flax, 197; Greater, 197; Lesser, 197.

Dog Rose, Trailing, 89

Dog Violet, 33

Dog's Mercury, 259

Dog-wood, 132

Dove's-foot Crane's-bill, 58

Downy Hemp-nettle, 228

Downy Wound-wort, 229

Downy-leaved Rose, 89

Drooping Saxifrage, 109

Drooping Star of Bethlehem, 286

Dropwort, 78, 83; Fine-leaved Water, 123; Hemlock Water, 123; Tubular Water, 122; Water, 114

Duck-weed, Lesser, 298

Duke of Argyll's Tea-tree, 207.

Dusky Crane's-bill, 57

Dutch Clover, 70

Dwale, 206

Dwarf Birch, 266

Dwarf Centaury, 193

Dwarf Cornel, 133

Dwarf Cudweed, 168

Dwarf Elder, 136

Dwarf Furze, 65

Dwarf Mallow, 50

Dwarf Orchis, 274

Dwarf Plume-thistle, 163

Dwarf Red-rattle, 214

Dwarf Spurge, 258

Dwarf Tufted Centaury, 193

Dyer's Green-weed, 66

Dyer's Rocket, 31

Early Field Scorpion-grass, 203

Early Purple Orchis, 273

Earth-nut, 114, 121

Earth-nut Pea, 75

Echium, Purple, 199

Eight-stamened Water-wort, 37

Elder, Common, 135; Dwarf, 136; Water, 136

Elecampane, 153, 172

Elm, Common, 263; Scotch, 263; Wych, 263

Enchanter's Nightshade, 93; Alpine, 95; Common, 95

English Catchfly, 41

English Scurvy Grass, 21

English Stonecrop, 105

Entire-leaved Peony, 9

Eryngo, 113; Field, 117; Sea, 117

European Chickweed, 239

Evening Campion, 42

Evening Primrose, 93; Common, 94

Evergreen Alkanet, 202

Everlasting, 152; White 167

Everlasting Pea, 75

Exogenous Plants, 1–268

Eye, Pheasant's, 2, 5

Eye-bright, 211; Common, 216

Fen Rag-wort, Great, 171

Fennel, 115; Common, 124; Marsh Hog's, 130; Sea Hog's, 130

Fenugreek, 64; Bird's-foot, 68

Feverfew, Common, 174; Corn, 174; Sea, 174

Field Bindweed, 196

Field Eryngo, 117

Field Flea-wort, 171

Field Gentian, 192

Field Lady's Mantle, 87

Field Madder, 139, 141

Field Mouse-ear Chickweed, 47

Field Pepper-wort, 20

2 B

LATIN INDEX

INDEX TO PIPE-WORTS, SEDGES, AND GRASSES

2 C

PRINTED BY
WILLIAM BRENDON AND SON, LTD.
PLYMOUTH